J. F. McM

THE POWER & THE GLORY

THE POWER AND THE GLORY

A Romance of the Great LaSalle

By GILBERT PARKER

AUTHOR OF

"Carnac's Folly," "No Defense," "The Money
Master," etc.

A. L. BURT COMPANY

Publishers   New York

Published by arrangement with Harper & Brothers
Printed in U. S. A.

TO

My Beloved Niece

LUCILLE ASPEGREN

CONTENTS

[vii]

Contents

WHILE this book is going through the press there comes the cable announcement from Rome of the beatification of Isaac Jogues, John de Brébeuf, Gabriel Lalemant and five other Jesuit priests who were martyred in Canada in the days of Louis XIV of France. Pope Pius, carried in the *Sedia Gestatoria,* "descended into St. Peter's, which was crowded by sixty thousand people, and knelt and venerated the new beatified priests."

How strange it is that only hundreds of years after the wonderful sacrifice of their lives, gladly, fearlessly, the formal recognition should come today when the religious faith of the world has been deepened by the late war and the souls of men freshly stimulated. I am not a Roman Catholic, but, a wide traveler, I have seen missions throughout the world, and today, as in the days of Brébeuf and Jogues, they have missionaries who give all for Christianity.

No greater heroism, no greater devotion to an ideal, ever inspired any men than that which led the Jesuit missionaries and explorers to the remote corners of North America. Though a layman, La Salle was of this noble company, and if the intense political hatreds of the time forced him into an opposing camp, it did nothing to dim the luster of his great spirit or the power and the glory of his achievement, which he shares with Jogues, Brébeuf and others. Canada and the United States are the heirs of their splendor.

August 1925.   GILBERT PARKER.

THE POWER & THE GLORY

"List to the Lark!
He soars and sings,
Wake to your work,
The Matin rings!
Praise God for work!

Noon-tide is near,
The board is spread;
Thanks be to Him
Who giveth bread!
Praise God for bread!

Sinks to his sleep
The pilgrim Sun,
Homeward to rest,
The day is done!
Praise God for rest!"

—ALBERT R. LEDOUX

Chapter I: AT THE CHÂTEAU
SAINT LOUIS

HIGH above the St. Lawrence stood Louis, Count Frontenac alone, soon after his arrival at Quebec as Governor. From a window of the Château St. Louis he was looking across the vast stream which is more renowned than any other in that hemisphere. As his eyes scanned the immense flood and saw the exquisite coloring of the foliage on the farther shore in the bright sunlight, his cheek flushed with admiration. He was now fifty-two, but in years only. His mind was twenty-five, his body framed to endure hardships and trials, and these were before him in immense degree.

As looking out he dreamed big dreams—he had a fiery, eloquent soul full of imagination and temperament—and compared his humble court with that of Louis XIV, where he had so much been, grim humor came to his eye. He could not feel he had mistaken his course. He was poorly paid, but the destiny of this unknown land had entered into his bones, and it remained there till the end of his powerful career in Canada, where he yielded up his breath to the suspirations of millions yet to come of another race, but bound to him as the skin is to the flesh.

There were not so very many homes in Lower Town far below the cliffs where was the Château St. Louis, but people were moving about briskly, and there came to Frontenac's ears the refrain of a song:

[1]

"In Heaven there is a dance,
    Alleluia!
All the young Virgins danced,
Benedicamus Domino,
    Alleluia! Alleluia!

It is for you and me,
    Alleluia!
We dance like the young Virgins,
Benedicamus Domino!
    Alleluia! Alleluia!"

These were only two of many verses, but the eyes of the Governor lighted, for they were the spirit of the place; at the same time there was the ringing of bells in the towers of the cathedral, and around the Bishop's palace came people eager for the blessing of Laval, the Bishop of Quebec, poor, unhandsome, but a power always.

From Lower Town there came the words of another song, that of the Fête of St. Anne:

"Now is the Fête of St. Anne,
    Eh! courage, hurrah!
Already at the bell one struts about,
    Eh! courage, hurrah! sa, sa!
Eh! courage, hurrah!"

The air was so clear that the Governor could hear the words floating up the cliffside to the Château from which could be seen Upper and Lower Town; and through it all there came the steady tramp, tramp of feet of soldiers near the citadel. Frontenac closed his eyes and he heard the footfalls of soldiers in his beloved France and other lands where he had led them.

His lips moved, speaking to himself, then he opened his eyes again. He now saw a canoe approach the shore hundreds of feet below, and a figure issue from it and begin to climb the hill leading to his Château St. Louis. Somehow this figure fitted in with his late dreaming. It belonged to one who knew the life of Canada,—bold, strong, in tattered clothes, as though he had come a long distance, with rugged, dauntless air, and yet with a curious union of triumph and tragedy. Presently he lost sight of the man, and turned to his desk.

As he did so, the door opened and his orderly announced: "Le Sieur de la Salle!"

This was not the man Frontenac had seen leaving the canoe, but a tall, alert, handsome, rather grim-faced man whose eyes looked clearly at those of Frontenac and at whose lips was a faint smile. He was clearly a man of splendid physique, and of iron will. Frontenac had immediately taken to him, for he saw in him, Réné Robert Cavelier, better known as La Salle, the true pioneer, who would put all away from him but the land he loved, and would live for that alone. Also he knew him opposed by the Jesuits who once had controlled in Canada by influencing Governor and Intendant, but had seen their power gradually decline.

Frontenac advanced to La Salle with outstretched hands, a warm smile on his distinguished face.

"You come at the right moment, Sieur de la Salle—I think of Canada's future! Who more welcome then than you!"

La Salle's face lighted. He had come to urge Frontenac to found a fort at the head of Lake Ontario where the Iroquois could be held in check, and trade with the English and Dutch from the Upper Lakes could be stayed. La Salle had discovered the Ohio and the Illinois, and was eager to trade and explore, the latter most to him of all. Hunger for wealth never entered his head, and all his life proved his freedom from lust of gain.

[3]

"Your Excellency! I am your faithful and devoted servant, and I have come to beg—"

"La Salle a beggar, but tell that to the wild men of China—you come not to beg, my friend!"

"I come to urge your building a fort at Lake Ontario, and if I may command it, good things may come to our dear France and Canada."

Frontenac laughed. "Yes, yes, that was in my mind. We shall do it, yet we are fought by powerful forces. We think alike, La Salle." He turned to a table on which lay a map and portfolio.

"You shall go ahead to Onondaga, the headquarters of the Iroquois, and ask their sachems to meet me in council. Then we shall build the fort. That is not popular, but we must stand firm or Laval—the starved and wonderful Monsieur de Quebec of high birth and educated by the Jesuits—will have us under his thumb." He laughed softly. "He is a big man, but there can only be one authority in Canada—the King, and not the Church. There is our fighting ground, La Salle, there and nowhere else. But we shall win, for God and the King will be with us—eh?"

La Salle bowed. "Though much be against us—the Bishop and Duchesneau and all, we shall win by the grace of God."

"Jacques Duchesneau—an Intendant that makes trouble, and will make more! The tool of the Jesuits, but not strong enough to conquer me, La Salle!"

At that moment came a tapping at the door, and an orderly entered. "M'sieu' Joliet would speak with Your Excellency."

"Joliet, the explorer—good!" said Frontenac. "Admit him."

Joliet entered, a man of vigor, firm and good to see, and about the same age as La Salle. He was tattered and wayworn, but determined and keen-eyed. He had studied for the Jesuit priesthood in Canada, where he was born, and had left it to become a fur-trader.

Frontenac saw he had news of importance. He offered his hand and said: "Well, M. Joliet, you have traveled far"—he pointed to his ragged clothes—"what have you to tell?"

Joliet bowed. "With Père Marquette we were sent by M. Talon, the late Intendant, to explore, and after trials and dangers on the Illinois, we entered the muddy surge of the Missouri. Out of this chaos we came at last upon the great quiet waters of the Mississippi."

"The Mississippi—the Mississippi!" said Frontenac astonished. "So, it flows south, not west."

"To the Gulf of Mexico!" said Joliet.

"It is a great deed," interposed La Salle. "By that, trade will not be stopped for months by ice in the river there. All the year round to France!"

"And the records of the journey?" said Frontenac.

"Naught, naught! We had escaped every peril from the Indians. I had passed forty-two rapids, and was landing at La Chine when my canoe was wrecked. I lost two men and my box of papers within sight of the settlements I had left years before. Nothing remains but my life—to use it as Your Excellency may direct, if you will!"

Frontenac's face was a study in pride, regret and sympathy. "What matter your records, man! The Mississippi! France will thank you, as it does now through its Governor. You shall have service with me, Joliet, and henceforth, so far as I can, all shall go well with you."

Joliet bowed low with gratitude. Then he said: "I will serve you proudly, monseigneur." He turned to leave, his eyes alight with pleasure.

"But a moment, Joliet. Here is to relieve your instant wants," and Frontenac placed a few gold pieces in his hand.

Joliet shook his head. "But no, Your Excellency. You need them more, for you must spend whether you will or no."

Frontenac smiled and took back the gold. "I have not seen such great faith, no, not in Israel!" he said cheerfully.

When Joliet had gone La Salle said: "The finding of the Mississippi is the summit of all. It opens up a marvelous field of trade for Louis, the Sun King!" His head lifted, his face shone, vision filled his eyes. "I see great things for France."

Frontenac, hand at his chin, looked meditatively at La Salle for a moment, and then said: "You live for your country and naught else, La Salle. You have the unselfish soul." He dropped a hand on La Salle's shoulder. "We can make New France the wider power of Old France—you and I!"

He smiled. The proud, irascible Frontenac felt himself in accord with this well-born son of Rouen, who was to bring to France and the new world high honor. La Salle, shy, and with few popular gifts, still with the power to win all who were not selfishly against him, said slowly:

"You honor me, Excellency. We have far to go. I shall find the mouth of the Mississippi and make from here to the Caribbean Sea subject to the King of France."

Frontenac laughed quietly. "You see far, La Salle! You have been at work here seven years and you have paid the utmost price for all you have got and done. For your first trip of exploration you sold your seigneury of La Chine and spent the money in exploration. You are a dreamer, but that you have vast practical qualities, your deeds show. All you have you give."

The sun shone brilliantly in the room where were few signs of distinction save the fleur-de-lis, a portrait of Louis XIV, of Cartier, and of Champlain, and a map roughly

[6]

drawn of New France, old oak chairs, wooden walls, dark with time, and a statue head of Brebeuf, the famous Jesuit missionary who had given his life under dreadful torture without a sign of pain. Frontenac's eyes were on this statue now. The Jesuits were against him, but his soul was too big to let his own wrongs affect his historical sense, and he had profound admiration for their courage and devotion, though he would fight to the last their national ambitions. The State first and last was his theory. Frontenac had vision and the sense of progress, and he was at one with La Salle.

La Salle said: "Excellency, I would receive direct from His Majesty my right to work in the Far West where foes retard all I do. The Church is against you as the head of all, and it is against me."

Frontenac interrupted: "I may be the head, but you are not the tail. You belong to our full body of progress. No, no, La Salle, you shall not fail. You must go to France. I will give you a letter to Colbert, the great minister of Louis." His eyes brightened, his lips laughed gently. "You will come back bigger than you went, and always, I hope, a friend of Frontenac."

La Salle inclined his head gratefully. "But not till you have opened the new Fort. We must have a large background of western trade before I go to France. It will have weight at Court."

Frontenac nodded.

At that moment came a tapping at the door, and an orderly announced the Intendant Duchesneau, the foe of Frontenac, and of La Salle whom he hated for his trade ambitions and because of his friendship with the Governor. A look of distrust crossed Frontenac's face, but he greeted the Intendant courteously. Duchesneau's eyes lowered sullenly when he saw La Salle, but he bowed to him with exaggerated impressiveness, while La Salle looked him steadily in the eyes and responded with grave precision. The Governor seeing, moved forward and shook La Salle warmly by the hand.

"*Bon voyage, cher Sieur de la Salle,*" he said, in courteous and suggestive dismissal.

"I thank Your Excellency," responded La Salle and left the room, knowing why the Governor had spoken as he did.

The Intendant's eyes showed he did not understand Frontenac's "*Bon voyage,*" but he did grasp the warm friendliness of the Governor.

"Your Excellency," he said, "that man has neither birth nor position in Canada. Your favor to him is not popular."

Frontenac's face showed satire. "Well, his family were burghers of Rouen. They were wealthy merchants with the elements of nobility, and La Salle was trained for a Jesuit. That's why he came to Canada poor—training for a Jesuit priest deprived him of his natural inheritance by the laws of France. I find him patriotic, unselfish, and sincere."

The Intendant scowled. "Sincere—a wild discoverer who sought to reach the Vermilion Sea on the way to China, and that's why his little Seigneury above Montreal was called La Chine!"

Frontenac sardonically replied; "La Chine! a good name, and his China will be here. He need not discover China. There is enough discovery here to last a lifetime."

Duchesneau smiled satirically. "*Bon voyage* to Sieur de la Salle!"

"*Bon voyage,* it shall be. Before him lies a wonder of achievement. History will record him,—France will be proud of him, this continent will adore him."

"His brother, the Abbé Cavelier, does not adore him,

Your Excellency. He is older and a good priest, and often disapproves of him."

"The Abbé Cavelier is a priest of St. Sulpice. He received part of La Salle's inheritance, and he is cold to La Salle as are those who receive something for nothing. Is the Abbé Cavelier a man of unselfishness and patriotism?"

"He is a devoted priest, and Your Excellency should like him for he is not a Jesuit."

Frontenac's eyes rested on the statue of Brebeuf. He pointed: *"Tiens,* there is proof that I love the Jesuit for his piety, fearlessness, and faith. In all spiritual matters I am his perfect friend. Now let us to business, Intendant. What surprises have you! What grievances and public virtues!" He spoke satirically.

"No surprises. The English and Dutch at Albany, as you know, mean to get the trade of our Indians and to set the Iroquois against us."

"Bon voyage, Sieur de la Salle!" said the Governor with deep meaning.

Chapter II: HAVE CARE, LA SALLE!

WHEN La Salle left the Château St. Louis, he walked towards the house of Rojet Ranard, Farmer of the King's Revenue, where he was an honored guest. The wife of Ranard was beautiful and her Christian name was Barbe. She, like Ranard, was a Jesuit and full of hatred for the man who had growing power in the country and had vast influence already with the Indians. La Salle had hesitated to accept the invitation, but did so because it might lessen Jesuit opposition; and so far nothing could have been more charming than Monsieur and Madame Ranard's treatment of him. They had a comfortable house just inside St. John's Gate, with a splendid view over the St. Lawrence, and he had been used with handsome familiarity.

Barbe Ranard was fair-haired, buoyant, graceful, slim, and of a vivacious temperament. She was quick of tongue, clever at repartee, and had the manner of the accomplished woman of the type of De Montespan and that class who prey upon the susceptibilities of men and their love of the beautiful and amusing. Barbe Ranard, at twenty-four, had beauty and distinction and was now the mistress of Duchesneau, who guessed why La Salle had been asked to stay with the Farmer of the King's Revenue. The Intendant would do much to destroy La Salle, and this way seemed possible and sure. Ranard, who did not know Duchesneau's relations with his wife—or pretended not to do so—was bent to secure advancement, and by playing up to Duchesneau and the Jesuits, saw his chance. He was a man of slower wit than his wife, but of straggling force and with a soul for mean things as had she, or they could not have plotted as they did.

When La Salle reached Montneuve, he entered full of joy at his interview with Frontenac and was going to his room, when he was met in the hall by his hostess.

She held up a hand in greeting: "Ah, dear monsieur, it is good we meet, for I wish a little talk, if you are not too busy. In my boudoir if you will."

Her eyes were laughing and innocent and she was becomingly dressed in a severely plain gown of pale gray, cut very low in front and showing soft shy breasts; and there was naught around her gracious neck save the glow of perfect health. Her golden hair hung in profusion, and her lips were like ripe cherries, soft, amorous, and tempting. As she ran up the stairs softly, La Salle could see her dress was pulled up so that her fine ankles showed, and her stockings were of tender pink. She was, as women go, a flower of the garden of Hesperides, and made a picture that to a lesser man than La Salle would have been all captivating. He had eyes for women, for grace and beauty, but there was that far deeper in his life—love of his work—and all else must yield to that.

Inside her boudoir, an exquisite room, brightly colored with silk and linen of grace and sweet design, she motioned him to a sofa, while she took a huge armchair beside the sofa. As La Salle sat down his mind was busy. Why had she brought him? It was as sweet a room as he had ever entered in Canada, and appealed to the sensuous side of him. For a few moments she gazed at him with a curious warm light in her eyes and sweet seduction in her carriage. She was essentially one of the women who helped at last to bring the French Revolution, and who have been at once the flaming morn and the somber sunset of more than one great land. She had brains to go far and she would go far; and this enterprise meant that favor with people in high places which could advance her own and her husband's interests—with the all-powerful Jesuit body, and with court life through Jacques Duchesneau, who stood well in France. She would have played for Frontenac, but he was too old, too uncertain, and he was opposed by the Jesuits, whose career he was retarding in Canada. Besides, Frontenac was not subject to women's wiles. He had, like La Salle, an ambition that was the State and its power. He was not selfish, but he was always, and to the end, the devout lover of France and her advancement. Barbe Ranard read him as such women do, with vital inseeing. She had the gift of the perfect Delilah.

Never had she looked better than she did this afternoon. She had no soul, but she had a marvelously sensitive temperament, and she was full of emotion, but was incapable of fidelity or true feeling. She was not immoral, she was non-moral. She could not see the vileness in her own mind and body. Truth and honor had never been a part of her, and never could be. From her birth she had gone the crooked path. Well born, she had married Rojet Ranard because he was in the Government, and her fixed idea was to get foot on the ladder and let her brains, body, and good fortune do the rest.

After a few moments in which she tried to impress the senses of La Salle, she said: "You have the mind that wins, Sieur de la Salle. You were trained for a Jesuit priest, but the wider things caught you—not the bigger things, but the wider things, and you would now do immense things for the land you love—we both love. I hate to say it, but I have studied you while you have stayed with us, and all I see makes me know the really patriotic thing is in you."

She blushed slightly and lowered her eyes with the skill

of her wonderful duplicity, and she added, almost brokenly: "I should like to help you—oh, I should! You will do so much for France in Canada! Oh!"

La Salle was impressed. It was an age when women played upon the senses of the biggest men. In sudden unsuspicious sympathy he half stretched a hand towards her, and she slid forward on her knees, buried her face in her hands and wept some fickle and easily commanded tears.

He almost touched her, but suddenly he felt it was not right to do so as a guest in the house, or at all, and in a voice of some emotion he said: "You are all too kind, madame. I wish I could accept your help, but I may not—I must not do so."

"Why must you not?" she sobbed, and bent over so that he could look down between her most attractive breasts and could smell the exquisite perfume she used. It was this act of hers that brought him to his feet in his fight for safety and escape.

"No, no, no I cannot accept your aid. You are not of the women one can meet in affairs of business and let it stay at that. No, no, madame, it must not be. It cannot be."

She sprang to her feet and threw her hands on his shoulders. "Oh, La Salle, most dear and wonderful La Salle, let me give you my help in all you do. I can influence so many—I can be what no wife could ever be to you. Can you not see, La Salle?"

He withdrew her hands from his shoulders, looked her in the eyes, and felt her utter shamelessness, her disregard of all the conventions of life, the utter rule of sex in her, and he said, firmly, "It shall not be," and hastened to the door and opened it.

Outside stood Rojet Ranard, who had helped to plan this hideous thing. Glancing back, La Salle saw Barbe with bitter passion in her eyes and lip curled in revolt. With a look of contempt at Ranard he left the house in anger.

"God save us!" he said, in stern appeal. "Is this what I shall have to face? Henceforth those two are against me—and the Jesuits and the Court folk behind them—Duchesneau and his kind here and in Paris." He went to old quarters he had known before and sent to Montneuve for his clothes.

Behind in Montneuve the humiliated wife said: "Rojet, that man has the nerve of the devil and the blood of an icicle. He has escaped us, and he will go on—curse him, like an eagle flamboyant—unless we do for him in another way. Yet he is handsome, too, in his grim way and I could almost have wished we were not playing a part. He has big things in him or he could not have withstood me. I am not easy to withstand, am I, dear Rojet?"

"No one could withstand you, Barbe, who was not sunk in his own importance. That man is a danger here, and we have failed. I almost wish I had challenged him."

A queer smile passed over the face of Barbe as she turned her head away. "He is a trained swordsman, Rojet, and you would have had a hard time. You did not mean to kill him, but to drive him from Quebec. It could have been done so easily if he had taken me in his arms—so easily!"

"Easy as eating. Not Frontenac—he is La Salle's friend—but the Intendant and the Jesuits would have made life unbearable for him here. He would have been ruined—and forever!"

"He will be ruined *forever* yet," she said. "Do you think a woman ever forgives such a slight? No, no, no! See you, Rojet, I will pursue him wherever he goes, till I defeat him in the end. He shall pay to the last centime for what he did to-day. Does he think he is bigger than Barbe Ranard? He shall see. I have brains. I have what he has not, duplicity. See you"—the beautiful savage teeth showed in menace, the blue eyes danced fire. "I will fight him every step of his way. He defeated me to-day. I will spend life and time in putting a blight on all he does, I will prevent his fame coming to fruition. When he goes to France—he is going, he told me so yesterday—I will be there."

"Why should he go to France?" he asked: "What can he do there?"

Her brilliant eyes answered. There flashed into them the look that has entered the brains of such women as Medea, or Lady Macbeth, and she said with ruthless lips: "Why indeed? It will be not so difficult to make France impossible. I see my way—I see it."

Ranard laughed. "You have resources, Barbe. If you say you will do a thing, it is done one way or another in the end. See, there has lately come into my employ a clever man from the North, Tuke Darois, who hates La Salle, and Du Lhut, the great *coureur de bois,* and we can use him at need. He has an eye for dark things—I see that."

"Tuke Darois! I like the 'Tuke,' it has dark possibilities. Who is the man? What has been his work?"

"He has been a trapper in the far North. His wife was Scotch and he has a daughter, a very pretty girl of eighteen or so. She is not like him—looks straight and honest; but he! well, behind his calm face is the soul of the devil. He is a most capable accountant, so I employ him. I have clearly instructed him to watch Du Lhut, and I know he hates La Salle—why I know not."

Barbe smiled. "Good, my Rojet. All comes our way. That man should help in good time—and his daughter, too!"

He shook his head. "No, she is of a different breed. I don't think we can use her."

"Well, let me try." Her face took on a look of rancor.

She turned to a table and picked up a letter. "I see one way here—in this letter. Read it. There's no reason why you should not. It is one of many that come into my life. Read it, Rojet."

He took the letter and read it, and a sour smile passed over his face.

"Nicolas Perrot, the explorer, too, and in love with you. What will come of this? What a fool to write like that!"

"It is not a fool of a letter, though. It tells the honest mind of the man. Suppose I"—she drew his head to her mouth and whispered. "Suppose—*that!* And when it is done, he cannot compel me—do you see, because by accident you had discovered the part he played—do you not see? La Salle goes to the West before he goes to France. If not there, then here."

Ranard was a bad man and lived in an age of good and evil, with, on the whole, the dominance of good, yet he almost shrank from the vile plot in her mind. He looked at her—so fair, and yet so black with dishonor behind her radiant face and exquisite hair and luring eyes! He felt stunned, for wickedness should not go with so much charm and soft luxuriance.

"By the eternal, you have the thing that knows not eclipse! You have no soul—"

"Don't say that. I am confessed and pardoned and go on again as before. No soul—eh, la la!"

"Do you confess all your sins?"

"Not all at once. Life is not so short as that. But a sin committed for the Church is forgiven. So I shall be forgiven—always."

He shook his head in pretended horror. "When shall you see Nicolas Perrot? He is in Quebec, I know."

"Yes, I saw him on Wednesday, and I can have him here at any time, and with your consent I will."

"Send for him now."

"The sooner the better. La Salle has raised what he cannot lay. He shall pay to the utmost."

Her note was of the briefest, "Dear Monsieur, come at once, please."

When she had dusted the ink and folded and sealed the letter, she said, "How long do you think La Salle can contend against me?"

Her eyes were still bitter, her cheek was flushed, her lithe figure was tense, and yet, resist it as she would, a longing for La Salle was on her. All the more she would destroy him—the paramount fool!

"As long as he lives, no longer," said Ranard, with enmity.

"His sun does not rise far," she replied.

She rang a bell and a manservant entered. "Bear this to M. Nicolas Perrot at Terre Bonne House, and answer no questions. Do you understand?"

The man bowed his head. "Perfectly, madame."

There was a queer look in Auguste's eyes. He had borne messages before to M. Duchesneau, and he was well paid for his services. If he betrayed his mistress, his life would end, and he knew it. He was a man of sound judgment.

"Come soon, Nicolas," said Barbe Ranard, aloud, with a satirical smile.

"He will not tarry. I go to my office," said Ranard.

Chapter III: THE MAN THAT MATTERED

BARBE RANARD was not long alone. She heard a voice in the hall, and in a moment the Intendant was in the room. He bowed over her hand and kissed it with passion, but malevolence was in his eyes. She saw both.

"What is it, dear monsieur?" she asked. "You have news."

"Always coming from the Château St. Louis, I have news."

"What is it now, Jacques?"

"Only that Frontenac and La Salle are closer than ever, and La Salle is going West—'*Bon Voyage, Sieur de la Salle,*' said Frontenac, and I said it later."

"Going West—yes, but he goes to France also."

"How do you know that?"

"He has been staying here, and he told me yesterday. What he is going for I know not and I care not. He left this house in anger a half-hour ago."

"In anger—why?"

"He is quick tempered, and—"

"Yes, yes, I know. Well?"

"I said something in jest, and he left in a fury. He is never returning here," she added viciously.

"Your humor is not bitter to your guests, I'm sure of that."

"You never found it so. I'll tell you what I tried to do. *He was too hard to move,* so he left us."

followed by canoes and two remaining divisions. Slowly they went to Cataraqui and met on the shore vast numbers of Iroquois, who had been amazed by the show of strength, the display of the old soldiers of the Carignan-Sallières regiment, and the uniforms of the Governor's guard.

The next morning the drums beat and all were drawn up under arms. A double line of men extended from Frontenac's tent to the Indian camp, and along this line sixty savage deputies came to the council. The deputies squatted on the sails of the flatboats in a ring and smoked their pipes. Once La Salle stooped and whispered to a chief called Garakontié, a friend of the French, and grunts of applause came from the Indians. At length Frontenac, La Salle, and his officers were all seated. They surveyed the assembled Indians, taking measure of their mettle, and gifts to the Iroquois were made ready. Behind the Indian warriors stood the squaws who had influence with their men.

At length Garakontié rose and in the name of the Five Nations paid deference and respect to Frontenac in a friendly speech to which his chiefs said loudly, "Hoh! Hoh!"

Then Frontenac in his splendid uniform spoke:

"Children! Mohawks, Oneidas, Onondagas, Cayugas, and Senecas, I am glad to see you here, where I have had a fire lighted for you to smoke by and for me to talk to you. You have done well, my children, to obey the command of your father. Take courage—you will hear his voice, which is full of power and tenderness. For do not think I have come to make war. My mind is full of peace and she walks by my side. Courage then, children, and take rest."

During the long speech the gifts were distributed—cloth, tinseled dresses, tobacco, beads. Never before had a Governor addressed them as "Children," but always as "Brothers," and yet this did not offend them, for Frontenac was dominant and decisive, and behind him was force. They

would not have borne it from another. They accepted
with applause, for they knew a man when they saw him.
Frontenac gave guns to the men, and prunes and raisins
and dried fruits to the wives and children.

This was the preliminary meeting. Afterwards the fort
was begun, and the Indians were astounded at the order and
alacrity of the work. Meanwhile Frontenac asked the
chiefs constantly to his table, fondled the Iroquois children,
gave them sweetmeats, and feasted the squaws, and they all
danced before him. When the fort was nearly finished,
Frontenac held a grand council with state and ceremony.
His perceptions were remarkable. He felt the Indians as
an artist feels the true atmosphere of a man, or a place.

He spoke, begging them to become Christians, and his
conscience and his policy were at one in this. His tone was
soft and gentle. Then he changed it, and he said, pointing
to his troops:

"If your father can come so far to make you a visit
of friendship, what would he do if you should rouse his
anger, so that he must punish his disobedient children? He
is the arbiter of peace and war. Beware how you offend him. You must not molest Indian friends of the
French—other tribes and peoples." He added, sharply,
that he would chastise them for any breaches of the peace.

After these threats he spoke with paternal kindness, saying he meant to build at Cataraqui a storehouse where they
could buy all they needed. They must not listen to bad
men, but only to such as Sieur de la Salle, whom he asked
now to address them.

La Salle had in mind the dreadful Iroquois in the past,
and recalled when Father Poncet, after sleeping in dank
weeds, had colic as he waded waist deep through a noxious
stream—how his feet were blistered, his legs benumbed.

The priest begged for a bowl of broth and he was given wild plums, and only at night as he lay fainting did he receive the broth. At last an old Indian took his hands, examined them, and told a child of five years old to cut off the left forefinger with a knife, which he did while Poncet sang the "Vexilla Regis." This was one of the innumerable tortures the fathers had borne at the hands of the Iroquois.

La Salle had great gifts of simple utterance, no rhetoric, no eloquence; his was straight and forceful speech, and he knew how to speak to Indians. His words were a true supplement to those of the Governor.

"Brothers, friends," he said, while Frontenac listened, delighted, "we have far to go together. The Governor gives me control of this fort. Food and supplies will come, and you shall have what you need in return for your peltries. In me you have a friend. I would not deceive you. My life among you will prove my fidelity. Brothers of the Five Nations, the French are your friends—King Louis, greatest of monarchs, is your father. He is of vast power and in Count Frontenac he sends one of his mightiest here. This Governor is kind, but he is firm and strong, and under him you may rest in peace and prosper. Here at Fort Frontenac is your *cache* for all good things. Brothers, I give you greeting!"

All this was well received—Indians shouting "Hoh! Hoh!" and the calumet chant was sung as the Indians rose to their feet and tramped round. The calumet is like a flag of truce and is the sign of good will and peace. This was the chant:

*"Heia, Heia, Yonkennonoué.
Heia, Heia, Yonkennonoué."*

The mission had been successful, and Frontenac left Cataraqui to the loud applause of the Iroquois. It was clear that the fort, with the aid of a vessel, could command Lake Ontario, help to keep peace with the Iroquois, and stop the trade with the English. With a fort at Niagara and another vessel on Lake Erie the French could command all the upper lakes. All this was part of La Salle's scheme.

Chapter V: THE FOUNTAIN OF POWER

WITH letters of commendation from Frontenac to Colbert, the great minister of King Louis, La Salle, went to France, but Barbe Ranard preceded him, knowing his purposes.

She had naught save malice for La Salle. The Intendant had written to Colbert that La Salle was a madman and should receive no favors from the King. To the enmity of the priests was added the malice of a woman who had failed of her purpose, and who, in truth, cared for La Salle in her own vicious, curious way.

Her bitterness came from defeat. Her husband had made much money in Canada, and she felt that at court she could defeat La Salle at every corner. She knew well the Abbé Potin, who was a prominent figure at court, the confessor of De Montespan, and the faithful friend of the Jesuits of Canada, and to him she went on arrival.

The apartments of the Abbé were near those of the Prince de Conti, Louis Armand de Bourbon, a cousin of King Louis, and a younger brother of the great Condé who had influence at court and was a favorite of King Louis.

The Abbé lived outwardly with austerity, but he had luxurious tastes and, though a Jesuit, had license from the Pope to spend money freely for the good of the Church. He had a mind not wholly Eden-like and a great vanity, for he was handsome and his cassock was ever scrupulously clean and fitted well his lean and graceful figure.

"So, my charming madame, you have come back to the gilded cage," he said to Barbe when she kissed his hand.

Her bright eyes shone as she said, "To the cage, yes, from the aviary, and it has nests of many strange birds."

The Abbé caught her meaning and he motioned her to a seat. Then he looked at her meditatively for a moment and said, "So I have heard, and another of the birds is to visit the court soon." He saw her surprise and added, "You see, I have the clairvoyant sense, *pétite madame*."

"Is it clairvoyance or an excellent correspondent in Quebec?"

He smiled with a subtle look in his eyes. "I speak of a foe of my Order who is coming to France. His name is Robert Cavelier, Sieur de la Salle, and he has a brother an abbé, an old acquaintance of mine. So I may be clairvoyant—eh!"

"Because I wished to pay humble respects to you, and to tell you of La Salle I come to you soon after I landed, Abbé. La Salle has come for favors from the court, and your Order in Canada and the Intendant wish to stay his hand."

"And as a true daughter of the Order, you would serve us with your beauty and your intellect—eh, madame?"

She read the double meaning in his words, yet only a flash of resentment came to her eyes. Such men as he, long trained in court life, could not easily be deceived, and she replied, "All I am is at the service of our Order, so I come direct to you."

Suddenly his manner changed. The careful, benignant look fled from his face and a steely expression came. He leaned a forearm on his knee and looked her steadily in the eyes:

"You wish me to help you, so let us bargain with clear minds. It is not our Order alone, though you are faithful to it, but you would not come to France at great expense for that alone. You hate La Salle, is it not so?"

She hesitated, then conquered by his infrangible mind and the danger of deception, she said:

"It is as you say, and for good reason."

He smiled subtly. "I know. You would have done a good thing for our Order, and, resisting you, you loathed him, and now you would bring him to naught at the court of the King. Is it that?"

She had regained her composure and she looked at him with the eyes of a child, and her sensitive smiling mouth told what she felt more surely than her eyes.

"Yes, be sure it is that—but first it was for our Order."

"And for the Intendant, the foe of La Salle and Frontenac?"

Now she flushed slightly and inclined her head.

"Yet you would have played with La Salle in spite of Duchesneau?"

"A woman is never sure of herself till she is tried to the full, M. l'Abbé."

"Quite so, I understand. You have the big thing in you, and we shall find you successful at Court, Madame Barbe."

He lingered over the last word, for it was a challenge of her purity of life. She understood, and she could not resist, for this man could help her in what she would do, and he was handsome and graceful, and if he had not been a priest—!

"With your help, dear Abbé, I hope to defeat La Salle. He is a menace to the good of that land where our Order ruled so well and so long. Under Laval's influence Canada did well; under Frontenac not so well. He grows rich with trade, and the land grows poorer. As Frontenac has increased, Canada has decreased."

"I understand. We have now clear way to walk and we must find what to do. The great Colbert—you would meet him? I can get to him through his son, Marquis de Seignelay. I expect him here to day. His message said he wished to see me—I know not on what business."

At that moment came a soft knocking on the door, and a Jesuit brother entered. He held a card in his hand. The Abbé took it.

"Admit him."

She was about to leave, but the Abbé, tapping her cheek with a finger, said:

"No, meet him before you go. It is well worth while."

Seignelay entered. He was to become Naval Minister soon. The Abbé saluted him with deference, and he turned to Barbe. The Abbé said:

"Madame Ranard has just come from Quebec, Monsieur. May I present her?"

Seignelay gave Barbe his hand, which she kissed, then a curious look flashed across his face.

"I have heard of the fame and position of madame. Has she a special mission here?"

"If Monsieur would allow me to call on him one day I could make all clear. It could not be done in a few words. But may I, Monsieur?" Barbe added, with an ingratiating smile, for the minister looked like one who could be impressed by a clever, pretty woman. Yet a queer look came into the Abbé's eyes. *He* knew that Seignelay was not easily moved by women—had he not seen it with the friends of the King's favorites, Vallière, Fontanges, De Montespan and De Maintenon.

Seignelay said to her: "I shall welcome madame to-morrow at twelve noon at Versailles—if that may please?"

Barbe curtsied. "I will joy to wait upon Monseigneur,"

and she met the enigmatical look in Seignelay's eyes with no real understanding. With a deep bow to them both she left the room.

"You have known madame long, Abbé? Handsome but not of noble family, eh?"

"I have known her ten years, Monsieur. She is not of noble family, but she married one in the government—Rojet Ranard, Farmer of His Majesty's revenue."

"Ah yes. I have heard—a man who blinks an eye, I fear. She plays a part with—one who matters in Canada. Now, Abbé"—with a friendly wave of the hand—"you can do the King's Government service by seeing the learned Abbé Renaudot. I would have him get from Madame Frontenac the latest inside news of her husband. He and she have not lived together many years, but she is a sagely clever woman, and she has, though poor, wide influence, yet she never appears at Court. She is the daughter of La Grange Trianon and once close friend of Montpensier, Louis' cousin, but they fell apart. She is still beautiful. She is devoted to his interests, and my father would know what Frontenac tells her about the Intendant and Indian affairs. They get official reports, but more is needed—if administration is to be handled well. Only one like Abbé Renaudot could gain her confidence, and he would do that for the King, of course."

"Monsieur, I will do what I can. I know the abbé fairly well. We are all patriots, are we not?"

Seignelay took a pinch of snuff and offered his box to the Abbé. He ignored the remark about patriotism.

"There are bad days in Canada, Abbé."

"Yet never better in France, Monsieur."

"As you say, never better in France."

[31]

"France has gone farther than in all her history—thanks to your father, Monseigneur Colbert, Monsieur."

"Thanks to the King," said Seignelay, with a reproving smile.

LA SALLE lodged in the Rue de la Truanderie at Paris, and he presently came to know the Abbé Renaudot, whom he met at the house of Comtesse Frontenac and with whom he immediately made friendship. The society at the home of Madame Frontenac and Mademoiselle Outrelaise did not appeal to him, for he was shy by nature, but he had from madame assurances that she would do all in her power for him, though her influence with the court was not direct.

The Abbé Renaudot had seen the Abbé Potin, and had accepted the commission to get from Madame Frontenac information, but to get it openly, and he presently told the countess all.

She smiled, for she had been a close friend of Madame de Montpensier—the granddaughter of Henry IV and cousin of King Louis XIV—and she knew Court life well—but she worked for Frontenac from outside, and she gave the Abbé all she could with intelligence and discrimination.

To La Salle she said, before he left her house:

"Here you shall always be welcome, Sieur de la Salle, and we will help you when we can." She had still great beauty and charm and wit, and he trusted her and liked her much.

The Abbé Renaudot was at once taken to his heart, for he was learned, reliable, a patriot, and superbly honest, and La Salle saw that at once. La Salle had few gifts for ingratiating himself at Court, and could not push his cause like most among his contemporaries.

So it was the Abbé Renaudot came to see him with a

rarely aroused interest. He had many talks with La Salle in the rooms in the Rue de la Truanderie, and he learned of La Salle's troubles, ambitions, and enterprises.

La Salle made it clear to the Abbé Renaudot that Frontenac had resource and determination and was to play a big part in the history of New France. His faults were on the surface—a quick temper, a stern will to have his dignity recognized, but a consummate courage where he had to contend against the Church and the Intendant, and the difficult, lawless folk of a new land.

Duchesneau had declared that Frontenac used the *coureurs de bois* to promote trade, compelled the Indians to pay his guards for protecting them, and he never allowed the inhabitants to trade until the Indians had given him packs of beaver skins, which he called "presents."

La Salle said to the Abbé Renaudot: "There never was a man who served the King more faithfully than he, and time and history will prove this. The best proof is he has taken the harder course—he has fought the old, powerful body of Jesuits, and they have fought him with the concentrated force of the Church. There was a time when four-fifths of the funds of the Province went to the Church, and there must come an end to that—*there must!* A lesser man would have sought the easier way. He chose the harder, and he is poor. He has not enough salary to support him. The man who did the most for Canada preceding Frontenac was Talon. That handsome man with his oval face and his shower of curls, his smooth features, the mouth formed for feminine sensibility than for masculine force, did great work; he opened the field for Frontenac. Talon prepared the way for Frontenac, my unconquerable leader."

Then La Salle told the Abbé of Madame Ranard, of her presence in France now, to spoil his chances of help in his explorations from the King and Colbert, and of her trap with her husband, for himself. He also said she was a member of a Jesuit society called the Sainte Famille, which met every Thursday at the cathedral with closed doors, where they told of all that had happened during the week, and nothing was told against the Jesuits. It was a sort of female inquisition, and the week after the trap had been laid for La Salle, Barbe told the assembled ladies of La Salle's attempt to conquer her virtue and of the opportune arrival of her husband. She told it with tears in her evil, beautiful eyes.

So it was that many left the Sainte Famille believing La Salle guilty of the crime, though there was no supporting evidence from his past history. Yet Barbe had done her work well, and, were it not that her relations with Duchesneau were guessed, there would have been greater effect, but it had set the unthinking against La Salle.

The Abbé shifted in his seat. "If Bishop Laval gives assent to this evil society, it is a dangerous precedent. We have naught like it in France, and the King would not permit it."

He laid a hand on La Salle's knee: "You were wise to come to France, and all will go well. You have foes, but you can overcome them. I do not fear the end."

La Salle lifted his head in gratitude. "You are a good friend, Abbé, but I have not met my powerful foes here. Duchesneau, the Intendant, has written, and Madame Ranard is here, and she can bring big guns to bear. An able lying woman is a dangerous foe." His eyes became darker in anxiety, his face looked troubled. "I can fight men—I know their games—but I cannot fight women. I am at sea till I find what she has done."

"She has seen the Abbé Potin, who came to me concerning the Comtesse Frontenac, and she has seen Seignelay—this I know—and also the Prince de Conti, who married a daughter of the King, Mademoiselle de Blois, and has tried to influence him."

"The Prince de Conti, eh, that great man, and twice most kind to me. He is interested in exploration, and I counted on his help. I named a post after him."

"You think she influenced him? But not at all. No woman, however adroit, can deceive him. He is sending here to-day Henri de Tonty, an Italian officer whose father was Governor of Gaeta and had to flee from Naples to France. In France he has invented the Tontine insurance policy and here his son has come—a young man of powerful intellect and great charm, as you shall see. He has a metal hand, for one was blown off at Libieso in the Sicilian wars. He became a captain. The Prince Conti has sent him, and that shows Madame Ranard has not influenced the great cousin of the King. I see in young De Tonty a comrade of yours. He has tact and skill, and the loyalty and enthusiasm of the Italian. He is poor, but he has what you lack, the great social gift, though he cannot impress people better with his honesty. Your foes are powerful, but the good God is with the right thing, and for you there shall be a secure future. You need one like Tonty with you. You can trust him, and able trusty men in France are few."

La Salle's figure became more restful. "Dear Abbé, you have helped me much already. I shall be glad to see him."

"You shall see him now, I think, for there is a knocking at the door."

Silence a moment, and then a servant entered and said, "Monsieur de Tonty."

Tonty entered, a tall spare figure with a face of dark color lightened by a pair of brilliant honest eyes with a feeling that comes of the soul within—the soul of a fighter, whose own native land was denied him, and who looked at

La Salle after the first greetings with eager eyes. What La Salle saw pleased him. He felt he could trust this man, who was the more appealing because of his metal left hand covered with a glove. He gave his right hand to La Salle, of whom he had heard, not always to his credit. But Tonty was a man who formed his own judgment, and that the Prince de Conti had sent him was sufficient.

La Salle smiled at him, and in the frank smile was a covert invitation, for at once La Salle wished to work with him. Tonty had the prodigious gift—he was a man of character, and he was, as the Abbé has said, unmarried and free for a life of peril and adventure.

"I have come from the Prince de Conti to a valued friend whom all France trusts—the Abbé here. We are fortunate, for men of trust are not plentiful in these days."

The Abbé's smile was that of content, for he saw these two men had made alliance of the heart already, and the way of success was more possible to La Salle. He knew that La Salle was lacking in those lighter qualities which Tonty had, and with character, too. He had the insight of the perfect priest who sees men as they not always see themselves, for his class are removed from the ambitions that influence others, and see more clearly than the average man.

"Sieur de la Salle has been telling me of life in Canada, and it is thrilling. It is full of danger and anxiety, but it is the upbuilding of an Empire of the West."

Tonty smiled and nodded. "I cannot return to Naples to build empire there, and France is now my nation. I would help build up New France. There is this drawback, of course—lifting up his metal hand—"but it would not prevent me, if I got the chance—if I got it."

He looked La Salle in the eyes, and La Salle said: "There is naught I wish more than to work with you. I need much a man of your caliber, for in Canada most men are out against me, even those I much admire. They are big, and they work against me and with the Intendant and certain old friends now hostile through trade, and others. I have far to go before I can win them to me—far to go."

Chapter VII: AT VERSAILLES

THE court assembled in the vast suite of apartments decorated by pictures and sculptures, tapestries, mosaics in light and splendor. Throngs feasted, gamed, promenaded, talked, and nowhere else in the world was there such magnificence. The suite was called the "Halls of Abundance"—of Venus, Mars, Diana, Mercury, Apollo; and Louis XIV met in the salon of Apollo with his courtiers, affable, gracious, august, a marvel of hard work and love of country, which under him was growing great and powerful.

Louis was his own Prime Minister and at the head of each department of state. His brain knew every important detail of every court in Europe. He formed his own policy and had an organization throughout France such as no government ever had. He was behind all the amazing progress of France. He had built it up from a series of fighting duchies from the days of the Fronde.

Louis has been traduced as the most arrogant ruler, who, a beardless king of seventeen, after a ride from Vincennes, strode, whip in hand, into the Parliament of Paris when they were discussing coinage, and said, sternly: "I forbid you, M. le Président, to discuss *my* edicts." The key to his policy lay in the words, *"L'état, C'est moi."* It has been called the sublimity of arrogance; yet his was the most brilliant reign of any modern French king; under him science and art flourished. Could it be that a man, however vain, who was an indefatigable worker, and who by his attitude to the world and to Canada, his new territory, shows his real nature by letters of such discernment and even justice, was so bad as has been painted? At one time he controlled Europe in effect. His army worshiped him.

We must not view the time of Louis XIV as we view life to-day—not in England, America, or in any other country. We must compare it with contemporary days. So doing, life under Louis in his seventy-two years' reign was most creditable to France. Vanity and arrogance are not crimes, else few great men would stand the test of time, and under Louis' powdered periwig and ringlets there was a brain of power; under his lace cravat there were a heart and mind that did honor to France; and behind his broad-skirted velvet coat and gold-headed cane and diamond-mounted stud, and jeweled snuff-box there was the courage of a man and the soul of a statesman. Extravagant he was and he loved display, but he worked like a slave with his Ministers, and no important detail escaped him. The letters he wrote to Frontenac and other Governors and Intendants, and to officials in New France are best tribute to a rare personality. Under the Generals Condé and Turenne, with Louvois as Minister of War; under Gremonville and Lionne as ambassadors, with Generals Vauban and Crequi and D'Enghien to come— France had reached to greater and greater days.

While the salon was full of courtiers awaiting the entrance of the Grand Monarch, things were happening on which depended the future of France in the New World. Were it not for La Salle, the vast territory from Fort Frontenac to the Gulf of Mexico would not have been taken in the name of France. We shall see how things went with La Salle.

It was at the house of the Prince de Conti that a meeting chanced which would influence the future of Canada. Tonty had given the Prince the result of his visit to the Abbé Renaudot, and Conti heard with pleasure that La Salle had asked Tonty to go to Canada. He said:

"I do not hear so well of La Salle's prospects as I had hoped, Tonty. He has bitter, powerful foes. If they influence King Louis and Colbert and Seignelay I shall have anxiety."

"But, Your Highness's influence is great at court, and you can set back the trio against La Salle."

The Prince smiled and tossed his fingers. "One never knows one's influence to be small or large till one tries, and I shall try to-day, but on the whole La Salle must fight his own fight, win his own case."

La Salle had done his best. He had written Colbert an account of his discoveries in modest yet convincing terms; had said that the new country of the far West was so fertile and beautiful that all could be produced that was produced in France; and more, that flocks and herds could be left out to pasture all winter, that the wild cattle had a fine wool for making cloth and hats, that hemp and cotton grew there naturally, that the Indians would adopt French ways and modes of life, and it was the knowledge of the poverty of Quebec, its dense forests, its harsh climate that had led him to plant colonies in the beautiful lands of the far West. He wrote of the dangers from the Iroquois and other tribes, the rapids and cataracts, the cost of men and provisions, and the rivalry of the English—of the Hudson's Bay Company and at Albany. But this last reason only animated La Salle the more and impelled him to confuse them by promptness of action as to settlement and forts.

The simplicity and directness of La Salle's appeal had good effect on Colbert, and he was ready to speak favorably to King Louis concerning his appeal. But meanwhile La Salle's foes were at work, and one of the most capable was the Abbé Potin. But Colbert, clean of mind and not corruptible, waited his opportunity. In the far West he saw a new empire for France, and not one to be a constant drain on the pocket of the King, who gave as freely as he could. Louis gave bounties on early marriages in Canada. Twenty livres were given to each youth who married before the age of twenty, and to each girl before sixteen. This was called the King's Gift, and exclusive of the dowry given every girl brought over by his orders, of whom about a thousand were sent over between 1665 and 1673. The dowry was sometimes a home, provisions for eight months, and often fifty livres and household supplies, and a barrel of salted meat. Also all *habitants* of Canada who had living ten children each received a pension.

Was all this direct out of King Louis' purse the act of a tyrant and a Nero?

As Prince Conti and Tonty talked in the Prince's house, La Salle and Barbe Ranard met in his anteroom, for both had come to see him. La Salle bowed to her with cold courtesy, and she, the perfect intrigante, came to him with outstretched hand.

"Ah, M. la Salle, we meet in France at last. May all you come to do be as the gods decide!"

La Salle looked at the insincere eyes, the smiling mouth, the powdered hair, with no nerve of assent roused, and with repugnance in his heart, but he said in reply to her equivocal words:

"As King Louis may decide—after such advice as Madame Ranard may give him direct or indirect, right or wrong, just or unjust, good or bad."

His face was composed as he spoke, but at his lips was a cold, ironical smile. He added:

"I do not forget, madame, what happened long ago, nor what you said at the Sainte Famille. Shall you use the same grotesque falsehood here in France—and to the ministers of the King?"

Her face underwent a sudden change. Her eyes became brilliant and fierce, her lips had a vicious look:

"I have told the minister what is well known in Quebec. I have not the gifts of fiction of the explorer. I think my word counts in France—my husband is in the Government service."

It was on La Salle's tongue to say that her husband's wife was in the service of the Intendant of Canada, but he forbore. He only said, satirically: "Madame is working for Canada here, of course. She has the patriot mind and the good of the Church at heart!"

"It is the strife between man and woman, Monsieur de la Salle, and in such contests it is not the man who wins. I have the secret of success in my pocket."

"Oh, in your pocket, madame! I knew you thought you had it—but not in your pocket! It is a powerful secret, but it does not always win."

"It wins when those who matter find it, M. de la Salle."

"We shall know about that soon, madame."

"Won't that depend on who sees the Minister last?"

"As for me, Madame Ranard, I abide by the customs of the place."

"Do you know the customs of this place so well, monsieur?" There was biting insult in her tone.

"Not so well as madame, I suppose, but enough to find my way about."

"The ways are dark, monsieur, and you will lose your path. You are not on the St. Lawrence or Lake Ontario. You are a backwoodsman. You do not know the halls of Versailles."

"I am a backwoodsman, as you say, yet I came from France and I am not so verdant. My family were of the Caveliers of Rouen, and I was educated for the priesthood of the Jesuits."

"You were a master in a Jesuit school!"

La Salle flushed slightly, for her tone and manner were contemptuous.

"Madame was never a mistress in a Jesuit school. She is the donnée of the Jesuits now, and what else be the will of God."

Barbe's anger now was great. Stepping close to La Salle, she slapped his face. "You insult a lady like that! If I were a man I would fight you—low born, low bred, thief of trade, tool of Frontenac, grotesque ape of social life, most in debt of any man of Canada, and most loathed."

La Salle smiled coldly. "If I am most in debt, it is proof I am not so much loathed, and as for my breeding, it ranks with that of a woman and her husband who stooped to the tricks of the ditch to bring a gentleman into disrepute. If you were a man I would make the world too small to hold you, madame."

Barbe turned and saw Tonty leaving the Prince de Conti's salon.

"Monsieur de Tonty, behold the man who abused the hospitality of my house, and now insults me at the door of the Prince de Conti."

Tonty looked at her satirically. "I think Sieur de la Salle never abused the hospitality of any household and never insulted a lady in his life. Madame Ranard, you have lost your temper—why I know not."

His handsome face had contempt for this brilliant and seductive figure, and he knew La Salle had in her a dangerous foe—one who would lose no chance to hurt him—by falsehood and every vile act of such a woman.

She saw his metal hand, and she now hit him with all malice:

"Not only is your hand metal, Henri de Tonty, your mind is also."

[44]

The insult brought a flush to Tonty's face, but he kept himself in hand. If a man had said such a thing—but it did not matter! She was of the most *incroyable* kind, and she was clever and vicious enough to give La Salle a bad time.

He turned from her slowly. "The Prince will see you now, La Salle."

La Salle said, with a courteous bow, "But ladies first!"

Madame Ranard moved forward, but Tonty said: "The Prince wished to speak to the Sieur de la Salle, madame. He knew, however, that you were here."

"I shall prefer to have the last word with the Prince," she said, with irony at her lips.

Bowing low, La Salle entered the salon and left her alone with Tonty.

"They will be some time. Will you not be seated, madame?" He courteously offered her a chair.

Her urbanity had returned. She smiled and seated herself and parted the ribbons at her throat. He could not fail to see how taking and alluring she was. All passions in her were in good control. She gave, she took away, with perfect measurement; her whole figure was alert, delicate, delicious. Even now her bosom throbbed as she looked sweetly at him. She was making a sudden and last attempt to win his approval.

He understood, and a strange drooping light came into his eyes. But all he said was:

"The roads are bad, madame, and the sky threatens."

She made no reply at once, then saw the curious look in his eyes and she quoted viciously lines from a song of Bourgoyne:

> "Eho! Eho! Eho!
> The lambs are on the plains.
> Eho! Eho! Eho!
> The wolves are in the woods!"

NEVER had the court at Versailles been more given to gayety and splendor. Yet behind all was an air of drama and grim event. Bright colors, perukes, swords, uniforms, laces, exquisite skirts, flamboyant ribbons, orders, velvet coats sometimes pure white, and everywhere signs of brilliance. Yet it was all possible, for Colbert had by his great finance made France rich, and unlike his predecessor, Cardinal Mazarin, he did not seek riches, and yet he could have made himself immensely rich. He was a figure as dear to France as later was Cavour to Italy, or Pitt to England, and he and his son Seignelay stood apart from the splendid superficial flippancy of Louis' reign. Marital felicity was derided in France, it was the sport of the theaters, but that was only at the capital; provincial France then, as now, was free from the sordid disregard of marital faith. Moscow was not Russia, Paris was not France, London was not England, Vienna was not Austria, Rome was not Italy, and behind all the outer show great causes and great minds were working, and all for the good of the land.

In the great Hall of Apollo stood Madame de Montespan, the favorite of Louis, surrounded by devoted courtiers, and she was not far from the King's throne. She was a most handsome woman, graceful in figure and with liquid and exasperating eyes. She knew well why these courtiers surrounded her, and she did not dislike it, for it was a tribute to her power with the monarch. But she was not deceived by it. She had a mind that would not stop at small things.

Barbe Ranard was of her class, but on a lower range of intellect and influence and poise. Even as a model to an artist takes on the air and imbibes the principles of art, so does the favorite of a great monarch grow more interesting because of her experience.

Madame de Montespan, the mother of seven children by Louis, seemed in excellent spirits, and was all smiles to those who flattered her, and she was as popular with the women as the men. She had that in her favor. She looked round the wonderful hall with pride. Here were princes, warriors, statesmen, philosophers, poets, artists, dramatists, all in the gaudy clothes of the court and all in the picture in sympathy with the magnificent architecture and decoration. She had worked her way brilliantly to her high place, yet she was not so vain as to believe that she might not be supplanted some day, and there was Fontanges, and there had been Vallière and others—and her mind was alert to hold Louis fast.

As she looked down the huge rooms, she saw approaching Abbé Potin, her confessor and secret-service agent. There was an ominous look in his face. She did not give her hand as he came near, but her suitors saw she wished to speak alone with him, and they drew aside.

She looked him in the eyes. "Well, Abbé, what is it? There's trouble. Is it grave?"

A satirical look crossed his face. "To have our plans thwarted is grave even in small things. This is not the biggest thing in the life of the Court, but it is a big thing in New France, in which His Majesty is so concerned. It would be bad for defeat to come now."

"Ah, it is the matter of La Salle—that?"

"Even that, madame. The Abbé Renaudot brought La Salle in touch with the Prince de Conti, and through him with Henri de Tonty, and through him with La Motte de

Lussière, and Barbe Ranard has not been able to influence Colbert or Seignelay or Prince de Conti."

"She is naught, but you, have you also failed? Tell me all, Abbé."

"I induced Abbé Renaudot, an astute and able man, to get information from the Comtesse Frontenac for Colbert, and he got what was required. But we could not win him to us. He is no friend of the Jesuits; he is a Recollet, if he is aught, and he made close friends with La Salle, whom he met at the home of Comtesse Frontenac. That we did not foresee. He has visited La Salle in his quarters, and La Salle has made progress. Yesterday La Salle and Tonty met Barbe Ranard at the house of Prince Conti, and Seignelay, would have naught to do with her action against La Salle—influenced perhaps by Conti."

De Montespan frowned. "Conti—Conti—he is pestilent! Louis' son-in-law!"

"He has weight, and has become a friend of La Salle. It is said by the servant of Conti who is in my pay, that Barbe Ranard failed to influence either the Prince or Seignelay, though she tried hard. She is handsome, captivating, and clever, and could influence men—and has influenced many."

"She is the friend of Duchesneau, the Intendant, in Quebec. She must have brains as well as charm. I would like to see her."

"She is here, madame. She shall be brought, if you so wish."

She inclined her head. "Is that all you have to tell?"

"But no, madame. Much more. There has been a meeting of Colbert, Seignelay, and the Grand Monarch. Colbert, insensible to my influence and to Barbe Ranard, has found much in La Salle to commend, and La Salle wrote a strikingly attractive report to the Minister of all that he has done and proposes to do. It has influenced the powerful and successful Colbert."

"Too powerful and too successful, Abbé, but it would be madness to try to move him, for the King gives him high place in affection."

"He cannot be removed, for he is the financial bulwark of France—an able man whom we detest, but he is incorruptible—as I know well."

"No blandishment of woman could move him!"

"You have not tried, madame!"

She looked at him with meaning in her eyes. "I have—and failed, but I shall try again, for there is much against me. It will be worth while testing my power. La Salle's report seems to have influenced them all. Ah, there Colbert is!"

In the distance Colbert could be seen, with Seignelay, coming slowly up the hall, and he was not surrounded, for few sought his company; he was too austere. But Seignelay had a more adaptable personality. He was a man not so great as his father, but he could not be purchased by gold or the Magdalene, and that was rare at Court.

"His Majesty will soon be here—his Ministers have come."

"And there is Barbe Ranard," said the Abbé. He sighed. "I have known her some years. She is a faithful friend of the Church."

"Summon her to me, Abbé."

The Abbé did not go himself, but sent a young officer of the King's Guard for her, and she came gracefully forward, her step light, her manner with an assumed modesty, her eyes tremulous with mock humility. She was becomingly dressed, her taking neck and fascinating face showing to advantage. She was no rival in beauty and distinction to De Montespan, and her pretended modesty pleased the favorite, though she saw through it; but seeing through it did not perturb her. The deceit was a tribute to herself, and she held out a hand in response to Barbe's curtsey. Barbe kissed it, and De Montespan said:

"You are welcome to old France, dear madame. You have lived in the wild places—how long?"

"Long enough to make me glad to feel the air of old France around me, madame. New France is not the same, though we have a small court there and we have a life that stirs in us the spirit of progress."

"So the Intendant, M. Duchesneau, says," she replied, with her eyes fixed on Barbe's face, "and Count Frontenac says it even more vigorously, I hear."

Barbe felt the thrust concerning Duchesneau, but she did not resent it, as why should she in a court like this, and before the favorite of the King.

"Count Frontenac has many foes in Canada," said Barbe.

"I am addressing one of them now, am I not? It is a contest between the Governor and the Intendant and you are with the Intendant. Between ourselves, I do not blame you, for I too am a Jesuit. I know all you have tried to do, and you have failed."

Barbe's face showed disconcerting changes of expression, but she looked respectfully at De Montespan.

"And will the great Madame la Marquise, perhaps, try now?" she said.

Montespan's face smiled inscrutably. "To try with so much against one is not easy. Your own failure and that of Abbé Potin is the best proof. Who am I that I should try? If they would not listen to you, do you guess they would heed me?"

She said this to flatter and also to tempt Barbe, for it would try her skill at reply.

"If they will not listen to madame, then no one need

essay. For madame has gifts beyond all others—man or woman—in France."

She was pleased. "Why not in all the world?"

"I only know France," was the adroit reply, "and France is all the world."

"Well said, well said, vain patriot," declared De Montespan.

"Madame, His Majesty," said the Abbé Potin, drawing near.

Slowly, yet with portentous dignity and magnificence, Louis came slowly up the room, preceded by his lords-in-waiting and his aides, and all the vast audience bowed low as the little man with his high red-heeled shoes came up the room.

As he advanced he spoke to Louvois, his Minister of War, to Madame de Longueville and the Duchess de Chevreuse, the most skillful and persistent intrigantes of the time, and Mazarin had said of the former that she was equal to ten provinces. But she had no weight with Louis. He also gave a word to Madame de Rambouillet, the owner of a great salon where many came, and to La Rochefoucauld, the Duchess de Chantillon; to the poets Racine and Molière; to Lulli, the composer, and Quinault, who wrote with him— and Louis spoke as warmly to them as to the more highly titled. Near his throne he saw mademoiselle the Duchess de Montpensier, who was his cousin and who lived at the Luxembourg, where she received in as picturesque a state as did no one else in Louis' empire. He had banished her more than once, but in the end he always pardoned her, though he never forgave her for having ordered attack upon his own soldiers at the Bastille. With her were Madame de Scudery, who gave famous Saturdays; the Abbé de Choisy, Madame de Lafayette, Madame de Sévigné. Nearer still to the throne stood the Dauphin, fat, over-dressed, handsome, brainless, and a danger to France, so lacking in kingly qualities was he. Not far from him stood Bossuet, his old tutor, whom Louis made Bishop of Metz, and also the Duc d'Enghien, son of the great Condé.

He had pride in picking out the "Untitled nobles"—like Molière and Lulli—as he called them, to receive recognition. It was not all vanity, for he was a man with artistic leanings and vast ambitious purposes, and he had faith that in good time he would, like Alexander, command the world. Littleness was in him, but also greatness, and his littleness was his age, and his greatness was for all time.

As he neared his throne he inclined his head to De Montespan and she came to him. He gave her his hand and she kissed it, and other courtiers drew near, and among them were the Abbé Potin, whom he did not wholly like, though he was De Montespan's confessor.

"Well, eyes of heaven, what have you to say. I see there is something," he said to De Montespan with a railing kind of tenderness.

"About New France, Sire. I would speak of that. Things go not well there, as you have told me."

"And so it vexes my sweetheart. And have only I, then, told you?" he asked, his eyes turning to the Abbé Potin and then to Barbe Ranard.

"I am concerned only with what you tell me, Sire."

"Well, I have decided about New France. M. Colbert," he said, in a voice raised a little, and the courtiers made way for Colbert. "Colbert, concerning New France, there is only one grave question there, and it is that of the Sieur de la Salle. I have decided, have I not?"

Colbert inclined his head. Montespan turned to Louis, and in a soft voice said:

"To give De la Salle no encouragement?"

King Louis smiled and gently replied: "What is encouragement? Is it the right to build forts and to find the way to the mouth of the Mississippi, to carry on trade with the Indians, and solely at his own cost? If that is encouragement, then I shall encourage La Salle."

"But, Sire, you have never approved of settlements in the West—it removed your subjects too far from your own control. You refused one, Louis Joliet, an explorer, to found a trading station in the Mississippi Valley."

"And may not a king change his mind? La Salle has the true thing in him, and I trust him. Frontenac supports him."

"And Duchesneau, the Intendant, and the Church and the principal people of Quebec distrust him, bear him no good will. Besides—"

King Louis frowned. "Yes, I know that 'Besides,' and it is in our presence now. It is not far from me. But no woman save one ever traduced La Salle. Quote not 'Besides,' for she does not influence me."

"Nor do I, Sire, any more."

The King pretended not to hear. "Colbert," said he, "is the Sieur de la Salle here to-night?"

"Sire, I think so."

Louis made a motion of his hand.

Officers of the King went searching, while De Montespan made effort to turn Louis' mind, but he did not listen gravely to her, and gently smiled and said: "If you had the facts as I know them, my dulciana, you would not be so vexed. You are too much of a Jesuit. The Church shall not control my Canada."

At that moment La Salle, with Tonty behind him, came forward, and all the court observed him. He was a figure men would turn to see, having looked once. It was not alone his handsomeness, for men like Tonty were handsomer. It was the upright precision and physical grace of his person;

it was the honesty in his face, his masculinity of form, his indomitable look, his apparent haughtiness, his clear energy, his concentrated look of inspiration, as though he had no thought but one, and that was his mission in life. As he came forward not only Colbert and Louis so appraised him, but he was such a contrast to the Court in the simplicity of his dress and the quiet nobility of his bearing, that all felt him to be a tower of courage and faith against whom danger and hardship would beat in vain.

The apparent haughtiness of his manner was understood by all. It was the self-reliance of a man that lived alone, the spirit overpowering what came before it. Never a wincing courtier, he would have foes always, but at King Louis' court he had made friends of four wise men—King Louis, Colbert, Seignelay, and Conti.

As he bowed to the King with profound respect, for he felt the august majesty of the scene, he won many hearts present, and even De Montespan was moved, for she had never seen him before, and she felt him a man who would do no mean thing—would never have done what Barbe Ranard had said! Women know men well—such women.

"Sieur de la Salle," said Louis, "we welcome you. It is our first sight of you, but we know your work and what you would do. This France of ours has vast designs—not only European; they include America and beyond—far beyond. We will be all-powerful, all-controlling, and we are giving you large powers of exploration and settlement in the sure hope that we shall not be dismayed. We would have you find the way to Mexico from Fort Frontenac, and you shall build forts as it seems good to you at your own cost, and you shall have sole right to trade in buffalo hides. That is our reply to your appeal, and may God be with you and strengthen you, Robert Cavelier, Sieur de la Salle." His hand was raised in kindly feeling.

Across La Salle's face there passed a swift emotion and his
eyes grew dim. He was receiving far more than he had
asked and it was given him in the most public manner and
with all display and honor. When Louis ceased speaking,
the attendant courtiers said in loud whispers: "How noble!
How great! How like Jove! How dear to France!" All
present seemed to bend in flattery save the Abbé Potin and
a few of his Jesuit brothers, and De Montespan—yet even
they put on airs of devotion to the Grand Monarch and hid
the bitterness in their souls.

As for De Montespan, she looked at Barbe and was almost
startled by the fierce fire of her eyes and the tragedy of her
figure. She had failed in what she had come from Quebec
to do, and her wild spirit was breaking loose upon this
court, yet not to other eyes than those of De Montespan,
who had a gift of seeing. She also had failed, and had suffered an affront which would trouble her vain, proud heart.
Not far away stood Prince de Conti, and the quiet triumph
in his eyes was like a stripe upon the raw flesh. He was a
strong, loyal, able man, and, though Louis did not love
him, he had pride that Conti was of his own blood and
family.

La Salle replied to King Louis briefly, and all present
were impressed by the calm, piercing emotion of his tone.
He had a voice with few inflections; it was rather monotonous, but that gave it power, and it moved even the blasé
circle of courtiers in the great hall. It was like the man
himself, direct, incisive, convincing, enduring, and he stood
a reproach to the phantasmagoria of life of which they were.
It was all poppyland, and he the wide wastes, the dark forests, the barren plains, the evil citizens of the Indian world,
ready to burn and destroy and never rebuild—treacherous,
brave yet cowardly, insolent yet amenable. Yet this Court
had seen and should see again Jesuits who had been tor-

tured and burned till their hands and limbs were like grotesque imitations of humanity. This King Louis had seen the broken relics of men who had escaped from the farthest regions where the fleur-de-lis waved, and yet returned to face it all again. A Court like this, outwardly insecure, had the elements of right, as was later shown when France, torn by revolution, would send to the guillotine just such people as these, and they would face their tragic end with a smile of disdain.

The flippancy and evil of the court were only the clothes. Beneath it all was the kind of truth that was in Cartier, Champlain, Frontenac, Maissoneuve, Marquette, Brebeuf, Jogues and La Salle. Tear away the laces, the velvets, the wigs and the outer fripperies, and stark, brave, true human life would prove that France at her worst was better than the surface showed. This court was a magnificent contradiction. Evil, yet good.

La Salle said: "Sire, I am honored by your commission. I have one thought, and shall ever have but one—the increase of the greatness of your realm. Naught shall divert me from that purpose. I have seen"—his eyes looked through Louis and far beyond—"the ways open to an overseas empire that shall be a home for millions of my fellow-countrymen, and for France a new garden where all things shall flourish. You give me hope that my life may prove evidence of your noble purposes and labors, and imperishable patriotism. I shall be ever Your Majesty's most faithful and devoted servant, Sire."

During these words the little, efficient, skilful, and powerful monarch looked at La Salle and round his Court with the air of the maker of the world. His ears were tuned to flattery, but in the words of La Salle was a new note—it gave his soul a spring of virtue and purpose, it lifted him to the height of his tallest grenadier morally. He smiled and gave him a hand to kiss, and when La Salle rose he met the eyes of Barbe Ranard, who would have killed him now if she could, for he saw the savage hatred in her eyes, though her lips were smiling.

In his heart was triumph, but his nature was free from guile or the smaller things. He knew he was now on a new and wider pathway of life and that behind him was—for the moment—the greatest monarch of the world, and a Minister—Colbert—who had even greater things in him than his master. Colbert was then in an age and at a Court where the small and the great were in sharp contrast, in hideous, yet beautiful amalgamation.

King Louis saw Prince Conti near, and inclined his head, and Conti came. Louis said: "My cousin, you have an eye—you see far. Is it done well to-day?"

Conti's face showed no feeling. "Your Majesty is right to-day, as he always is. In the Sieur de la Salle is a subject who will bring honor to France—to you. I have no tongue for flattery, Sire."

"I know it well," and Louis lightly dusted some powder from a scarf and gazed round him kindly. He saw La Salle talking to Tonty. "Ah, that Henri de Tonty, the Italian, is he a friend of La Salle, my cousin?"

"I brought them together, and Tonty goes to Canada with La Salle. He is a strong, brave man."

"I am glad. I have honored La Salle before my court. He knows all it means to him."

"Did not his speech assure?"

"I have never heard such a speech at Court and I have heard many. There is something in his voice that gets to the core of things."

Louis turned to De Montespan. "Well, my seraph, what think you of La Salle?"

De Montespan, who had the true sense of things behind

her fripperies and sordidness, said: "My sovereign was benign, and La Salle is a man of men. He has not the Church behind him, but he is the soul of the new life— over there."

Louis was pleased now. He did not see the falsehood in the woman, for he was fond of her as yet, and he thought that he—not La Salle—had conquered her. He whispered in her ear, and what he said brought a slight flush to her face. Her eyes looked into his and dropped so that their light was for him only.

Barbe Ranard and Abbé Potin watched them. She said: "La Salle has beaten us Abbé, but he has not yet left Paris for New France. There is still that to do!"

The Abbé touched her arm. "Not *that*. It must not be. He must return to Quebec, and then! Not here. Louis would search it out after to-night. Let be. It is not the way to fly in the face of Fate."

She clenched her hands. "The face of Fate shall be with me yet, then."

Chapter IX: FOES MEET

LA SALLE found his reception at Court had done great
things for him, but he needed money. Through the
Abbé Renaudot and Henri de Tonty he came to Simmonet, a
notary, and Raoul, an advocate, and one Dumont, who between them lent him thirty-four thousand francs, and his
cousin François Plet, a merchant, lent him a large sum at
the stiff rate of forty per cent. His chief helpers were his
family, his brothers who gave all they could at last, and
before his discoveries were ended he had cost them, so they
said in their extravagant memorial to King Louis, five hundred thousand francs. And on his return even Frontenac
found a loan secured by a mortgage on Fort Frontenac.

The Abbé Renaudot had proved a stalwart friend by
tongue and pen, and did his best to prevent Bellinzani,
director of trade, who had been trained by Cardinal Mazarin, from extorting money from La Salle, but did not succeed. He thought it well, as did La Salle and Tonty, not
to appeal to Colbert or Seignelay lest worst might chance
in the end, but the money the director got was later re-
claimed by the Abbé when Bellinzani fell into disgrace with
Seignelay.

One day before La Salle sailed from Rochelle he was
summoned to the home of the Comtesse Frontenac, where
she lived with Mademoiselle Outrelaise—and the two were
known in France and Canada as "The Divines," so popular
and courted were they. Outrelaise was not present at this

visit. The Comtesse was in high spirits, and gave him warm commendation for having triumphed at Court and she said:

"You have done great service to my husband, for your success has strengthened him against intrigues. He cannot well meet all the charges made, and I stay here to help him, for I have no love for the primitive life, and yet I never go to Court. I am too poor for that life but I will not live in the dark!"

"Madame la Comtesse could never live in the dark," said La Salle. "Her life is too bright and Les Divines are more powerful than if they were at court. I have named a river 'Les Divines.'"

This pleased the Comtesse. "You will be surprised to hear that Madame Ranard is coming to-day and that is one reason why I asked you. I know what she has done and still tries to do against you, but you will conquer in the end, though she represents the Jesuits—but herself before all and most of all! I know madame is a foe of my Frontenac, too, but I shall see her here and find what real stuff she is. She has some power through Duchesneau, the Intendant, but that is insufficient. Frontenac—and you will win!"

La Salle smiled. "I shall be pleased to see madame again. She is vastly able, but she did not have power against the friends of Count Frontenac—Prince de Conti, Colbert, Seignelay, and King Louis himself, though she had Madame de Montespan behind her."

At that moment a servant announced Madame Ranard, and she entered with aplomb. She could never be nonplused, and not even now when she saw La Salle near Comtesse Frontenac. After Madame Frontenac had greeted her with cordiality and had motioned her to a chair, she turned to La Salle, who bowed low.

"Ah, Sieur de la Salle," she said, "last time I saw you

you were in close touch with the Grand Monarch. You were in high favor—for the moment—but prince's favors are like spring showers. They do not much enrich the ground. Is it not so?"

La Salle smiled. "I am new to Court life and I am glad to have the moment's favors. Better these than naught. The favors of King Louis have their uses, and in Canada their perfect potential uses, as Madame Ranard knows. When they cease, those who lived by them cease. It is a place of mixed interests."

"A salad—a French salad, which the oil of the Grand Monarch's favor makes good for all," said Madame Ranard, lightly.

"And the acid of intrigue makes bad for all," said the Comtesse Frontenac.

"But the oil endures to the good of all," said La Salle.

Madame Ranard smiled subtly and her tongue was soft.

"The good of all is not found without some contest of mixed interests. The Sieur de la Salle has far to go in the wild West and much to do—at his own expense!"

There was that in her tone which La Salle and the Comtesse did not miss. "Nothing can be got for nothing in this world," said La Salle. "The expense may be high, but I can meet it and outlast it."

As he said this he met the eyes of Barbe, which had a veiled but bitter malice, and yet she waved a hand cheerfully:

"Prophet—prophet! God save the prophet! May he outlast his prophecy!"

For the first time in his life La Salle was the sinister courtier. He leaned over, took Barbe's fingers and kissed them, as they turned cold at his lips.

"Ah, Madame Ranard, you have given me the great hope. May it be fulfilled!"

This was too much. She withdrew her hand sharply and looked him fiercely in the eyes:

"Your experience at Court has given you grace of words, Sieur de la Salle, but there is no grace of heart behind. Your path will be steep—and hideous!"

"Yet, as you said, with God's help I shall win, madame."

The Comtesse interposed: "Madame sees that Sieur de la Salle has the true spirit of the pioneer. With Frontenac's help he will win."

Suddenly Madame Ranard rose and turned on her with savage irony. "You brought me here to meet this man, Comtesse. Know then that I understand. I go back to Canada with the spirit you have shown me here. You brought me here to shame me; in Canada I will bring shame to you."

"You are wrong, madame. I brought you not to shame you, but in the hope that you and the Sieur de la Salle might find peace here in the house of the Governor of Canada."

"Peace—peace, to talk of peace between us! He used me vilely in Quebec."

"Madame, that has no glint of truth," said La Salle.

Without a word, but with a sweeping curtsey to Madame Frontenac, she turned brusquely with an acrid laugh, and left the room.

The Comtesse raised her hand in disdain.

"I am glad she came, rude as she was, for now I understand her. She is able and beautiful and bad. She will stop at naught!"

"She has been stopped. She will start again. I go back to Count Frontenac with a strong heart."

The Comtesse looked at him sadly: "Strength is good, but love is better, Sieur de la Salle."

La Salle inclined his head and smiled as he looked into the distance:

"There is a wonderful Canadian chanson, madame: The sentimentalists sing it there. It is popular—and forceful!"

> "Il ya longtemps que je t'aime,
> Jamais je ne t'oublierai."

The Comtesse turned away sadly.

Chapter X: LYA

TUKE DAROIS had found employment in the offices of the Farmer of the King's revenue. He had been in the employ of the Hudson's Bay Company. He spoke the French language perfectly and came as a spy on the doings of La Salle and the *coureurs de bois,* who were rivals in trade with the Hudson's Bay Company in the far West and North. With his combined origin, Darois was a capable man and had no morals. He had a good-looking and enterprising face, he was bearded, was about medium height, and had an attractive personality. He did not say he had been with the Hudson's Bay Company, but had been a trapper in the North, and he was welcomed to Quebec by officials of the Province, for he had the rare ability to write and keep accounts, and his services were welcome in the department of Rojet Ranard.

His daughter, Lya, with brown hair, brown eyes, rather a large mouth exquisitely shaped, and a broad, low, fine forehead, lived with him. Her hands were capable and fine and she had a long firm grip. From her hand you would judge her character. It told so much. She had been commanded not to say they had been with the Hudson's Bay Company; and this was to prevent prejudice against her father. She had no mother—her mother had died at giving her birth, and she had living with her an old black-eyed, lame Frenchwoman called Luce Hontard, who was devoted to her. She was one who might go far in the world, if aught could be judged by outer form.

Lya

One day after La Salle and Tonty had arrived from France with La Motte de Lussière, they were coming from the citadel where Frontenac had received them with cordiality, and La Salle saw Lya walking towards her father's office. She had so much spirit, yet was so modest, so simply yet becomingly dressed, with none of the hair-dressings and flounces of other girls of the city, and with a resolution of her slight figure at variance with her vivacious face. Somehow she arrested La Salle's attention. He had never been impressionable, and no woman ever had a hold on him. He drew Tonty's attention to her. Tonty was also attracted and was unable to say why.

"A newcomer and a beauty. Who?" said Tonty.

La Salle shook his head in negation. They saw her enter her father's office.

Tonty spoke. "Ah, Tuke Darois's daughter, no doubt! That is his office. I met him this morning. He is watching the *coureurs de bois,* of whom Du Lhut is chief. How do I know? I don't. It is only instinct, but I'm right, for I saw signs of it in his office. He does not ring true. He's got a twist somewhere. I saw on his table a manuscript marked *Du Lhut.* So, I made up my mind. He is working against the *coureurs de bois* and Du Lhut. But not his beautiful daughter—no, if that is she! She is as straight as the sun!"

La Salle nodded and gave a short, hasty laugh. "Perhaps you are right. Let us go to his office. I have some business with him. It concerns the accounts of Fort Frontenac. He is a man to know. We start for the West in two days, my friend. See! There is Rojet Ranard coming towards us. How cheerful—as though he had not a care in the world. But he is Mephistopheles—as black as a pan."

Tonty nodded, and M. Ranard came towards them,

[65]

smiling. He knew Tonty and had not seen him yet, as he had been in the West.

He raised a hand in greeting. "Ah, M. Tonty, I welcome you to Quebec. You would do much here, I know, and you have left much behind you." He held out a hand and Tonty took it with a bow.

"I greet you well, M. Ranard, and I left behind naught I could not afford to leave. I work with my friend Sieur de la Salle."

M. Ranard turned slowly to La Salle. "Sieur de la Salle and I are old friends, and we meet as always—in good feeling."

La Salle looked coldly at him. "It is as M. Ranard says, we meet in the feeling we had when I left for France."

"I am told you met my wife there, Sieur de la Salle."

"I had that felicity, monsieur—at the home of Comtesse de Frontenac, and before that at the palace of the Prince de Conti."

"She was charmed by your success—you were received by the Grand Monarch at Versailles and were given your commission before the court. It was a triumph for you, Sieur de la Salle." There was veiled sarcasm in Ranard's tone.

"It was a triumph for New France, let us say," remarked Tonty. "It had the soul of exploration and trade."

"It had the soul of Sieur de la Salle," said Ranard, with a biting tongue.

"And his is the soul of New France," said Tonty.

"May it flourish for the good of old France!" returned Ranard.

"If all here say Yea, who shall say Nay?" said La Salle, ironically.

"But all say Yea," sneered Ranard.

"Then things have changed since I went to France," said La Salle.

"What else could happen? Your absence is a vast event," remarked Ranard maliciously.

"Especially when Madame Ranard was gone also, bent upon the good of Canada, and helpful to me in France!"

A dark light came into Ranard's eyes. "She will always help you in the same way, as you well know, Sieur de la Salle. She never changes, and if you but visited our house again, you would flourish more."

"I have flourished because I did not remain in your house, monsieur, and I hope I shall never enter it again!"

"Yet we shall meet often in this small place, Quebec, and we cannot escape each other's influence, can we?"

"That is made plain by the difference between the Governor and the Intendant, and yet we know our influence on the Intendant," said Tonty.

The eyes of Ranard grew sullen, for he felt what Tonty would convey, but with a sneer he said:

"Monsieur Duchesneau is not like you or me—or he would take return for your insolence, M. Tonty."

He laid his hand angrily upon his sword, and Tonty shrugged a shoulder. "I was not insolent to the Intendant, monsieur."

"You were insolent to me—then draw, monsieur, and see which can uphold his honor best."

A cold light blazed in Tonty's eyes. "I do not care to fight you, monsieur, but you have ways I do not like. I would find what is inside you—blood or ditch water."

They at once began to fight, and had made but a few strokes, in which Tonty was at an advantage, when Bishop Laval came upon them on his way from the Church council. He was, as always, plainly dressed, and his striking face with long nose and piercing eyes gave him a singular personality. He had been master of New France in other days.

"Messieurs, messieurs," the bishop said, in amazement, "what do you broiling in the street! Is Canada to be governed thus! Stop fighting, messieurs!"

"He insulted the Intendant," said Ranard.

"I did not insult the Intendant, Monsieur de Quebec. I said what monsieur thought reflected on the Intendant, but it was not meant so. I came with Sieur de la Salle from France."

The Bishop turned towards La Salle and smiled in a frigid way. "The Sieur de la Salle has a high place in the heart of Canada, M. Tonty."

He held out his hand, this spare, almost emaciated bishop, but there was power in his whole bearing and authority in all he said. He lived a life of abject poverty, had been a Jesuit in his youth, and had brought to Canada two things— self-effacement physically, and the ever-present love of his Church—its advancement. He had no love for La Salle, for he would extend immigration in the West, and that he and the Church did not wish. His Church had once been all-powerful, and received four-fifths of the revenue sent by the King, but of late years that power had declined, and the old man resented it in so far as his nature could. The Bishop had done much for Canada, and his thin lips now drew tighter as he turned to M. Ranard.

"It is not seemly, M. Ranard, that you should act so— an officer of the Government; yet maybe your temper took umbrage where none was meant."

At first Tonty would say that umbrage was meant to Ranard, but he abstained; and all seemed settled, for the two men put up their swords, but La Salle said:

"M. Tonty took up the quarrel on his own part, but the difference of opinion was with me, monseigneur, and I would gladly have fought with M. Ranard, for a reason which he and you will understand. I do not forget what happened in his house and what was said at the Saint Famille. These things should not be handed over to one's friends. M. Tonty said what I would have said with more point."

The Bishop's face flushed slightly at the mention of Saint Famille, for he knew what had been said there, and he had given this society of Jesuit ladies his approval; but he said:

"Sieur de la Salle, we have no knowledge of your difference with M. Ranard—"

"And his wife," interrupted La Salle.

"And his wife; but this is a small place and we should live in peace. There have been misunderstandings, no doubt, but we should overcome our feelings for the sake of unity in this pioneer land. Why should we not all be friends?"

"Why not?" said Ranard.

"I will say, why not, then!" said La Salle. "The greatest Governor Canada ever had is opposed by good men like Le Moyne and his sons, and Le Ber and La Chesnaye, Damours, De Villeray and De Lotbinière, and many others, and they are all against me because I open new territory and advance new trade in furs. I know what forces are against me, and what intrigue goes to hurt good things, but the good will prevail, monseigneur. I will help advance that, but I will yield naught in all I do to open up the West and South."

He held himself modestly, firmly erect, for this was the first time he had opened his mind to the Bishop, and he wished it to be plain what sort of man he was and what he meant to do. Bishop Laval liked La Salle—he knew him as one who never spared himself and fought with clean hands. But his ambitions clashed with those of the Church and the Intendant, and that was against him sorely.

He said, quietly: "Your designs have support from all who care for Canada, but your methods are not those we all approve. Our ways are not your ways, and we work by different rules. Yet"—he raised his hand in benediction, and the men dropped to their knees—"I give you blessing in your work, for I know your heart is full of high purpose."

As they all stood up, Ranard said: "Monsieur de Quebec, I shall wipe this dark thing from my mind. I will be a friend to Sieur de la Salle. I offer him my hand."

La Salle instantly said: "I have no faith in the friendship of M. Ranard. I cannot take his hand."

The Bishop looked at him sternly for a moment, then his face cleared and he said, "At least the Sieur de la Salle is an honest man," and he turned and went towards his palace.

Habitants and rivermen and a few *coureurs de bois* and a burgher or two had gathered, but they came not among them, and though they wondered what the quarrel and the consultation were, they were too much in awe of Bishop Laval to come too near. Quebec was too often roused by combats to be astonished.

Ranard looked at La Salle with grim irony. "You have refused my hand; be sure you can justify that."

"I am ready to sustain it," answered La Salle, with bitter coolness, for this man and his wife were the limit of endurance—so clever, so corrupt, so bad, and yet outwardly so fair.

Lifting his hand in courtesy La Salle moved away with Tonty, while Ranard stood for a moment in furtive mood, and then walked on with malign purpose.

As they passed along the street there came to their ears a song of the pioneers of France, brought to Canada by the Carignan-Sallières Regiment. It floated out on the clear air with sweet melody and happy resonance:

"I am a very good knife-grinder,
I am a very good knife-grinder,
And for my daughter I have great fear—
And in the islands I have a great fear
    When I am there,
As she is very good."

"If I go on the sea,
If I go on the sea,
It will be never to return,
And in the islands I have a great fear,
    When I am there,
For she is very good."

As they listened, Tonty laughed: "He may be a good knife-grinder but I doubt it, and for his daughter, he may well have a great fear, for she *is* good! That's so, isn't it?"

La Salle nodded. "He's bad enough, I doubt not, and she's good, I doubt not, and we shall see them both soon. Here we are at his door." La Salle now said to Tonty: "We are on the bank of a turbulent river, but we shall cross it safely. Our heaviest trials are before us. Naught borne in the past can equal what I must bear—what we must bear— in the future. As I open this door, I open a new and horrible chapter of life. This I know."

He opened the door and Father Louis Hennepin stepped out. Hennepin was clothed in a coarse gray capote and peaked hood, with sandaled feet, a crucifix at his side, and a cord of St. Francis at his waist. From a convent at Artois he had gone to Calais at the herring-fishing season, had made friends of sailors and become enamored of foreign lands. After many requests there came permission to go to Canada, and he sailed in the same ship as La Salle, and scolded a party of girls who were enjoying themselves with officers and passengers on deck. La Salle had told him he was acting like a pedagogue, and Hennepin retorted that

La Salle had once been a pedagogue in a Jesuit school! This La Salle resented, for his foes were now Jesuits and he wished not to be linked with them. Besides, he pierced the hollowness of Hennepin's character.

Hennepin had a quick, cheerful spirit, and his enthusiasm, physical health, and stature were great. Now when he saw La Salle, he bowed and smiled, and said:

"I am deeply glad to see you, Sieur de la Salle. I would join you in your explorations. If I had permission from my superior— Ah, may I not go?"

La Salle had mind to see all sides of a question, and, while he had not faith in him, Hennepin was not a Jesuit. After studying the friar briefly, he said:

"I will get you permission, and you must start at once. We shall meet at Fort Frontenac."

Hennepin raised hands in joy.

"You give me great news, and I will serve you to my life's end."

It was clear Hennepin wished to stand well with him, and that was much in Canada where so many were against him. La Salle said:

"Be ready to start to-morrow."

With an exclaimed blessing Hennepin paced away, bold and hardy and daring, but as false a friar as ever wore the gray capote, who would grossly exaggerate, a conscious but contented liar.

As Hennepin walked away, Tonty said: "Are you sure of that man, La Salle? What is he doing here with Darois?"

"He is strong, he has a vivid mind, and he will succeed with the Indians, and we need that. He is a Recollet, and not a Jesuit. Who knows what he has been doing here? One is sure of this—he is not deliberately my foe! That is not in his mind now."

By this time they were inside the office of Darois. He

was standing with back to them, talking to a clerk in a silky voice with ragged edges. At last, the clerk disappearing, he swung slowly on La Salle and Tonty, and looking at them softly said:

"I welcome Sieur de la Salle and M. de Tonty."

La Salle bowed: "I have come upon business, Monsieur Darois—the accounts of Fort Frontenac. They are not complicated, and they are few."

Darois bowed, and his bearded face showed no apparent feeling, yet his eyes had a furtive look which did not escape Tonty.

"Will you sit down, messieurs?" he said.

In Tonty's mind was the thought about the girl, Lya Darois. She was not here, but she had evidently gone into another room—that into which the clerk had entered. Tonty liked the face and figure of the girl. It did not seem possible she was the daughter of this smooth and subtle man who was now examining accounts of La Salle. It is clear he had a mind of business capacity, and a tongue that did its work well, but he was sure he was a spy on the *coureurs de bois*.

These *coureurs de bois* were indocile, debauched, wearing the sword and decked out with lace. They would not cultivate the soil, swaggered like lords, spent all their gains in dress and revelry, and despised the peasants. Yet they were a wonderful body of men, brave, chivalrous, carrying all before them when properly led, and expert traders with the Indians, and that was why the Hudson's Bay Company had sent Darois—he did not yet know that Darois had been sent to spy upon La Salle as well. But he disliked Darois' face as he bent over the papers with La Salle.

Lya Darois, that unusual and reliant girl, that pure product of the northern plains—where was she? Tonty wished to know.

THE Abbé Jean Cavelier was La Salle's eldest brother, a priest of St. Sulpice who had gone to Canada before La Salle, and he proved of far less caliber than the great explorer. He impeded rather than assisted La Salle by his small character and his interfering ways. He was in Quebec, though he lived at Montreal, and La Salle went to see him before starting for the West. The Abbé's thin, almost cadaverous face was in sharp contrast to that of La Salle— strong, vigorous, immobile, handsome, full of character. In his quarters at the small Seminary of St. Sulpice he awaited La Salle, and when he came, said:

"I come from Montreal to welcome you. You did well in France, brother."

La Salle shook hands warmly and received the Abbé's blessing.

"I have Fort Frontenac, and the rights to build forts and to find the mouth of the Mississippi, and have been raised to the nobility. All this was given me at Versailles by King Louis and with my foes at work. Even De Montespan with a Jesuit confessor was against me, and Madame Ranard was there—acting for Duchesneau, but Louis is his own adviser, and he and Colbert and Seignelay were with me."

The Abbé chuckled, for he was a courtier and he loved success. He could not condone effort with failure. His soul was small. La Salle recalled how, when it was reported that he was living at Fort Frontenac—this lie was spread by his foes—with a girl he had seduced, the Abbé had gone out in great indignation and had found him at the head of an exemplary household with two Recollet friars in attendance and had come back to Montreal a wiser man. The Abbé had borne the hard journey well, for he was a healthy man, and as a St. Sulpice priest he could save money, which he did; but he helped his brother little.

His thin hand fluttered over La Salle's head in blessing, and seemed full of piety, but this had little effect upon La Salle, who knew the Abbé had not come to help him. If his journey to France had been a failure, he would have been cold and unsympathetic. La Salle wished to keep a friendly attitude, for it would go ill if in the minds of the public, dissonance were known between him and his brother.

Presently the Abbé said: "Have you enough funds for your work?"

"I have not funds enough. Our cousin, François Plet, loaned me money at forty per cent—"

"Forty per cent—avaricious cousin!" said the Abbé.

"More came from other sources in France, and Count Frontenac has raised some by mortgage on Fort Frontenac. The Governor is my friend and I have a few others I can trust. So I can go on."

"I have some money—not much, but I can loan you twenty thousand at half the interest of François Plet—his is excessive—and you will pay me back in good time, is it not so?"

La Salle at once said: "I will take the twenty thousand gladly, and at twenty per cent interest, which is better than François Plet, but it came from one who does not know Canada and before I received my commission from King Louis at court."

The Abbé rubbed his hands together, for he was an avaricious man.

"You shall have the twenty thousand to-morrow—no, now!"

He went to a drawer and counted out the money, then sat at a table and drafted the note-of-hand at twenty per cent.

As he wrote the explorer watched him. La Salle knew him to be without human sympathy—a time-server, a courtier, a priestly follower of the Church, because it was part of his attitude towards life. He had started fair—honestly, so far as was in him, a priest. Then he had fallen from his original honesty and was now of the false life of France transplanted to Quebec. He would sacrifice anyone for gold, even his own brother.

La Salle's spirit revolted, but yet they were of the same father, had lived in the same house, drawn milk from the same breast, had the same country and the same God!

At last the Abbé stood up. "You have many foes, but in me you have a friend."

He gave La Salle the money and La Salle took it and sat down at a table to sign the note.

"One true friend is worth ten foes!" said La Salle, with grim softness, and he smiled at his brother, who did not realize the satire.

AT Fort Frontenac La Salle entered upon a new and interesting phase. He had De Tonty with him and La Motte de Lussière and Father Hennepin, and soon after his arrival there came to him Nicolas Perrot, called Jolycœur, who had been employed by the Jesuits and was an explorer of courage and skill. La Salle welcomed Perrot warmly, and did not know that he now worked for Barbe Ranard, so had the beauty of the woman acted upon the impressionable nature of the brave explorer.

La Salle had a servant, Nika, a Shawanoe hunter, ever with him, and from the first this acute native suspected Perrot, though he could not tell why. Yet he kept watch.

Time was spent in improving the fort and attracting Indians. Trade in fur steadily grew, while La Salle planned to build the first vessel that ever sailed the western Lakes, the *Griffon,* at Niagara.

La Salle liked Perrot, but could not understand why there shot into his mind at times a doubt—yet the man worked hard and had influence with the natives. One day Nika, La Salle's servant, was absent, and La Salle and Perrot had a meal together. Before the dinner Perrot mixed a salad and La Salle ate it, but three hours later was seized with convulsions. He had no suspicion of poison, yet it was one of the most frequent crimes in all Europe.

In the night he called and Perrot came to his bed.

"I am ill—most ill," said La Salle. "Give me an emetic. It may do me good."

Perrot mixed an emetic with no joy, for it might save La Salle's life, and he was thinking only of Barbe Ranard. La Salle took the emetic, yet it seemed not to cure him, for in the morning he was again seized by convulsions, and would have died had it not been for Nika, who, returning, at once guessed the truth and gave La Salle a drink of Indian herbs. He found what La Salle had eaten the night before, and discovered a few leaves of the salad, saw they were discolored, and wrapped them in paper and kept them. At last Tonty returned, and Nika told him what he feared. Tonty, who had some medical knowledge, analyzed the leaves and found in them hemlock and verdegris.

Perrot was kept away from La Salle's bed. He seemed now morose, now cheerful, and both kept strict watch of him and fought for La Salle's life. At last La Salle was out of danger, and then Tonty acted. He told La Salle of his analysis, and La Salle was convinced. He had studied medicine first in France, and afterwards with a doctor in Quebec for the good of his explorations.

"Why should he wish to kill me?" asked La Salle. "He is able, well known, himself an explorer. It is incredible."

"He is working for the Jesuits," said Tonty.

"No. They would not go so far with me," said La Salle. "I will accuse Perrot. He made the salad—the cook cannot make one, and I trust my cook. He has been with me five years."

"I will speak to Perrot first, and I will do it carefully," said Tonty.

"Very well," said La Salle, now thin, worn and feeble.

In another room Tonty, smoking a pipe, said to Perrot: "This is a curious illness of Sieur de la Salle. I think he has been foully treated. I was not here when he was seized. You were. What were the symptoms, Perrot?"

Perrot told him briefly, a startled look in his eyes, for he knew Tonty to be an able man.

"That looks like poison," said Tonty, looking steadily into the gray eyes of Perrot, his own black ones subtly shining.

"That cook—I can hardly think it," said Perrot.

"But did he cook all the meal—all?" said Tonty, fastening the now shifting eyes of Jolycœur.

"He prepared the dinner."

"What did you have?" asked Tonty.

"Fish from the lake, a black squirrel, some potatoes grown here, and a raisin pudding. Naught else, I think."

"But yes—a salat, m'sieu'," said Nika, standing near. "I saw the leafs, and the cook he can no make a salat—no."

"You made the salad," said Tonty, with sudden anger, and he clenched the table with one hand and stared into the fluttering eyes of Perrot.

Perrot suddenly seized a knife at his belt, but Tonty's pistol was in his face. "None of that, Nicolas Perrot. Come and say to La Salle what you've said to us. Come—now!"

Perrot saw no chance of resistance. A glance at the eyes of Nika, who hated him, hastened his footsteps to La Salle's bedside.

La Salle looked at him without speaking, then at last he said:

"I heard what passed. You have had my hospitality—we have worked—fought together—had the same trade of exploration. Why did you poison me?"

Perrot at once lied. "The Jesuits hate you. One will do much for one's church."

La Salle frowned. He was at first inclined to believe Perrot, then his mind revolted. He could not think the Jesuits would do that. Cold-blooded murder, and the tool a well-known explorer like Jolycœur, seemed beyond comprehension.

Nika put it right: "That man, he lie—it is no Jesuits—
no."

La Salle looked at Nika. Nika had instincts, and these
were all-important. Nika's instinct was poison, and poison
it had been. Right once by instinct, why not right twice.

"It was not the Jesuits, Perrot. Who was it? Answer,
man! Who was it?"

"I have naught to say," said Perrot.

"Was it the Jesuits? Answer me," said La Salle. "You
have but a short time to live, so tell the truth. Do not
enter your grave with a lie on your lips. Was it the
Jesuits?"

"It was not," said Perrot, sullenly, for he was in their
power.

La Salle's forehead cleared. He was glad, for, foes as
the Jesuits were, they had done vast service for the country
and for France, and murder like this had seemed too
shameless.

"Then who was it—your own evil heart, Jolycœur?"

"I had no hate of Sieur de la Salle."

Now Tonty spoke. "We believe you. Then it was a
woman—eh?"

Perrot did not answer, but his head hung low and despair
was in his body.

"It was Madame Ranard," said Tonty; but before he said
this he motioned Nika out of the room. "She—eh?"

Perrot inclined his head. He had lost all he had hoped
to win by La Salle's death, and his mind was sullen.

La Salle's eyes flared. That woman still pursued him and
was the agent of so much that had been done against him.
She was still active, and she had brains and skill, and her
soul was like the pit of Avernus. What should he do? The
right thing was to have Perrot shot at once as a would-be

murderer, or sent to Quebec to be tried, but in that case notoriety would ensue and the end would be bad.

"Have him disarmed, Tonty, and kept a prisoner, and come to me again."

Perrot, conscious of Tonty's and Nika's arms, yielded up at once his knife and pistol, and soon afterwards was in a small room by himself, unbound, but guarded by Nika, who had fastened the door.

Tonty returned to La Salle.

"What will you do, La Salle?" asked Tonty, with anger on his cheek. To think that La Salle, the man who was to do so much for Canada and France in this hemisphere, should have been so near death! As La Salle lay feeble, but with so stern a face and so resolute a look, Tonty almost wept, for in this explorer he found that new thing—an absolutely honest man, with no fear and with high faith.

After a moment's silence La Salle said: "I shall pardon him, Tonty. He has been sent mad by that woman, and in his heart he does not hate me. He would have killed me for her sake, but so would many a man have done. Perrot is not a bad man—he is simply a mad-man, and I shall set him free."

Tonty protested. This shocked him. "It is most unwise, La Salle. He will be your foe in the future."

"Nearness to death makes the brain clear and the spirit understand; besides, Perrot is a fine explorer and he will do good work. I shall free him."

Tonty sat with bowed head for a moment, and when he raised it again his eyes were smiling. He grasped one of La Salle's hands.

"In my soul I know you are right, La Salle. Shall I bring Perrot to you? Is that it?"

"At once, Tonty—he must not remain here under guard. Bring him, please."

In a few moments Perrot was again in La Salle's room. He held himself erect, for his manhood had reasserted itself and he was ready for all that might come. He came to La Salle's bedside and La Salle said, "Sit down, Perrot."

Perrot sat. La Salle looked at him a moment sternly, yet sadly, and said: "I am glad you did not succeed, Perrot, not only for my own life's sake, but for that I wish to do for our beloved land. I am of no account, but Canada is and France is. For a wicked moment you forgot both. But you are a man who can do great work for your land, and I implore you to do it, and—"

Perrot looked up astonished. Was he then to live? His eyes became blurred.

"You shall go from here with no stain on your character, so far as the world is concerned. It was not your real self that attempted my life, but a woman who would injure me and who had no regard for you. Did you think she would turn to you when you had killed me? You were in her power and you could do naught; you would have been a murderer. Did you not know that? She is the friend of the Intendant. Do you not see how she inveigled you?"

Perrot's face underwent many changes, but the last expression was one of sullenness. Suddenly he shivered with fury. He had been made a tool and would have killed this man. And for what? For a sordid passion which made him slay his own soul for a woman's body, for the rage of the flesh which had twisted his life to do a brutal deed.

La Salle felt the thoughts passing through Perrot's mind and his great spirit spoke. He saw how distraught Perrot's face was, and he knew the man truly repented of his dastardly act. He was not all bad—he had had a fit of elemental lunacy, and he now saw himself as he really was—the victim of an evil force which would have sacrificed him in the end. And how easy! To make him the victim of public disapproval, of her husband's sword or the Intendant's power, and she to go through it all unmoved save in her vanity, with smiling face. That was what vexed him now, which made him see himself in the light of this man's face whom he had tried to kill. He saw her now in her graceful, luxurious gown, her pale face and dark, fascinating eyes, her slight yet sumptuous figure, her ravishing power over the lower side of man.

Suddenly he dropped on his knees and his head bowed in shame. With a broken voice he said:

"Sieur, I have naught to say. My eyes are open. May God forgive me for the evil I have done you and myself! I am the scum—the dregs—I, Nicolas Perrot, once an honest man, now the dung of the world."

His body shook. But La Salle touched his shoulder.

"Be still, Perrot. I shall soon be at work again, and you shall work for your native land. I cannot employ you. Your evil deed would be ever before your eyes. But be my friend in the world where I need friends. Speak of me as you know me, a man who is the lover of his land and his King. Speak me fair, Perrot—eh?"

Perrot rose to his feet. His eyes shone, his face lighted.

"You spare my life! You spare my life! You are of the greatest of the world, and I will help you when I can. My tongue will always speak for you. I go not to Quebec, for I should do some mad thing to that woman, but into the northern fields. May I go now, Sieur de la Salle?"

A smile seldom came to La Salle's face, but one came now and he said, gently, "Go in peace, Jolycœur—and may God be with you."

For a moment Perrot stood looking at him with strange intentness; then he stretched out a hand as if in good-by, and, turning, left the room, meeting Tonty at the door.

Tonty knew what La Salle had done, and his eyes gazed

sternly at Perrot, for it was too bad that he should go free.
But to arrest him or have him shot was not good, for it
would be evil for La Salle in the end. Yes, La Salle was
right, so Tonty made way for Perrot to pass, with the
words:

"Adieu, Perrot! May the path you tread be clean!"

Perrot looked him firmly in the eyes. "*Merci*, M. Tonty.
It shall not be a bog."

As he passed out of the fort, Nika's eyes watched him
with anger, for he was of a race that never forgave, and he
could not grasp La Salle's action. Yet he fought the thought
of having Perrot captured by Indians and tortured, for that
would be unfair to La Salle, whom he loved. But he followed Perrot to the door, gave him his arms, and said, with
eyes glowering:

"It is good luck to you—no. Good to torture you, but
for Sieur's sake, no!"

When he was gone Nika stood still looking at the door.
Unmoved he stood for five minutes, brooding, his mind
alive with evil thoughts. He saw Perrot tied to a tree, and
his tribe peeling bits of skin from his body and burning it
and eating it. He saw little stabs in every part of his body
and live coals thrust in the wounds made. He saw the white
body grow red and purple and a mass of gashes, and a face
contorted with pain. He heard a voice in horrible agony,
and then Tonty's voice behind him:

"Wake up, Nika. It is all over. He is gone. Go in to
your master."

Nika drew himself together and slowly, heavily, he went
to La Salle's room with a look at Tonty which had in it the
primitive faith that would know no change. He was true.

Chapter XIII: LYA MAKES A DISCOVERY

LYA DAROIS was fitting her life to that of the capital.
Sometimes she went to her father's office, but she
kept much to herself, though young ladies sought her
company. She was more plainly dressed than they, and
she wore no glittering bodkins or aigrettes. The hair of
the young ladies of Quebec was always curled and powdered.
Those of high rank got up at seven, dressed till nine, drinking coffee at the same time, then they placed themselves at
a window and, in a dirty jacket and a coarse petticoat not
reaching to the middle of the legs, they took up some needle-
work and kept their eyes on the street. They were lazy,
but on the whole they had good manners, wit, and delicacy,
and good voices, and a great fondness for dancing. When
they undertook to catch a lover he could not easily escape.

Lya had little to do with them. She lived with her father
and old Luce Hontard, and she had not yet been to the
court of Frontenac. But one day Frontenac saw her
with her father and she was invited to his next reception.
Frontenac, a good judge of character, distrusting Darois,
for there was a look in his face he did not like, had confidence in the daughter, and felt her to be honest, true, and
very intelligent, though so young—only eighteen.

So, simply yet prettily dressed, Lya went to Frontenac's
reception, and was cordially received. The lady who acted
hostess was the wife of Count Louvigny on Frontenac's
staff, a relative of the Governor, and she at once liked the
young girl, but presently Lya was left to herself and she

stood not far from the Intendant and Madame Ranard. With rare gift of hearing the words of Madame Ranard came to her:

"That leper, La Salle, escaped Nicolas Perrot, who did his work ill. Now this must follow."

She then begged Duchesneau to incite La Salle's creditors to seize his properties at Quebec, and put men in his employ who would desert and leave him too few to meet the demands of his title-deeds.

Duchesneau said: "With the help of Tuke Darois we will destroy him. Darois is our man. Why he hates La Salle I know not, care not, but he can do our will. He watches Du Lhut there and does not hate Du Lhut—as who could—but he watches and hates La Salle."

This startled Lya, as she had not known her father's especial task, but if it was to watch La Salle and Du Lhut and be foes to them both, then he was a spy—a spy—her father a spy! It made her sick in mind, for such a life was detestable and low. A spy! Her father a spy! She shuddered slightly, but she listened sharply still.

Madame Ranard's eyes glinted wickedly. "His daughter—I'll make up to her. There's more in her than in her father. I'll find what she knows. That Nicolas Perrot, it sickens me! He, an explorer too, and to fail! He has not come to Quebec since."

Barbe went slowly to Lya, unaware that all between them had been heard. She said:

"Ah, dear mademoiselle, I am glad to meet you—very."

Lya curtsied. "I do not know your name, madame, but that does not matter."

Barbe looked alertly at her, but felt no intended insult in the words. She was, however, piqued, for that anyone should not know Madame Ranard seemed too ignorant—

in so small a place as Quebec! She hid her irritation and smoothly said:

"I am Madame Ranard and my husband is Farmer to the King's Revenue. Your father works for him."

Lya showed mock surprise. "Ah yes, I have heard of you, madame. You belong to that wonderful society, the Sainte Famille."

Barbe looked at her rather suspiciously now, but before she could reply Madame Louvigny came and said to Lya:

"Will you not hear Monsieur Du Lhut talk? He is of the interesting men in Canada. He has done great service for the King."

Barbe slightly sneered. "He is a *coureur de bois* who breaks the laws of the King. His reputation is known."

"If the laws are broken, His Excellency, the Governor, is responsible for him."

So said Madame Louvigny with point, for she knew the dark nature of this radiant woman.

"His Excellency, I have been told, is responsible for trade with the English at Albany, Madame Louvigny."

Madame Louvigny shrugged her shoulder slightly.

"Madame Ranard has listened too intently to the gossip of the Intendant's office. It has been written to France by the Intendant we know, but we kill that in this salon, madame. It does not last, that sort of falsehood."

Then turning to Lya she said: "Come and hear Du Lhut, my dear. The King is proud of him."

"Monsieur Darois is a faithful listener to Monsieur Du Lhut, madame. So his daughter should listen also."

Something in her words wrung Lya's spirit, but she smiled at Madame Louvigny and said: "I would like to hear monsieur. His face is well known. He leads men."

Madame Ranard's eyes had smothered fires as she said:

[87]

"He leads the *coureurs de bois,* who break the laws of trade in fur that the King has made."

Madame Louvigny smiled serenely at Barbe and led Lya away from the malicious foe of La Salle. Barbe watched them until they drew near to Du Lhut, then she returned to the Intendant.

"They fight, but we shall win in the end, Jacques."

"It is not so easy winning here. What did they say?"

Madame Ranard told him, and the Intendant frowned.

"The girl has brains. She is not all on the surface. I wonder does she know what her father is?"

"I'm sure she does not," answered Barbe. "She is demure and ignorant, but clever in her way. She has a mind of her own—that's plain."

Presenting Lya to Du Lhut—to her father's disgust—madame presently left the powerful Du Lhut talking with respect and vivacity to Lya. He was won by her winsome honesty, and others listened with envy, for he talked directly to her.

Madame Louvigny went to Frontenac and told him quietly what Madame Ranard had said, and Frontenac showed naught in his face, knowing that the Intendant and Madame Ranard were watching, but he nodded sedately and smiled, as though listening to pleasant things. Then he turned to Louvigny.

"Sedition is spoken here, Louvigny. The Intendant says I am trading through Du Lhut with the English and Dutch at Albany. What fools! Do they think they can defeat Louis Frontenac?"

A frown showed on his forehead, a sneer touched his lips.

"Am I so small, think you, my Louvigny?"

"The sparrow fights the eagle, Excellency. We know which will win."

Louvigny smiled, for he knew the Intendant's eyes were on him, while Frontenac's back was towards them.

Frontenac laughed now. "Due care should be had when the crows are flying low, Louvigny."

"The crows and the vultures, Monseigneur," said Louvigny, smiling grimly, for he was thinking of the Intendant and Madame Ranard and the Jesuits.

"They may all work together, Louvigny, but when I move they must give way. Here Bishop Laval comes. Now for frontier diplomacy—and the eagle's claw!"

So saying, Frontenac met Bishop Laval with friendly courtesy. The Bishop was a big man in reputation and character—one of the biggest Quebec had known. As he came to Frontenac, his ugly nose seemed larger than usual, but his eyes were glowing, his figure thin, yet slightly stooped, and one hand fingered gently the crucifix on his breast.

"I am proud to greet you here, Monsieur de Quebec. You give distinction to my poor court," said Frontenac, with courtesy.

He looked on the assembly where were penniless and improvident nobles like the Marquis de la Sablonnière and numerous, black-robed Jesuits, Recollets in gray robes, beautiful women from the Court of France. Also men who had left France broken in fortune and were living here as officials or adventurers, officers of the Carignan-Sallières Regiment, who had received seignories, gentlemen of Canada like the Le Moyne family, Le Ber, Chesnaye, Du Villiers, Lotbinières, Robillards, Martinoyes, Caron, Sechets, Benjoinville, Lauriers, and others all in laces and velvets and swords, all eager to serve their own interest. Many of them were foes of Frontenac, who, as they thought, stole from them, by support of La Salle, their share of the fur trade. Among them were *coureurs de bois,* who were welcome at Frontenac's court, and who, many of them, were little removed from peasants, while some were nobly born like Du Lhut, and lived lives of adventure and profit and would fight with *élan* and success at any time. They were the figures in the life of Quebec, bold, strident, conquering. Frontenac eyed the throng with no emotion except that which said: "Of these I am the master, and none shall defeat me. I know my way."

It was not a scene like that at the Palais Royal at Versailles or Fontainebleau, for there was none of the glittering architecture of those places, no vast tapestries and paintings and sculpture, no lofty ceilings, yet it had distant view like Versailles. It was however a court with brilliant charm, for the dresses of all were showy and were a gallant foreground for the dark timbers of the ceilings and the brown wood of the walls, along which there showed a few good pictures of France and the ancient spears and flags of armies of kings that lived before Louis XIV. It was a large room, and it looked important. It had a glamour of its own.

Laval quietly said, in a smooth and careful voice: "Your court does no dishonor to Versailles, though it is smaller, but here there are fewer shreds of humanity. We are a people with good things in us."

"I like to hear you say so, Monseigneur, for sometimes I have doubted it, yet you should know better than anyone else. Perhaps my office makes me too exacting."

"Your office has been filled by none more distinguished than Count Frontenac. I have seen many come and go."

"That says much, for some Governors were of your own choosing. You honor me."

"There have been moments when I doubted Your Excellency was the best fitted for the post, but I have faith now."

His keen eyes shone. He was evidently anxious to get something from Frontenac. He continued: "Even a bishop can make mistakes in a land where mistakes are common. We have crossed swords, Your Excellency, but I found you most competent."

Frontenac felt some purpose in these compliments, but he could say naught to help the matter on.

"I have never crossed swords with a bishop in my life, but if our wills are meant—yes. I found Monsieur de Quebec no amateur in mind and purpose."

The Bishop smiled. Presently he said, softly:

"I wish to know if you approve the purposes of Sieur de la Salle. He would extend discovery and the King's rule on this continent and develop settlement largely. Is that good? Is life to be lived with gold and silver as the end of all? Are not the souls of men more? We Church-men wish to convert the Indians and to save their souls for God, but we seek not money. To us it is better to make the Indians true sons of the Church than to use them for gain, as do the new settlers La Salle takes to the West. Is that not so?"

Frontenac looked with a grave smile at the Bishop.

"I do not understand. The Church had been the true servant of exploration and trade. I do not forget the martyrs who have given their lives, like Brebeuf and Lalemant and Jogues and so many others. And they were traders, too. Even Marquette, whose late discovery of the Mississippi with Joliet would develop territory, and with it trade. The greatest Intendant ever here, Talon, who increased trade and showed the way to manufacture of many things, knew that this land could not always be the foster-child of King Louis. It would pay its way, and only by trade can it do so. Even the house the present Intendant lives in was a brewery built by Talon, and you have schools for children which he started. Your Church has ever been the friend of exploration and trade, but now you wish the Indians only to be sons of the Church!"

The Bishop's face hardened as he listened to the Governor.

"We have had first in our minds the salvation of the Indians, and that could only be by exploration. We have been friends of trade, but it is not our chief aim. The soul— the soul of the Indian, that is first."

"Yet, frankly, Monsieur de Quebec, your missions only prove that you can give the world great martyrs. There you are supreme. To be sons of the Church *only* is not the policy of King Louis."

"It was until lately," was the rather tart reply of Laval. "Your Excellency changed it. He would not let Joliet build forts on the Illinois and the Mississippi. La Salle would not have received these wide powers save through Your Excellency's intervention. Your Excellency has great influence at Court."

Frontenac smiled. "Monseigneur, I had no influence. He himself did all, save for the letter I gave him to Colbert. But others had written to Colbert—the Intendant and his friends here. No, La Salle himself carved his own way in France. He had against him—so the Comtesse Frontenac wrote me—the constant efforts of Madame Ranard"—the Bishop stiffened—"who was acting indirectly for the Intendant. La Salle convinced them all, and before the whole Court King Louis gave him his commission. But La Salle did it in spite of De Montespan and her Jesuit confessor, and the Intendant, I chance to know, and not through me. I have good correspondents in France, and my wife is on the spot."

"We have always lamented she is not here, Your Excellency."

"We cannot say all, my lord Bishop. She has no love of frontier life. She is not strong. It is better to have in France some one wholly loyal to me, and so she stays there. Her use to me in France has been shown again and again. She does not go to Court, but she is a perfect chronicler."

"They say she has the golden key to the Court, though she does not enter it. You will not try to influence La Salle against his present course—is that your will, Excellency?"

Frontenac said, firmly: "I have helped La Salle in every way possible. I borrowed money for him. To all he does I give assent, for he is an honest man, and that cannot be said of many in New France—as I have found."

The Bishop had good self-control. He showed no feeling, but he said: "I regret to oppose you in this policy, Your Excellency. You may find it successful, but I doubt it— ah, I really doubt it."

"When the Bishop doubts, the Governor must take heed!" said Frontenac, with quiet point, and then they moved away from the crowd, the Intendant and Madame Ranard watching intently.

From the side of Du Lhut, Lya at length detached herself. She felt him a man of rare ability and she liked him; and upon this man her own father was a spy, and upon a far greater man, La Salle.

She went to her father. "I would go home," she said.

Darois saw a shadow in her eyes and he thought it fatigue.

"Come then. We will have a quiet walk in the bright night. I have had enough of this."

Outside he said, "You found Monsieur De Lhut interesting?"

[93]

"One of the most interesting men in Canada, don't you think?"

"To me one of the most interesting."

Darois smiled grimly as he said it.

NEWS of La Salle and Tonty came but slowly to Quebec city, and meanwhile life went on. Du Lhut vanished with his *coureurs de bois*. Not very many of these were nobly born like Du Lhut, and some of the best men of the colony pleaded with Duchesneau to obey the King's orders and suppress them.

It was an old source of trouble between Frontenac and the Intendant, and letters had gone to France in protest from the latter and in defiance from the former. King Louis and Colbert believed in Frontenac, but they both reproved him and they both chided Duchesneau. The difference was that Frontenac would develop the King's estate regardless of himself, but to do so he must evade the commands of the King in this one respect, while Jacques Duchesneau was only, and always, for himself, with no high patriotism, and with intent to grow rich.

Word had come that La Salle was building a ship which was to go over the Great Lakes and down the Mississippi, and the ship was to be called the *Griffon* in honor of the coat of arms of Frontenac, and against the purposes of the Jesuits. Yet La Salle had got from Louis the right to build forts and to open up trade on the Mississippi.

Here it was Tuke Darois did his work. He was intent to destroy Du Lhut and ten times more eager to ruin La Salle, for increase of trade meant injury to the Hudson's Bay Company, and he was their spy in the service of Duchesneau. His enmity to Du Lhut and La Salle had the support of the

Jesuits and the Intendant and Ranard, who did not know that he was a spy of the Hudson's Bay Company.

Darois at last determined to go to Fort Frontenac and to try and spoil the purposes of La Salle in two ways—by letting the *Griffon* be built at considerable cost, and then giving her a pilot who would sink her, and by weaning from La Salle his workers and so place him in difficulty with Louis and Colbert, who had demanded that he keep so many men at his fort. La Salle had borrowed money in France and in Canada and to ruin him financially would be the last great blow.

He did not tell his daughter where he was going when he started. She thought it was only to Montreal and Three Rivers, for he was astute. He did not know she had an inkling of his real position, and he hid the truth from her. Lya visited but little, yet she had many invitations, for the notice taken of her at the Château by Frontenac and Madame Louvigny and Du Lhut had its influence. It was only by chance that Lya found her father's true purpose, for one day, coming past the Bishop's palace, she met Madame Ranard, who stopped and spoke to her.

"Ah, dear mademoiselle, you are alone, I hear." She smiled sweetly, but Lya was not to be deceived by that. She smiled also, and said:

"No, not alone, dear madame. Our old servant is with me, and I have much to keep me busy."

"But busy—for so long alone!" said Madame Ranard, raising her eyebrows.

At once Lya seized some hidden meaning in the words "so long."

She said, "What is a few weeks in a lifetime, madame?"

"A few weeks—but no, a few months, my child."

"Well, even a few months—what of that? I did not know my father would stay so long in Montreal." Her eyes caught those of Madame Ranard with a hidden suspicion, for she recalled that night at the Château.

Madame Ranard now struck with venom, but softly and subtly:

"Montreal is naught—weeks—but your father goes far beyond that!"

Lya shrugged a shoulder. "Does my father, then, confide his plans to madame?" she asked in irony.

"He is under my husband in office, and I know where he goes, and why."

Madame Ranard smiled. She was convinced that Lya did not know her father's purposes or where he was going. So it was she had struck so deftly. She wished Lya to be hurt, for she felt the girl against her.

Lya's face showed naught of what she felt, but her tongue said:

"Well, *why* may I ask?"

Madame Ranard thought hard. What difference could it make if she told that which would irritate the girl, who loved her father, would not expose him to Frontenac or seek to remove him from his post. Lya was in a quandary, and it did Ranard's dark spirit good to think she was stabbing this slim, lonely girl through her gentle bosom.

"Oh, you shall know, if you do not. He goes to bring La Salle to his senses and to do true service for King Louis."

"You mean he goes to ruin La Salle?" asked Lya, intently.

"Your father does his duty—as do all who love France and the King more than themselves."

"But the Governor is La Salle's friend and believes in him!" said the girl, with slightly heightened color—she wished to show she had been struck hard.

"Frontenac—oh, he—yes, he is La Salle's friend, but Frontenac's days are numbered here, as are La Salle's. Do you think that Frontenac and La Salle can fight the Church and the Bishop and the great traders forever? Why, no, my child, that can't be done, and the biggest man in this country is the Intendant!"

She had calculated her stroke well. The girl would not go to Frontenac and tell him what she, Madame Ranard, had said, for she loved her father, and if she told Frontenac anything, she must tell all, and that she would not do.

"Well, madame, if what you say is true, I am sorry we came here, that is all. Oh, why did you tell me? I must fight it all out by myself."

"Oh no, not that. There's always the Church. You can unburden your heart to a priest."

"No priest can help me. For months—for months! Madame, you have—"

She stopped as though her feelings had overcome her. They had walked far, and she was now near her own home. She had fully deceived Madame Ranard, who left her with a furtive look and with the certainty that the girl's lips were sealed.

When she had gone Lya's face lost its affected misery and her eyes blazed up.

"My God! does she think me made of wood? Does she think I know not what to do? My father gone to Fort Frontenac, has he? And to destroy La Salle! Well, there is a way for me, too. She knew well I would not go to Frontenac. But she forgets—forgets I have courage and endurance. I am—"

She said no more, but quickly reached her home.

Chapter XV: THE ARGONAUTS

IT WAS late Autumn, and in the East snow had not yet begun to fall. Lya had made her arrangements quickly and told no one save Luce Hontard of her destination. She found two faithful *habitants* of the Du Lhut corps, who knew the woods as they knew their own hands. These men, who loved mystery, assented gladly, for they meant to join Du Lhut in the West, and to them she was like some sweet bird flying to a new nest. Lya had a gift of inspiring confidence, given to few, and she had no fear in travelling with these two. In her heart of hearts she knew life, and her soul was as radiant as the drops of water hanging in the leaves after a rain, through which the sun shines.

It was Luce Hontard who put her in the way of getting these good men, both of whom were near fifty years of age, both bearded and with eyes that showed not singular integrity, but temperament which would honor every law that made a girl safe in the darkest places. Both had been married and both were as widowers, though one had lost his wife by desertion and not by death. This made him not gloomy, but firm, and with a sense of chivalry which is and always had been characteristic of the French Canadian. He was Jules Ladaux and he was short, thick-set and with endurance and great skill of the woods.

The other was Luc Maste, whose wife was true and faithful, and he was built like wire, and his roving nature had a stern sense of duty. He had wandered far, had been in danger often, had been prisoner of the Iroquois, had even been tortured, but he had come through all with a nature which would not stoop to the mean thing. He had killed Indians, had been in raids for skins against the law, had the air of a *petit gentilhomme* and was at times dressed like other courtiers, with velvet and lace, and he did this solely to make the *coureurs de bois* more prominent. His was the vanity of the good men of the lower orders. He was a *habitant,* and yet was a cut above, with a kind of natural dignity, and it was strengthened by the gallantry and grace of the well-born Du Lhut.

At their first meeting with Lya, she said:

"I am told you are going West to join the great Du Lhut. Is it so?"

"It's so, for sure," said Luc Maste, and Jules Ladaux nodded.

"I wish you to go with me farther West than you have meant perhaps. I cannot tell you where yet. I cannot pay you high, for I am poor, but I will give you each—"

Luc Maste interrupted her.

"We will serve you, m'm'selle, without bargain. We are not hucksters—*nom d'un pipe.*"

Her eyes lighted and a smile came to her lips. "Let it be so, then. I like you to feel you are doing good to one who loves France and Canada and all that concerns their good, as you do."

"Your love of both would not be doubted—no!" said Jules.

"I do not mean myself. I mean one who has many foes, yet thinks not of himself."

"Your father?" said Luc Maste, with a faintly furtive eye, for he had his doubts about Tuke Darois, and this was Tuke Darois' daughter! The instinct of the French Canadian is always acute, and he feels where he cannot think—

he feels first. Luc caught the swift flash of her eye as she said in reply:

"I do not mean my father. He has many friends and he does think much of himself."

Jules interposed: "It matters not. We shall go where you will, seek whom you seek, and our mouths will be like ice in winter. You want that, is it not?"

Lya's breast heaved: "It is so. You will not regret it. I will start in twenty-four hours. Can you be ready then?"

They both looked at the young, slight, yet firm figure, at the composed yet fiery face, at the self-reliant eye, and their reply was instant: "We can be ready—bagosh."

She gave a hand to each, and they took them in their own, and with the other hand raised above their heads made a silent vow, looking into her eyes the while. A glimmer of a tear showed in her eyes, but her lips were firm, and she said:

"No one must know till we are on our way. No one must guess where we are going."

"We do not know, m'm'selle, and we do not gossip. You can trust us. *Tiens!* we have never been one of those who blabbed."

"Yes, yes, I know."

"No lady has ever taken the risks you are about to take, m'm'selle."

"I do my duty, that's all."

"There will be great dangers and we are but three."

"I understand. I have been brought up with a gun in my hands. When great things are at stake, risks must be."

At that moment Luce Hontard entered. She was portly and slow, but she had a body of great endurance and an unwavering mind. She did not hesitate to let Lya go, for, though no one had said why the journey was taken, she understood. She had an uncanny gift of prescience. Her eyes settled on the three for a moment. She saw that all was well. Then she looked the two men in the eyes.

"You, you—good, good!" she said, and no more.

Both men kissed her on the cheek. She flushed slightly, she even smiled:

"Me—good, good!" she said, and no more.

"*Tonnerre!*—but yes," said Luc Maste.

Twenty hours later, at break of day, when the broad river was flowing gently past Quebec, the three started in a canoe with no watchers near—only a stray *habitant* who had no interest in the three and gave them scarce a glance. It was no unusual thing for men to start on journeys at dawn. The canoe was well loaded, yet not so heavy that they could not carry it, and all, beyond the rapids of La Chine. After those were passed there would be no further trouble, and at La Chine they could get help, if needed, from *habitants*.

As the canoe sped away quickly Lya looked back. There was the Château of St. Louis on the heights, looking grim and stern in the early light; there was the palace of the Intendant Duchesneau, massive and striking and long; there was the Jesuit College buildings in the square, with the glow of the rising sun touching the white walls; there was the palace of the Bishop, the cathedral, and the house of M. Rojet Ranard by itself, and in it was the woman who had done harm to La Salle and would do more, if she could; and there was her own small house which maybe she might never see again. Then there were the homes of Lower Town, the warehouses, the few shops, the places of business, the mart.

Lya was dressed in chamois from head to foot, her cap was Indian with a small tail, and she looked like a priestess of the wilds. This was an expedition which would demand all the endurance of a stern pioneer, all the courage of La Salle himself, all the faith of a saint. At last with a tremor, not of fear, but of excitement, she looked ahead.

There was the broad river, there were the mists, and there was the lovely shore of the river at the North; there were the sure dangers, but the sun was breaking through the mists, and she suddenly felt all would be well. Here and there along the shore was a house, here and there a *habitant* at his plow or in the field, and now and then an Indian with his bow and arrow or a gun. All the land seemed a place of beauty and strength, and to Lya there came visions of the future when these shores would be inhabited and all this land a glorious empire of the King of France.

At last she took a paddle as well, and worked like a man, while the two *coureurs de bois* sang one of the songs so much beloved in Canada:

> "There is no land like this—no, no;
>   Fly away, my heart, fly away!
> There is no hope like this—no, no;
>   Fly away, my heart, fly away!
> Here is a bride to kiss, yes, yes;
>   Stay here, my heart, oh, stay!"

Softly Lya joined in the song, and the lilt of their voices with the strange deep feeling of these people came out like the song of the birds in the trees of the shore. Somehow, at the very start of their voyage the fibre of these people of the woods and streams was a guaranty of success. Yet Lya knew that few dangers would come till they had passed Montreal and were far up the river by Lake Ontario. She liked these men; they were of the right sort, and it touched her grimly that it was they, with La Salle, her father was set against in his work.

Their meals were made on the shore—game, Indian corn, bread, prunes, baked pumpkin, and spring water and tea and coffee, of which they had plenty, and she quickly tidied up after the meals. When night came, after a thirty-miles' row, they camped on the shore, and she slept in a tent, but the men on the open ground. She slept soundly, and at dawn she went for a bathe at a secluded spot; yet she knew that this could not continue, for, once they had passed Montreal it would not be safe, and so Luc Maste made plain to her when she said at breakfast that she had had a bathe.

"It would be madness in the wilds—*bidemme!*" said Luc, and he looked her straight in the eyes.

"I know. When we pass Montreal I will not bathe in the river. But till then, oh yes! I know how careful we must be."

"You have the woodman's sense," said Jules.

"And the riverman's mind," said Luc.

"And the woman's instinct," said Lya, and she laughed.

"And some other things also, bless the good God, or we should not be here," added Luc.

It was after passing the rapids of La Chine, and the river widened and grew more beautiful with the maples, elms, and oaks deepening in exquisite color on the banks, and the air was like a vivid wine, that the real dangers came. One night they camped on shore, and Lya did not undress, for she felt peril near. Her sleep was not sound, and she was suddenly waked by seeing the cloth of her small tent raised. She softly drew her gun to her. Then the body of a man appeared. It was an Indian, and there were two others behind him. They were in war paint and feathers. As the Indian stooped to enter, there was the sound of two shots, and two Indians fell, but not him who was now inside her tent. As he half turned to the door she fired. He fell at her feet with a sharp cry, but raised his tomahawk to strike. She seized his arm, and with her knife struck him in the chest, and he fell and lay still. Outside there was further discharge of guns and wild whoops of fury, and then sudden

[104]

silence, and Luc Maste came running to her tent. He saw the dead Indian at her feet, and said:

"They nearly caught us, the five of them, but they are all dead. They think we were no good—eh! Jules has a very slight wound in the leg, but we're both all right." They both looked at her with grave, proud eyes. "You are a true *coureur de bois,* but yes!"

At that point Jules appeared, and the two men carried out the body of the Iroquois. They carried the five into the woods and left them without burial. It was near morning and they did not lie down again, but built a fire and waited for the dawn.

As they sat waiting, an anxious, drawn look came into the face of Lya. This Indian was the first man she had ever killed. She had seen many, many killed, and thrice had wounded Indians, but had never killed till now. Her youth, her composed beauty, her self-possession, were all there, and the two men worshipped her.

Looking up from the fire, she at last said:

"You have trusted me. You have followed my will. Now I tell you where we go. It is to Fort Frontenac, where my father has gone." They both nodded, and Luc Maste said, sarcastically, yet carefully:

"Your father goes upon the finances of the Fort, and to see that all is after the will of the King."

"That is so. Yet why not trust La Salle, who is a good friend of France? I did not know my father was going to Fort Frontenac!" Her eyes were searching those of the men.

Luc Maste laughed a little. "Yet you go—and why? It is a hard journey, and we are not yet there. You go not upon the finances of Fort Frontenac. It is much danger for one so young—and a woman!"

Lya gave a low half-ironical laugh. "Well, my father and

I are queer. We are mysteries, and why he went, and why
I go, are mysteries. Let it stand. Danger—I am used to
that, and so are you. You work for nothing, and you risk
your lives for me. I will never forget while I live. How
long before we reach Fort Frontenac?"

Jules Ladaux' eyes were shining. The French love mystery and melodrama, and this adventure was meat and drink
and inspiration. "It all depends—yes. If it freezes and
we have to walk much, it will be long. If we can go by
canoe all the way—another week. Yes, if it freezes we shall
have to leave the canoe, and we must take our chances on
that—*sacré bleu*. Then we shall be in danger always, for
the Indians are many on shore."

"We are in the hands of God," said Lya.

"Then God be with us," said Jules Ladaux, and they both
signed the cross with their fingers.

At last dawn broke, and the reddish glow made the river
very beautiful, and all the vast expanse a glory of wild life.
It did not seem that death and danger could be near. The
roseate glow was like a balm to a troubled world—the sun
was a feast of the eye.

To Luc Maste his friend said, while Lya made breakfast:
"It isn't plain why he or she should go to Fort Frontenac."

Luc Maste laughed low. "It's plain to me. Darois is
the foe of La Salle and means him harm and our Du Lhut
also, and this girl goes to stop the harm, if she can. She
is as straight as her father is crooked—that's my view. I've
not seen one like her since I was born. Mystery, she says,
but we know it's no mystery. We will get her there safely,
in the name of God!"

When they were within two days of Fort Frontenac by
river it froze, and they had to take to the land. They could
only carry enough to feed them, and enough clothing for the
heavy frost. The tent for Lya had to be left behind, and

much else, but this they had known from the start, and so they turned the canoe on the few things they abandoned, and walked on, each loaded to the limit. As they marched, Luc ahead and Lya in the middle, the men sang softly a chanson:

"Peasant, give me your daughter,
    And that is all!
Peasant give me your daughter,
    And that is all!
I pray you give her to me,
    You will make my heart happy!
I pray you give her to me,
    You will make my heart happy,
And that is all."

They had no want of food, and they had hominy and brandy. They had seen Indians now and then, and more than once they were anxious, but they were not attacked, for the Indians were not Iroquois, but Algonquins, and were not inimical to whites. One of the men slept for four hours by turn, and they would not let Lya take turn at watching. As they each got at least seven hours' sleep a night, each morning found them vital. They had no more adventures till they reached Fort Frontenac and saw the bastions, the narrow gateway, and the strong walls, and round these walls tribes of Indians La Salle had gathered there.

As they neared the fort of a late afternoon, Indians came to greet them, and there was warm welcome, and Indian women made special welcome by clapping hands on open mouths, and they gathered round Lya excitedly, fingering her dress and admiring her. She was the first white woman who had ever come this hard journey to Fort Frontenac. They took what she was carrying, the Indians did the same with Jules and Luc, and they entered the gateway of the fort with much clamor. Inside were Indians. Some had brought furs to exchange for goods, and bartering was at its height. It all had color and display.

Now suddenly there appeared in the doorway of the fort three white men. Two were Recollet friars, and one had the air of an official. They did not at first see the new-comers, but presently the hurly-burly reached them and one priest, pointing, said:

"Arrivals from the East. Two men and a woman."

"Two men and a woman? That's strange!" said Tuke Darois, and came forward. He was amazed to see his daughter, and he turned pale. A frown came, then he hurried forward. With a searching look at her two escorts he embraced Lya and said:

"God in Heaven! What brings you here?"

Her reply was firm, "Not what brings you here, father?"

Of the two men who had come with her, Luc said:

"Now begins the real story. What is it?"

Chapter XVI: FACE TO FACE

TO her father Lya said, "Why did you come, please?" With a scowl he replied, "When I know why you have come."

Lya shook her head. "Anyone will tell me. I know why you came." Her voice was pierced and strong. "Why did you say you were going to Montreal only? Why did you deceive me?"

"I have my own business."

She came close to him, her eyes flashing. "You are a spy and the foe of La Salle. You came to injure him. There are those who know."

He was startled. An ugly look came into his face. "Who told you that? Who says I am a spy? If so, you are, then, the daughter of a spy. Do you like it?"

Her face was flushed, her mouth bitter. "I could kill you for degrading yourself and me. You hid it all from me. You—a spy! A spy!"

"You could kill me—you!" he seized her arm. "Who told you I was a spy? Who? What devil lied so?"

"No one lied. That night at the Château St. Louis I heard it, and now I know it true."

"You heard it—from whom?" There was anger, yet a fear in his eyes.

"From Madame Ranard and the Intendant. You are their agent and they know why you are in Quebec. You spy for the Hudson's Bay Company, but they do not know that, and you spy for them. Why do you hate La Salle and what he does?"

"Spying is not dishonorable. Better men have done it. It is the clash of race and interests—two vast concerns one against the other." He said this roughly.

"So you are more English than French—is that it?" You work for French Canada as well as the Hudson's Bay Company? Does the Intendant know that? You don't want the French to trade, therefore you hate La Salle because he does trade. His foes don't want him to trade, and so you spy for them on La Salle and Du Lhut. That is it, is it?"

"They don't know I'm a spy of the Hudson's Bay Company. They only know I am against La Salle and Du Lhut. It coincides, that is all."

"You are here to hurt La Salle, and I have come against you. If you go on against La Salle, I will expose you."

Scorn, anger, and sorrow were in her voice. All her being revolted at his work.

"You would tell then what I am—you, my daughter!"

"I will tell them, and I will tell Count Frontenac. If he knew, your life would be worth little."

His eyes grew big with amazement. He had a child that would send him to his death—to oblivion—because her soul was just and true. He had known she had ability, but this new vein was bigger than all. She had character, and her journey out was wonderful. No woman had ever made it, and she had done it with two men whom it was his duty to overcome. She had gone through how much danger and anxiety for the sake of conscience. He had to deal with a brain better than his own, and a character to which his own was as a distant star to the sun. Down deep in his crooked nature was love of her. His mind was confused, his purposes seemed suddenly dark and treacherous, his soul was awakened a little. Yet he was bitter that she should oppose him so. He caught her arm fiercely.

"Let go my arm," she said, with sudden anger. "I am not your slave. You shall treat me with respect, even if you do not love me."

He dropped her arm at once. He saw that he must go warily, or it could be ill for him, for she loved truth more than she loved him.

"What is it you would have me do?" he asked.

"Cease to spy for the Hudson's Bay Company. You are your own foe. I will not bear your treachery. I can make my own living, and I will."

For a moment he looked at her with malice.

"You will do this, you will do that, and you will give me up to the hands of Count Frontenac. Then I will make you no promise. I will go on as I have done. If you and I clash, then the stronger wins, and I am the stronger." He added, moodily, "Do these who brought you know what I am?"

She waved an indignant hand. "They know naught. They brought me here free of charge. They risked their lives for me. Once I was near death and they fought to protect me."

She told in a few words the attack by the Iroquois, and her father's face was a study. He realized that she was one in ten million, and that she would carry through what she meant to do. But he must make a fight for his authority or all would be lost. He would see it through in his own way.

"Come into the fort," he said, "and we will talk of this later."

Her face hardened. "Unless you promise, I will take my own course," she said. "You are not all I have in the world."

"Whom have you, then?" he asked, in a surly voice.

"What you have forgotten—the truth of things."

They were now at the door of the fort, and they were admitted with no formalities. The first person they saw was the astounded Tonty. His fine, distinguished figure, his black handsome eyes, his healthy face, his air of ease and culture, fascinated her at once, and she smiled into his face.

"Ah, you came to see your father do his duty here," he said, with outstretched hand which took her own.

"I came to see my father do his duty," she said, with a curious grave smile, which did not escape the quick thought of Tonty, for he felt things more than saw them.

"You show no ill-effects from your long hard journey—no lady has ever taken it! You shall rest here while your father does his duty."

There was a delicate inflection in his voice which did not escape the girl, and she knew it was in reply to her, but Tuke Darois did not feel or see it.

"You shall see the Sieur de la Salle at dinner—or perhaps before," he said, as he showed her into a room some distance from her father's. There with a bow he left her, and with a pleasant nod she saw her bundle placed in her bedroom, and with a scowl her father disappear.

Left alone, Lya looked round the room. It was bare, yet from the few drawings on the wall, the narrow bed, the plain deal table and the chairs and washstand, she had a sense of home. It was a new feeling, and after unpacking her few things she sat on the edge of the bed and looked at the opposite wall. It had a shelf on which were two books, and one of these was the plays of Corneille, and one the essays of Bossuet, and her sense of culture awoke. Culture? What had she to do with culture? She had lived in the wilds always, and she had read much, but never the plays of Cor-

neille or the essays of Bossuet. She went over, brought
them back, and opened them. In the Corneille volume the
first words she saw were:

"The spirit is a fire, and it burns up all that shames;"
and from Bossuet these words met her eyes:

"Blessed is the soul that holds the truth."

She laid the books beside her on the bed. So this was the
first message she had after her dangerous journey! She was
to burn up all that shamed, and hold to the truth. She must
hold fast on the course she had entered, and she would
warn—carefully—both Tonty and La Salle. She looked
at herself in a small mirror on the wall. Yes, hers was an
honest face, and a kind one, and in her eyes was a steady
light which would not be diminished. She sighed heavily
and sat down on the bed again. What should she do? In
any case she would warn La Salle that the Jesuits and the
Intendant were out against him, and that Madame Ranard
was a constant and deadly foe, and she could do this without implicating her father. Perhaps he knew all this; but
he did not know that her father was a spy, and she could
not tell him that; yet she would go far to save La Salle. She
had made a desperate journey, and she would go through
with it. In a sense she felt responsible, for she was the
daughter of a man who was La Salle's foe and who would go
far to ruin him. Her coming would at best put them on
their guard. She was glad she had come.

For a half-hour she sat in meditation, then there came a
firm knock on her door. She opened it. Luc Maste and
Jules Ladaux stood there. Luc Maste smiled and he said:

"We come to ask if all is well with m'm'selle?"

She gave each a hand. "All is well, dear friends, and you
shall have commends from me to Sieur de la Salle. Will
you go into his service? Is that possible?"

They both shook heads. "No, we go to follow the great

Du Lhut," said Luc Maste. "He is not so big as La Salle, but we cannot change our service."

"Are you well roomed in the fort?" she asked.

"As well as can be, after our outdoor nights. This is the best fort in Canada. It is managed like a game of chess."

At that moment Tonty entered. He saw the two men and shook them warmly by the hand. "You good men brought mademoiselle a hard and dangerous journey."

They smiled and bowed low. Luc Maste said:

"It was not work, it was honor. We were glad all came right, even when attacked by the Iroquois!"

"Attacked by the Iroquois!"

They told him briefly what had happened. Tonty turned to Lya with pride in his eyes. "We are glad you are here—safe. Now enjoy your rest, my men, and be sure La Salle will thank you."

The two disappeared. Then Tonty turned to Lya.

"La Salle will see you now if you will come."

Lya lifted up her head in pride. So she was to talk with La Salle. Her hands clenched at her side and her face turned slightly pale, and Tonty saw both. He had had more than one love-affair in his life, yet never had he felt what was in him now for this girl. She had a way with her, greater than any lady he had ever known. It was not the airs or graces of the life in Paris or in Rome, but those of a capital city called Nature, in which she was supreme. She was sensitive, but composed and self-possessed—she was alive in the highest and truest sense. She had culture which comes from pure heart and soul, the grace of perfect naturalness. He was moved in some deep part of him, as he had been when he first saw her in Quebec. As he walked beside her he was aware how soft and gliding was her footstep, how lissom was her figure, how buoyant was her carriage. She was not tall, yet she was perfectly made, and had rare dignity. Presently they stopped before a door and Tonty turned the handle and they entered. La Salle was seated with a map before him on the table, but he rose and came forward.

Like Tonty, he had been impressed at Quebec by her appearance, but here, shut off from the world where no ladies had ever been, she was like a ray of sunlight in a dark place, and for the first time in his life his soul was stirred by a woman. How wonderful she was, her eyes shining, her face aglow with health and understanding, her sense of being like a thread of fire in the cold.

After a word of introduction Tonty left, and Lya was alone with this great man. His handsome face was not like Tonty's, full of temperament; it was rather set and a little stern, but there was in it the purpose of a lifetime, and the unchanging faith and hope of a patriot who would sacrifice himself and all with him for his cause. Only his marvelous eyes showed the soul of the man. They were alive and ample and lustrous, and in them was his life-long ambition, which for the first time was caught on its course by the spirit of a woman. He smiled at her.

"You are welcome, and may your stay be long, mademoiselle."

At first her heart had throbbed so that it was difficult to speak, but the quiet steadiness of La Salle's personality restored her balance and her heart ceased its wild beating. Yet it was not easy to hold her poise. Her lips trembled a little as she said:

"My stay cannot be long, monsieur, but I am better for the coming. I am where the wheel of your great work is."

In La Salle's mind was the sudden wish to say: "Stay here where the pivot is and help me," but that was madness and he did not say it. Why did this one girl of all he had seen or known seize so upon his powerful being?

Others were as beautiful and more beautiful, others were as clever, no doubt—others as graceful, others as fine, and yet she had her own place unrivaled. She was unique— one of those flashes of Time that have no explanation and no traceable origin. When her hand touched his a fire swept through his arm and body, a vivid life. Her fingers were slim, yet her hand had firm softness.

"Will you not sit down?" he said, and she took a chair.

For a moment neither spoke, but at last he said:

"You made this dangerous journey to be with your father, I suppose; yet why did you not come with him?"

She hesitated, then she said: "He would not have brought me, so I came after him. We girls are not so weak as he thinks. I've proved it to him."

For a moment La Salle looked as though he believed her, then he said: "He might have known you would do all man could do to the level of your strength. Women have not the same physical endurance as men."

Suddenly he stood up and bent towards her, looking her steadily in the eyes.

"Will you not tell me frankly why you came?"

Slowly she rose. "Yes, I will tell you, monsieur. I came to warn you that you have foes in Quebec who plot your fall. They will leave no stone unturned to do it. You have great purposes, and they have not. You would in- crease trade and immigration, and they would not—you have foes high up. That is why I came—to warn you!"

La Salle smiled grimly:

"All this I know. But tell me how you came to know, and your special reason for coming. I have many foes, yet I sur- mount them all. Will you not say more?"

She pointed to the map on the table: "There lies your chart of action, I suppose. You are studying the possible course of the Mississippi. You mean to build a ship and go down the Mississippi. Is it not so?"

"It is so. What then, mademoiselle?"

"May I look at your map, Sieur?"

"Surely. It is for your eyes. There is not much to see yet, but it is the rough drawings of what we know and what we expect to find."

As she bent over the map and saw spread out the course of the tributaries of the Mississippi, her heart rose in her like a wave. She felt his great dream and ambition, and she would give all she was, and could be, to help him.

"I see—I see," she said, and her eyes glowed, and she pointed to the map. "To here you know, but beyond this you do not know, and you work to know for France's—for Canada's sake."

His fine head bent over, his hand also touched the map, his eyes shone, and he had the sudden will to take her fingers in his own and clasp her to his breast, but he put the wild thought from him, for he had one idea and one only, and there could be no diversion from the straight course he had drawn for himself. He must fight down this sudden swell of human feeling. He drew back from the map.

Then Lya said: "I will tell you what I know." She then told of the evening at the Château St. Louis, and what Duchesneau and Madame Ranard had said, and how it had weighed on her mind, and that was why she had come to Fort Frontenac.

For an instant it seemed she spoke the truth, and then he felt it was not the whole truth. Where was her father in all this? Why had she come where her father came? What Tonty had said about Darois in Quebec came to his mind. Was he a spy upon Du Lhut? If on Du Lhut—why not on himself? Suddenly it flashed upon him that she had come to warn him against her father. Why had Darois come to

Fort Frontenac? It was not imperative. Why had he come?

Tonty doubted him from the first, and his daughter, whose truth was clear, had come after Darois, daring the perils of the wilds—not on account of Duchesneau and Madame Ranard, but because of her father. He was their agent, but the girl would not betray her father. Yet he determined that she should—not directly, but sufficiently. He said, seriously:

"Yes, yes, I know that Duchesneau and Madame Ranard and the Jesuits are against me. I have known it long, but how does that concern the visit of your father here? What has he to do with Duchesneau and Madame Ranard?

She turned slowly towards him, and her eyes took in his face with a hidden anxiety that could not be seen save by one like La Salle.

"My father came on his usual business, I suppose, but how should I know if he acts for Duchesneau and Madame Ranard and the rest? I do not know. I am not in his mind, but if he works for them, then I am against him too."

This was what La Salle suspected, but he took no advantage of it.

"How could his coming affect my future plans? How could he or they injure me?"

"Are you not obliged in your contract with King Louis to keep so many soldiers here, and will you not build a ship? Could they not hurt you there?"

"Ah, that—yes! They could seduce away my white men, and they could put a false pilot on my ship, that's true! Also they could stir up the Iroquois against me! All this I know."

"But do you feel it in the *deepest* part of you? Is that so?" She asked it with all her soul, for it seemed that she was on the verge of tragedy and in that tragedy her father played a part. She was set that her visit should not prove a failure. She did not wish her father exposed, and yet she would expose him in the last resort. Also, La Salle felt it would be unwise, even had he proof, and there was none, to have Darois exposed and dismissed, for that would be rupture with all concerned. They were powerful and combined, and an open break would be bad. He was not sure that silent watching was not best. Yet somehow, this girl's agitation, however controlled, was not burdened by the fact that Darois was an agent of his foes.

"Yes, I feel it in the deepest part of me," he replied, with a stern hand on himself, for her pleading eyes got into his soul. He knew she had not told him all, yet he could not guess what more there was to tell, and he would not try further to make her confess. "I am glad you came," he continued, "for I will keep my eyes open better now, and your father will return soon to Quebec. I have employed one of his men to stay here. Deslaurier is his name, and he will work with me."

"Deslaurier," said the girl, in slight confusion, for she did not know the name.

"Frankly, I would not employ any of my father's men. Suppose he works against you—acts as agent for your foes at Quebec?"

"My eyes are wide open since you came, and so are Tonty's, and we will try to keep things in the path of safety. I shall begin my ship the *Griffon* very soon, and then we shall have the test of loyalty and devotion."

Suddenly all she was, and had done, overcame him. Never had there come to La Salle such tumult in his mind. Never had passion and love stormed so across the moat and assailed the towers. He first flushed red, then he turned pale, then his face became set, and only his eyes showed what was going on in him.

The girl was woman enough to understand, yet it only confounded her—that this big man should be enamored of her was like some wild dream.

As it was, she could have thrown herself at his feet, so big was her spirit with what he meant to Canada and to France. She had the great thing in her, and yet she had no glint of love for him. He was too far removed, too prodigious. Yet she remained looking at him with eyes that saw what he felt, and also the fight going on in him. She could have loved him if she had not realized that he was not for her—that he was for the far bigger end—the immortal hours. To be loved by such a man was a vision of life, but she knew it was not for her. Some lesser man. She loved La Salle as only they can love who are free from self. It would carry her to farthest heights of self-sacrifice and endeavor—not the love of mother for child, or sister for brother, or child for parent—but the holier thing, for it was removed from all sense of relationship, except that larger affinity born of the Eternal.

So she looked at him as he looked at her, and both knew, with no words spoken, that the tale of their lives in this one sense had been told, and that never again would such vital speech be between them. His lips opened to speak, but no words came, and for an instant they stood looking at each other, as though they were meeting for the last time. He took her hand at length, and then he spoke. There was in his face now strength of purpose, though the fight was not all over, and could not be while she was still at Fort Frontenac.

With slow, firm voice he said, "I understand *altogether* why you have come, and while I live I shall be grateful."

He went to a window and opened it. The strong sharp air of early winter came in, and the sun beat down upon the opening. The window looked into the deep, decoying woods far off, and between were the high walls of the fort and an empty space, for no one ever camped before this window— that La Salle had insisted on, that he had as part of his daily rules of life, and that was why he had such power— discipline!

"These woods look south, and it is south that I am making for—south and always south. The mouth of the Mississippi shall be mine in the name of the King!"

For a moment there was deep silence, and in it the future with all its care and trouble and tragedy and triumph gleamed.

"All in the name of the King!" said Lya—no more.

As she left the room his eyes followed her, and when the door closed he sat down at the table and his head dropped in his hand. For long he sat so.

At last he rose, went to the window and opened the heavy shutters. Beyond them were the dark woods, and beyond these dark woods was his future, his destiny, the carrying out of his commission. He turned from the window towards the table where his map was, then there came softly through the night the sound of an instrument and a voice singing—a man's voice. It was that of Jules Ladaux, who had with Luc Maste brought Lya to Fort Frontenac. The song was tender and in the kind night mystical. These were the words:

> "I did plant a rose-tree,
>   Small, very pretty,
> I did plant it at night;
> The next morning,
>   The next morning I took it up."

La Salle did not speak aloud, but in his heart he said: "That is it! Sweet girl! To-night yes, but to-morrow— no."

Chapter XVII: THE WAY OUT

PERHAPS the most acute of La Salle's followers was Nika, the Indian, who had but one thought—to serve his chief with a constant and faithful mind always. He had the native's instinct, and from the first he had no faith in Tuke Darois, and yet he had instant faith in Lya, as all did. When she came from La Salle's room Nika saw glow in her face, and he knew there had been a meeting which would affect their lives. He had never seen his chief touched by thought of any woman, yet he felt she had transformed Fort Frontenac since her coming. He could see the change in Tonty, and he was sure that when he saw La Salle again he would see a change in him. He watched Lya move towards her own room, and then waited immovable and with bowed head till he should be summoned by La Salle. In about a half hour the summons came, and when he entered on La Salle he saw a man over whom had passed some vast influence. He was not outwardly changed, and yet his bearing was more forceful, his eyes more alive than he had ever seen them.

La Salle looked at Nika steadfastly for a moment, and then said:

"Nika, you will bring all Tuke Darois' movements to me. You understand?"

Nika understood. He made an assenting gesture. There was between these two a perfect respect—the barbarian and the high and cultured chief, and they needed few words.

Presently Nika said, "I have watch him since he come—he must to be watched!"

"Ah—what have you seen, Nika?"

"With the eyes, so little, but with the mind—" he made a big enveloping gesture with his arms.

"Quite so. Tell me the little."

Nika said he had seen Tuke Darois speaking to the men and with Deslaurier in the woods, and he thought him a twisted stick. La Salle smiled slowly, for this man was a good judge of devotion and he was faithful. Then Nika said, "To watch *her*—no!"

La Salle's eyes half closed, for there shot into them the memory of her. "No, not her—Nika, never!"

That night after dinner, Tuke Darois came to his daughter's room. His face was gloomy and his eyes were hard, but he knew he must go warily. He had seen no signs of doubt in either La Salle or Tonty, and yet he felt they did not trust him. There was no warmth in their talk with him, yet to his daughter there was apparent confidence.

He shut the door and came towards her. "You had talks with La Salle and Tonty," he said. "What was said between you?"

"I warned La Salle of danger to his plans."

"What did you say of me?"

"Can you not judge? If I had told the truth would you have been sitting at their dinner table? They do not trust you, but not because of me. Such men are not blind—even to you so clever and so bad!"

There was scorn in her tone. He came close to her. "So bad, am I? What will you do when you go to Quebec again? Tell me that, my wench. Is it war between us?"

"War! Oh no! You are my father. I will not give you up. I will watch you in Quebec, and if you try to injure La Salle there I will see you are stopped."

Her eyes filled with tears, then became dry and cold and hard. "I hate you for what you are, and yet I love you in a way as my father. I could kill you and love, and because I love you kill you. You are a pest to Canada. I will not expose you now, for that would not be good for La Salle. It would only bring disaster to you and evil to La Salle, for all his foes would work harder; but I will see that La Salle is kept safe from you and all who work with you."

The man was moved by the wonderful uprightness and wisdom of his girl. He had arranged for a false pilot for the *Griffon*, and he had also set an evil influence in young Deslaurier at work, and he thought that La Salle and Tonty did not know. He feared his daughter, yet he loved her, but not sufficiently to alter his way of life—not yet. He felt himself secure, and yet he knew she was the strongest foe to his purposes. He could not see his way clearly, but he knew that he must return to Quebec. He had sowed the wind and La Salle must reap the whirlwind.

"We start in two days for Quebec," he said. "Why should we wait longer here?"

"I would start to-morrow," said Lya. "I have done what I planned to do. If ill comes, you will be the cause."

His face became relieved and he said, "Well, kiss me good night, and to-morrow make ready."

Lya's face took on a somber look. "No, I will not kiss you good night, and to-morrow I shall make ready for our return the day after."

He frowned. "You would control the King's officer, eh?"

"Shall we go at dawn the day after to-morrow? That I wish to know."

He saw that if he wished to retain her affection he must be temperate, so he said: "Very well, your father will start when you say, and the King's officer will go also. I can influence him." He smiled futilely at his feeble joke.

The attempt at humor was lost on her. It was cheap, but Lya had an inner satisfaction, for she saw that he was coming to do her will, and that was much.

"I wish to go to bed," she said. "Good night." She paused an instant, then she added, "Good night—father."

"Good night, my daughter," and with a face in which love and gloom and bitterness showed, he turned and left the room. On the whole Lya had triumphed.

She watched him go with a strange sinking at the heart. Here was the one being on earth related to her, and he was such a man! For a moment she looked at the closed door, then she began to undress. She bolted the door and then sat on the side of the bed, and her thoughts dwelt on La Salle and Tonty. Presently she knelt and said a prayer for herself, and for her father, with a heart that hurt her. Then she blew out the candle. There in the dark of the night she thought of La Salle and Tonty again, and her heart grew big with joy to think that La Salle had been drawn towards her—to her! Had their stars been the same, she could have loved him—she loved him now in an everlasting way, but he was not for her. As for Tonty, her heart leapt up. There was a man of men—on a lower scale than La Salle, but big in his way, and upright and a patriot, and, oh, so handsome! His metal hand was but evidence of his bravery in war, and it gave new interest to him. Already there was growing in her the feeling that only comes once in this world, the first opening of the imagination and heart to love, and imagination is bigger in all such feelings. In the soft embrace of this exquisite illusion she slept till daylight.

The first person she saw when she issued from her room was Nika. She offered him her hand.

"Nika," she said, softly, "you serve one of the greatest men in all the world."

"Him—me always," was the slow reply.

So it was with Nika. He would never leave La Salle, and was with him till the end.

The next person Lya saw was Tonty. Her eyes were like soft pools of light and Tonty met her with outstretched hand. "I am glad that to-day we will have here a gathering of the Iroquois, and you will see how La Salle controls them—the cleverest, cruelest, deadliest foes that France and La Salle could have."

"To be here at such a time is good," said Lya, with features alive. "Did you know it yesterday?"

"No. Only this morning. Couriers from the Iroquois brought us word."

Lya thought of her father. Would he try to influence the Iroquois? Here was something she did not like. Her father—her spying, treacherous father! She would warn him and watch him. She would see him at his evil work among the terrible Iroquois, who had slain and tortured so many and who were the best governed of all the natives in Canada—the renowned Five Nations. She saw in Tonty's eyes an understanding of herself. The light in them was true, and she felt him the perfect friend of LaSalle.

"How long will the Iroquois stay?" she asked.

"Two days, perhaps—not more."

These foes of France were here with one of the best friends of France—La Salle—and one of the worst foes of France—her father, and he would be free to talk with them.

"They will be here in about three hours," said Tonty. "Come to breakfast now."

At breakfast La Salle was silent, watchful, filling the place with his presence. He had no word for Darois—he only inclined his head; but for Lya he had a gentle smile and a word of cordial courtesy. Then the breakfast of sagamite, fruits, salads, and fish from the lake was eaten. La Salle ate little, but Darois prodigiously.

After breakfast she went into the yard of the fort, and saw Indians and half-breeds and Frenchmen—Luc Maste and Jules Ladaux and others of the men who followed Du Lhut or La Salle, and a picturesque sight it was.

Her father had been very silent at breakfast, but she saw his eyes subtly flash at talk of the arrival of the Iroquois, and she waited for him in the yard. There she said to him: "The Iroquois are coming. Remember you may pay for treachery with your life."

Anger leapt up in him. "I will do what I wish, with no thought of anyone."

"But you will think of me," she sweetly said, "and that will keep you from doing all you wish. Your love for your daughter will keep you from mad things."

At the moment Nika passed them.

"That Indian is not an Iroquois and he hates them—and you, too," she said.

"Nika—yes, he hates the Iroquois and me," was the reply. "I feel that."

"Then beware of what will put you in his power."

"In *his* power—tush! I am an officer of King Louis."

"You are an official of the Hudson's Bay Company," she said, with bitter taunt.

"Well, watch the day's doings," he replied.

"I shall watch *you*," was her reply.

Chapter XVIII: THE POW POW

UNDER instructions from La Salle a feast had been arranged for the Iroquois and all at the fort were excited. There were Algonquins, Winnebagoes, Ottawas, Miamis, and other Indians camped about the fort. At the coming of their ancient foes, they were holding themselves erect and confident, for here was their friend, La Salle, and his few soldiers, and the Iroquois would stand no chance if they meant treachery.

The faces of the Iroquois were painted in all colors, and so were their bodies, blue and red and yellow, and above all was their marvelous headdress—distinguished and impressive. A Jesuit writer had said of the Iroquois that "they approach like foxes, attack like lions, and disappear like birds." Yet it was only in the woods that their great fighting qualities showed. They seldom could defeat the French in the open, even with more men. Their gifts were woodland gifts, their subtle minds worked only well in the umbrage of the forest.

Their women, who had great influence and even became chiefs, were experts on torture. When a prisoner was fed up against his burning, the women were assiduous in their attentions, bringing broth and corn and beans and wild oats or rice and a drink of dried bilberries, and oil of sunflower to anoint them, and enticing food; and stroked their cheeks as though they loved them.

The prisoner was ready for his torture when it came, and would run the gantlet through a myriad of fires, being beaten by flaming torches as he leaped from one end of the encampment to the other. For hours this would go on, till at last, burned and lacerated and broken, he would fall, never to rise again, having borne tortures with stoic endurance.

If a French prisoner, he was tortured terribly. A nail would be torn off, a finger cut off with a scallop, a piece of skin peeled from the body, the eyes scorched out, and strips of flesh eaten. Jogues, the Jesuit priest, when he at last escaped to France from Albany, had been so tortured that his hands were useless, and as no one with mutilated hands could say mass, and he was received at court and the people surrounded and kissed his mangled fingers, Louis XIV got from the Pope permission for Jogues to say mass again.

And Jogues came back to Canada and went among the Indians who had tortured him before, and was at last again tortured and killed. Too much cannot be said for the Jesuits who surrendered estates and great social place and gave themselves to hideous poverty and danger in the wilds of Canada. Nowhere in history is there such record of noble defiance of danger and death, and there was no Jesuit but looked forward to being tortured and slain for the faith to which in a vicious age he had given all that he had and was. In their long history the evil the Jesuits did was little beside all the good they did, for they showed in Canada the basis of the steady discipline which, after the British conquest, gave a quiet, steady people whose only guide was the Church, and whose steadying influence goes on even to this day.

It was about noon when the first Iroquois came, and the cries of those assembled Indians and French could be heard like a vast wind. They came in war dress and with tomahawks raised and it looked like war, and as they circled round, whooping, and La Salle and Tonty watched them, they filled the yard, about two hundred, beating their tomahawks and shrieking. The other Indians, the French and the *coureurs de bois* watched them with malice, for their blood was up and they would willingly have fought now, and then the worst would have come for Canada, for the Iroquois were many and combined. At last their Chief shouted:

"Farewell war, farewell tomahawks. We have been fools till now. Henceforth we will be brothers; we will be brothers."

Then they put up their tomahawks, and after the Chief had embraced La Salle they all sat down on the mats which had been spread, and for a long time there was a deep silence, broken only by a concerted "Hoh! Hoh! Hoh!" from the Iroquois. It was a strange sight on this lovely, bright morning. Behind La Salle stood Tonty, Lya, her father, and Jules Ladaux and Luc Maste and De Lussière and Hennepin, and at the sides the Indians who were the ancient foes of the Iroquois—squaws, and others, even many girls, some almost beautiful, and in their eyes hatred of their foes. Here they all were in these far spaces, laying the foundation of which are now vast cities of the West and South, and would embrace Chicago, Toronto, St. Louis, New Orleans, and vast populations.

At last La Salle stood up and began to speak with belts of wampum in his hands. He said he was their faithful friend save when attacked, and that his great master Frontenac, who acted for the King of all the world, had ordered him to give presents, and so he now gave them cloth. There lay before the chiefs rolls of cloth. Then overcoats were given, and tobacco, to the shrill applause of the Iroquois; then other presents—hatchets and knives and axes—La Salle walking up and down like an actor, opening his heart to them, eloquent and convincing. In dealing with natives, La Salle could succeed where others failed. Though he had no confidence that what he was now doing would have permanent results, he did it with an air of certainty. He said:

"We have been foes, my brothers, now we are one family. Here at Fort Frontenac you come and get all you need for your camps. You are powerful, but I come of a race more powerful. You may defeat us once or twice, or ten times, but we have men without number and untold wealth, and in the end we triumph. We mean well by you—we are your brothers—we are sworn to you by the crucifix which here we raise above you." He pointed to the crucifix near the building. It stood high and dominant. "It is our totem, and all our sachems and councilors and chiefs of the Grand Monarch bow before it. It is the only symbol that lasts, it belongs to all the ages. It is the one thing that lives when we all go to the happy hunting grounds where there is peace for all. It has been the conquering sign for sixteen hundred years. It is the key of the Hereafter—the only *oki* in the universe. It is the true hope and faith of millions who are to you as the stars of heaven to the leaves upon one tree. Be sure, my brothers, that we are here to stay. Yesterday we saw sun dogs—a sign of warmer weather. You point your javelins upward against Jannava, the Thunder Demon, to divert him from his purposes. We also point our javelins upward in defiance against the demons of disorder and misrule.

"We wish only to clasp you to our hearts and live in peace. The sky of our God and His Church is over all, and while life lasts we are your brothers. Look how glad the world is to-day—all sun. It is the sun of life that is in our hearts to you. Our King is called the Sun King. He warms all those who serve him well. I pray you be his children."

When he had finished, the Chief stood up and, clasping

his arms around La Salle in his handsome scarlet tunic and laces and plumed hat, said to his men, his black eyes glowing: "As I embrace this brother, so we all embrace their faith. Their Oki shall be our Oki, their God our God—and I have spoken!"

"Hoh! Hoh! Hoh!" said all the Iroquois, their hands clapping their mouths with assent, and all in the yard shouted assent, for La Salle's speech had conquered all—save a few like Darois—and some Iroquois, who yet were for combat.

When this was ended, the feast was brought—after the calumet pipe had been smoked by La Salle and the chief, and it had been passed to others. It was in great kettles and apart—Indian corn, green peas, beans, prunes, eels and fat, fresh salmon, sturgeon and wild pigeons, squirrels, deer's meat, partridge, quail, black birds, owls, and fish from the lake. Dried berries soaked in warm water were used as a sauce to the food not in the kettles, and a nut-meat gravy used with squash, and pumpkins and potatoes; and all ate greedily with spoons made of bark. La Salle had arranged that as they ate there should be music, and so there was music by drum, trumpet and cymbal, and a violin played by Jules Ladaux, and as they all gazed and ate freely, hens fluttered about picking up bits dropped by the feasters, and dogs snatched pieces of food let fall.

Tuke Darois had listened to La Salle with hidden hatred, for he saw the effect on the Iroquois, but Lya felt the greatness of the man. His gifts were rare, and he had captured the Iroquois, who loved rhetoric and saw in him a master of it. She stood near La Salle, with Tonty beside her, and her face shone while La Salle talked. Many eyes were turned to her, and she knew she was watched closely by the Iroquois, who had tried to kill her as she came to Fort Frontenac. That did not disturb her. She was alive to their duplicity, yet she saw that all was well for the moment. She watched her father. She knew he was not the fool— to be treacherous in the open day with Nika watching. The day drew on, and it was late in the afternoon the feasting ceased. It was clear at last that the Iroquois meant to stay the night. La Salle had prepared. He ordered that they should all sleep in the huge yard, and that they should not go among the other Indians or into the woods.

NIGHT fell under a shower of stars and a young moon. The Iroquois wrapped themselves in their robes of beaver furs decorated inside with painted figures and by the quills of the hedgehog. Some wore their hair loose on one side and tight-braided on the other. Others were close shaved, with one or more cherished locks. A few women with long black hair gathered behind their necks wore disks of copper and were gay in beads, and lay among them, and Fort Frontenac was in the circle of peace—outwardly.

Yet La Salle took no chances. It would have been impossible for the foe—if such they still were—to have made successful attack. Indeed, they had no wish to do so. They were for the moment at peace and the presents given had been ample. Besides, they were in numbers fewer than their hosts.

One chief had noticed a curious look in the face of an official—Tuke Darois—and had gathered that he wished speech with him. He knew the official not to belong to La Salle, but to Quebec—told so by one of the *coureurs do bois.* For long he lay on the edge of the crowd of Indians and at last fell asleep. He was waked about three in the morning by a tug at his robe, and a voice whispered, "Follow me, chief."

He rose and followed Tuke Darois to a corner of the yard where there was little light. Darois, speaking Iroquois well, said in a low voice: "Why are you friends with La Salle— you and your Five Nations? He is your foe and the foe of all great merchants in this country. He does not mean well by you."

"What is to-day is not to-morrow," said the Chief, ironically, and his look was ugly.

"But what is to-day should not be at all."

Treachery was part of the policy of the Chief and all his friends, but he had not looked for it in a Frenchman. His black eyes fastened on Darois.

"Your King gives him orders—your Governor helps him. What then?"

"He takes away your trade and the trade of the merchants. He will become rich and powerful and a tyrant here."

The Chief said naught at first; then he laughed a low, morose laugh.

"We can destroy them all, but we choose not yet."

"If there should come to you all—wealth, eh?"

He got no further, for Nika, the servant of La Salle, came softly and he said: "Sleep time. Let be."

Then Darois with anger turned away, and the Chief sullenly went back and lay down. At the door of the fort Nika said to Darois, "Night is sleep time—yes." With a look of fury Darois entered the fort and went to his room.

In the morning Nika reported the meeting to La Salle, who had expected it, but the explorer said naught save that he would see Darois left that day for Quebec. His face clouded, for he was sorry for Lya, and he told all to Tonty.

At breakfast time Du Lhut and twenty of his men arrived on the scene, and they were received with clamor by the Indians and all at the fort, who had not expected them. The Iroquois were preparing to leave, but they joined in the welcome, and Du Lhut gave all cheerful greetings. The Iroquois and the French respected him, for, though he broke the law, he was high in favor with Frontenac.

After greetings with La Salle and Tonty he saw Tuke Darois and his daughter. He had heard of their coming, and he felt by instinct that Darois was his own foe and the foe of La Salle. His greeting to Darois was distant, but to his daughter sincere and emphatic.

To her he gently said: "I see you here in the wilds where never has been a white woman. Your coming has done good!"

She raised her eyes in friendship. "I have seen what never else I could have seen, and I return with my father."

At that moment Luc Maste and Jules Ladaux came to Du Lhut, and their welcome was warm. "We brought her here, m'sieu'," they said.

"You brought her here? Then she did not come with her father!"

"No."

La Salle intervened. "Her father would not bring her, but she came. He will, however, take her back to Quebec. *All has gone well!*"

As he said these last words, he looked hard at Darois, who bowed low. "It goes well with Sieur de la Salle always," he said.

Three hours later, when the sun was hot and the woods showy with autumn colors, and the Iroquois had gone, Darois and Lya stood at the gate with three *habitants*, and said farewell to La Salle and Tonty and Du Lhut.

"A safe journey," said Du Lhut.

"A strong tide with you," said Tonty.

"You will soon be there," said La Salle.

Darois made no reply, but shrank a little from the stern eyes of La Salle. As she looked into La Salle's eyes Lya said: "You will find your way to the mouth of the Mississippi. That will be yours and France's glory."

La Salle's face shone with the light of ambition and hope,

and then came another look—it was the struggle between love and duty to a cause, and it turned her eyes to Tonty. Tonty came close to Lya. He took her hand, pressed it warmly, and looked into her eyes. This look said to her: "You have given a new sun for my sky. You have planted in my heart the seeds of love. You have set aflame the vast prairie of the future. I shall walk in the fire and shall come out ready to kill Goliath. Look into my eyes—tell me if you understand—child of life and love!"

All this was said without words, but the girl understood, and into her eyes there came a moisture of Eden. There were no words, but the language of the soul was there. She smiled at him, and he breathed quickly in emotion, and then kissed her hand.

La Salle saw all and at first he had a bitter pang, then the spirit of renunciation came upon him. He knew that the girl loved him in a deep, mysterious way in which there was no passion. He knew she felt him far removed from her, and with powerful will he mastered himself and said, "So—so, it is the hand of God!"

La Salle watched her go with conquest in his eyes. *That* was over, and he must face the unknown but hopeful future. He smiled at Tonty.

"All shall go well," he said.

Chapter XX: THE BUILDING OF THE "GRIFFON"

ONE day months after their journey to Fort Frontenac Lya received a letter from Tonty.

DEAR MADEMOISELLE:

I know you would hear what has chanced since you left us that black day, taking the sun from our sky. I have never forgotten you one moment—never can. You are always here. La Salle and I started for Niagara to the fort built by Hennepin and De Lussière. On Christmas Eve we were near wrecked in the Bay of Quinté by a treacherous pilot. La Salle would do naught with this pilot, for he risked his own life with that of La Salle, and so a Jesuit would without hesitation—eternal reward would be his. I see La Salle with the man before him. "Not again, not again, monsieur!" he said and dismissed him. In such wise had La Salle conquered the would-be murderer, Jolycœur, and it will ever be so with him. He is too gigantic to be moved.

When we came to the Seneca town, he spoke to the assembled chiefs, who had been eloquently but hopelessly addressed by Hennepin, and his reasoning, that building a vessel for trade would be good, at last convinced them, and they smoked the pipe of peace and took his presents with applause. When things are at their worst with La Salle, he can get money for his enterprises and gain the confidence of the most unlikely people. His cousin, François Plet, from whom he borrowed, is coming to Canada, and La Salle will have him conduct the business at Fort Frontenac.

So with the Senecas, he left them with good will behind him, and came on to the lovely, stupendous and gorgeous Niagara, all thundering and bright with color and shining! At Niagara La Salle's vessel was wrecked on the coast, and only the anchors and cables for a new vessel to be built were saved. On the high point where Fort Niagara now stands, La Salle marked out two block-houses, one of which he called Fort Conti. Then, after a time, hearing bad news from Quebec, he set out on foot for Fort Frontenac—two hundred and fifty miles through the Iroquois country and ice of Lake Ontario. He and his comrades had at last only a bag of parched corn and they made the last two days fasting.

It was left for me to finish the vessel at Niagara, which I did. She was forty-five tons and she was called the *Griffon*. When she was finished a Te Deum was sung and the Indians were loud in their excitement. La Salle had said he would make the *Griffon* fly above the crows—make Frontenac triumph over the Jesuits! We made her fast in the swift current and waited long for La Salle. Spring and more than half the summer passed and only in August he appeared, calm and reserved. He brought a tale of disaster. His foes had seized all his property and the Intendant had placed a seal on his furs at Quebec.

The *Griffon* was forced up the current by tow-ropes and sails till she reached Lake Erie. So we sailed this great lake to the Strait of Detroit, entered Lake St. Clair, and went on to Lake Huron. We had a wonderful journey, and passed through a noble country—had plenty of game and were in high spirits. Then a vast storm came and we were in grave danger. All fell to prayers and La Salle vowed that St. Anthony of Padua should have a chapel if we were saved. St. Anthony heard our prayers! We moved on till we came to St. Ignace of Michillimackinac. Here were Jesuit priests, their home and chapel, inclosed with palisades, compact houses of French traders, and grouped wigwams of an Ottawa village, a Huron village with its cabins and its fence of tall pickets, and they all gave La Salle warm welcome. At the Ottawa village La Salle heard mass in mantle of scarlet fringed with gold, with soldiers, sailors, artisans, black Jesuits, gray Recollets and Indians who called the *Griffon* "a floating fort."

You see how troubled is our way. Thus we move forward over seamy cracks and on the edge of chasms. If my will was not as hard as my left hand, I could not carry on. When I strike a bad Indian with my metal hand, he says, not knowing what it is, "Great medicine!" He does not know it is artificial. He thinks it is the devil in me. So with the will, when it strikes with Heaven behind it—the reply is "Great medicine!" Even the Church cannot conquer when the saints are with the metal will. That is how it will be with La Salle in the end.

At Green Bay, near Lake Michigan in the country of the Menomonies and Sacs Indians, La Salle made the one great error of his career. Here he found faithful servants who had collected furs, and he sent these furs in the *Griffon* to satisfy his creditors. She set sail for Niagara, and I cannot forget how I felt when it was done, for the *Griffon* was his true source of income, his perfect capital for the future. Yet he trusted her to an inimical pilot, he who had lost the small vessel on the Niagara. Then La Salle with fourteen men and loaded canoes left for the Illinois River. It was a hard journey for La Salle. Storms pursued him, and great difficulties stayed their progress. Things grew bad. The men paddled all day with only Indian corn, and sick with haws and wild berries, and La Salle gave them a confection of hyacinth to make them well. But we came at last upon plenty of bear's meat and buzzards and wild grapes.

Then the boatmen began to pick up spirit and to sing. They had great numbers of chansons, and, though primitive, have point always and an allusiveness not found among the Latins and the Celts. As they paddled one started a song of the river which I have often heard. He was thinking of his home, and of the marketplace, and as he sang all his comrades joined him:

> "When the lame girl goes to market,
>   She never goes without her basket,
> She never goes without her basket,
>   Niou, ioup-è-nif, è-nif, è-nif, è-nif,
>   She never goes without her basket.
>   "Lir lon, fa, ma lura dondé."

As he sang in the bright morning, a tender bite in the air and the sky cloudless and vibrant, all the voyageurs' eyes shone and they were transformed from wild woodmen and boatmen into men of home and quiet days. Even La Salle's eyes showed how much this domestic spirit touched him. He smiled and he joined in the refrain:

> "Lir lon, fa, ma lura dondé."

The party in eight canoes, numbering thirty-three, ascended the St. Joseph, looking for the portage leading to the headquarters of the Illinois. As we made our way to the head of the Illinois and could see far off the lodges of the Miamis, one Duplessis, an agent of Darois, raised his gun to shoot La Salle in the back, but his comrades stopped him. I knew of this, but did not tell La Salle, for it could do no good and Duplessis stayed with us. But I challenged him and he has now promised loyalty. He was a man of spasmodic emotions. In this I followed the example of La Salle.

Right and left were the prairies, with gray wintry forests and strewn with carcasses of buffaloes. Food became scarce, and all Nika, the Shawanoe, could shoot were two lean deer with a few wild geese and swans, and crows and owls. At length came a wonderful country with wooded hills and green prairie, a pasturage for buffalo and deer. Near by was a high cliff called Starved Rock, crested with trees, and along the right bank of the river were the lodges of a great Indian settlement built of framework of poles, covered with mats and rushes. This vast town was empty of people, but we found the caches in covered pits where was hid their stock of corn. La Salle hesitated, but at last took thirty minots of corn, hoping to compensate the Indians later.

At last they saw the Illinois wigwams on both sides of the river. The eight canoes were placed in line abreast. The men laid down their paddles and seized their guns, and the current brought them to the Indian camp. Here came immense excitement. The Indians snatched bows and war clubs, and all fiercely shrieked and howled, but La Salle with his little group of armed men landed and prepared to fight. But a chief came with a calumet, and La Salle showed another. The uproar was stopped, and feasting began, and the Frenchmen were fed by the fingers of the Indians, and their feet were rubbed with bear's grease.

La Salle gave tobacco and hatchets, and told them of the thirty minots of corn, for which he offered, and they accepted payment. He told them he meant to travel the Mississippi to the sea, and if they would not help him he would go to the Osages, their foes, who would reap the benefits of trade. This conquered them, and they feasted late, but still La Salle kept watch.

That night a Mascoutin chief, Monso, brought knives, hatchets, and kettles to the Illinois. He warned them against La Salle, and denounced him as a friend of the Iroquois, who would stir up the Mississippi tribes to join against the Illinois. Omawha, a friendly chief, came secretly to La Salle and told him all.

Next day Nicanopé, brother of the head chief, gave a feast. Before the feast Nicanopé warned them against the Mississippi, saying it had savage tribes, and the waters were full of alligators and serpents and whirlpools.

This had effect upon La Salle's followers, but La Salle coolly told them he knew what Monso had done, and as for enmity, they could have slain their tribes without help from the Iroquois.

"Even now," La Salle said, boldly, "we could put you all to death with your young men away. But we have brought you goods and tools! Bring back this coward, Monso, who comes and goes in the night, and let me face him. After a moment, Nicanopé grunted assent, and the feast went on all day. But La Salle kept guard at night as before, and in the morning found that six of his men had fled. He summoned the rest before him and said they should all return to Quebec in the spring if they would have it so.

La Salle left the Indian camp, and a half league below, on a low hill two hundred yards from the southern beach, he set his camp. On either side was a deep ravine and in front a marshy tract overflowed at high water. They dug a ditch between the two ravines, and an embankment was made and it was guarded by a *chevaux-de-frise* and a palisade twenty-five feet high was built. The fort was called Fort Crèvecœur.

Here came news to La Salle that the *Griffon* was no more. A young Indian joined his camp and told him that he saw a white man of the description of the pilot of the *Griffon* among a tribe beyond the Mississippi. With four others he had been captured while traveling to the Sioux in canoes loaded with goods. This fixed in La Salle's mind that the *Griffon* was lost. One day a young Illinois coming from a distant war excursion came upon La Salle, who gave him a turkey and other presents, and learned the truth about the Mississippi. La Salle added to his presents a hatchet, and made him promise to say naught to his people.

Then he went to the camp of the Illinois, and at a feast of bear's meat sat upon the rushes and smoked with them. At last he rose and said they had tried to deceive him, but the Master of Life had said to him all was well on the Mississippi. He told them something of what he had heard. His astonished hearers clapped their mouths and confessed that all they had said meant that he should stay with them. Later when a band of Chickasaws, Arkansas, and

Osages warriors told him that the river was navigable to the sea, La Salle's followers took heart again.

Then La Salle said he would not wait to get pit-sawyers, but would himself build a vessel, if he could get men to help him. They responded, and within six weeks the hold of the vessel was half finished.

I shall never forget the parting with La Salle when, with Nika and four Frenchmen he marched to Fort Frontenac for necessities lost in the *Griffon*, or we should be retarded a whole year. The forest was still leafless, and the ground frozen. Near by was the unfinished ship upon the stocks. In La Salle was not only unconquerable will, but anxiety, too, for this journey would test not only his endurance, but his faith in himself. Yet to the eye, all to be seen was a firm, serene face.

I was to remain behind with about three honest men and a dozen scoundrels to hold Fort Crèvecœur in his absence. It was a journey of about five hundred leagues in a direct line, and the dangers of meeting hostile Indians was great. They watched by night and marched by day, loaded with baggage—blankets, clothing, kettles, hatchets, gunpowder, lead, and skins to make moccasins. Sometimes pushing through marshes, they had to carry their canoes. Again and again progress was barred.

Day by day they toiled among pools and snow and ice, and at last they came to Peoria Lake, sheeted with ice, and dragged canoes half a league, launched them, and again had to take to the woods; but a sharp frost came and they could use their snowshoes. At last they reached the great town of the Illinois, empty of its people, where they got food by killing buffalo, and they met Illinois Indians. La Salle feasted then, and induced a promise to send food to us at Fort Crèvecœur. Later they made a desperate journey in the bitter cold, when the prairie was mud and water and snow, and came at length to the fort they had raised at the mouth of the St. Joseph. At length after hard trials, dogged by sickness, they built a canoe and floated in it down the Huron River. Lake Erie was reached, and in snow, sleet, and rain they made for Niagara.

Here La Salle found men who confirmed not only that the *Griffon* was lost, but that a ship from France loaded with goods for him had been wrecked, and that twenty hired men had been detained by his foe, Duchesneau, at Quebec.

Undaunted still, he traveled a thousand miles through a country beset with perils to Fort Frontenac. There he found his friends had plundered him, his creditors had seized his property, and canoes laden with furs had been lost in the St. Lawrence. So he hastened to Montreal there to face the enmity against him.

This is my sad tale, and it only tells a true friend what we have been doing since the winter fell between us and her good eyes. Our ship has far to go, and the perils are great, but we have one unchangeable star and by it we sail. It is La Salle. He is our North Star and our Southern Cross. And so, with quenchless admiration, most dear mademoiselle, goes to you the friendliest thoughts.

HENRI DE TONTY.

Chapter XXI: THE DARK CORNERS

ARRIVING at Quebec City, La Salle went at once to the Château St. Louis and was received most warmly by Count Frontenac. He had come straight from the shore to the Château in the dim evening, and was recognized by very few as he passed; but one of the few was Darois, who took the news to the house of Madame Ranard.

"Welcome, thrice welcome, La Salle," said Frontenac. "God knows, I wished news of you, and you bring them! Black things are said about you, and done to you, but you survive them all. What has chanced since you left here?"

In the long two hours La Salle took in telling his grim tale, Frontenac sat enthralled, or walked slowly up and down, having given orders against interruption, his big eyes fixed on La Salle's face. Now and then he would ask a swift question.

When La Salle had finished his rare and piercing story, Frontenac said: "The facts are these, then: you have lost the *Griffon,* you have lost canoes of furs, your goods from France has been wrecked in the St. Lawrence, your property has been seized, your men from France have been detained, your credit is at its lowest ebb, your forts have been destroyed, your men have deserted from you, you have been the victim of treachery. They think you are ruined. Your foes and mine would destroy us both. Is that not so?"

"It is so, Your Excellency, but I have no fear while you believe in me. With you behind me, I can live on—

fight on—and win in the end." La Salle reached out a firm hand and opened and shut it with vigor.

Frontenac smiled and laid a hand on his shoulder. "La Salle, La Salle, if there were a few like you in this country, naught could defeat us. We have against us powerful folk— the Bishop, the Jesuits, the Intendant, and their friends, but we must be confident and fearless. In Paris you fought them and you won, and in Canada you will do the same. What I fear most is that they will poison the minds of the Iroquois, who will destroy the Hurons, the Neutrals, the Eries, Andastes and Algonquins; inveigle the Miamis, and attack and destroy the Illinois. They league to prevent your trading, and they will stop at naught. They care not for consequences, if you are destroyed and trade is prevented and they can sell brandy and furs themselves."

His eyes darkened, a frown came on his forehead, then suddenly his face cleared and he said: "They cannot beat me thus. I have the King and Colbert and Seignelay with me, and so have you. They can injure, but they cannot destroy. We shall win—you and I!"

La Salle got to his feet, for this was one who had in him the splendid faith that made himself what he was—intrepid and unshakable. He now determined to tell Frontenac about Tuke Darois.

He said: "Excellency, there is in the employ of the Intendant and the Ranards an astute foe. It is Tuke Darois."

The Governor's eyes flashed. "Tuke Darois—that man! Yes, it may be so. I have never trusted him. Yet his daughter—I think there is a girl of truth and faith."

La Salle smiled half pensively. "She—she is straight and true." Then he told of her visit to Fort Frontenac and what had chanced there. "She is as true as he is false, and she is with us."

Frontenac laughed outright: "Yes, yes, I heard she had

gone the stark journey to Fort Frontenac, but I did not guess why. He can do less harm with her watching him than if he were dismissed. I could have him dismissed, but is it wise?"

La Salle's face shone now with a new light. "It is not wise, Your Excellency, and he should be left where he is at present—the tool of the Intendant and Madame Ranard."

Frontenac stamped a foot lightly on the floor. "Do they think, these silly folk, that they ruin us! I say *us*, because your fate and mine are one. Both want the glory of France and Canada more than aught else, and Canada first—always first."

Fontenac then went into the question of furs—trade in the West. He questioned concerning trade with the tribes in the Huron and Illinois country, and applauded the effective concentration at Fort Frontenac. He said La Salle would find money in Quebec, and he would see that his men should be released by the Intendant and be free to work for him. La Salle had been wise to visit Quebec, for he could start again with new power.

La Salle's face underwent many changes as they talked. It was as though Frontenac gave him a new commission, new impetus. He had little demonstration, but he showed in his eyes the enthusiasm of his soul. They were the windows of his inner life, the power-house of his purposes.

When he left the Château St. Louis, he walked towards his lodgings with a heart cheered by his talk with Frontenac. Somehow he felt that in spite of all he would prevail. As he passed from the Château and footed it in the moonlit night, he heard from the windows of a house this song:

> "Michau kept vigil
> The evening in his cottage,
> Near the hamlet

> He guarded his flock.
> The heavens sparkled
> With a brilliant light,
> And he began to sing:
> 'I am, I am the star of the shepherd,
> I am, I am the star of the shepherd.' "

This was a chanson of his native Normandy, and it startled him now. He raised his face to the star-lit sky and his heart beat faster. It cheered and inspired him—the Star of the Shepherd. He was the shepherd and his star was above him. A quiet smile lighted his face.

In this city were forces working against him of which he knew, but it did not affect him now.

Tuke Darois had gone straight to Madame Ranard and in her house had said, "That mad devil has come again to Quebec and has gone to the Château St. Louis, madame."

Madame Ranard fiercely said: "He is mad, but he is clever, and he is hard to defeat with Frontenac at his back. He is on the verge of financial and political ruin. You did well to come at once. You had his *Griffon* sunk, and other of his vessels and canoes, and the work you do is good. But in your daughter we have a foe. She went to Fort Frontenac to stop you. It was brave, but it was as mad as aught that La Salle or his friend Tonty do. You have little power over her, I fear."

"Power to prevent her having me dismissed!"

"Dismissed! Why dismissed? You are not Frontenac's servant. You are employed by the Intendant under my husband."

She did not know that he was a Hudson's Bay Company spy, and no one save his daughter knew, and *her* tongue was tied. Even Madame Ranard and Duchesneau would not have kept a spy of the Hudson's Bay Company in their employ. They only knew him as the foe of Du Lhut and La Salle and so they had employed him.

It enraged Barbe Ranard to think that La Salle should defeat her purposes, and always when she seemed on the edge of success. She was a woman who would sell her soul for men's favors, and she could not resist now playing, even with her tool, as he was. She looked into his eyes with a soft passion that inflamed his blood. She uncovered herself spiritually before his eyes, and he thirsted for this exquisite being higher in social life.

At last she said: "I will see the Intendant and he must stop this madman from restoring himself. If there were men in Quebec of real character he would have no chance. He is a cog in the wheel that stops its progress, and that cog should not be there."

Darois knew what she meant. "There *are* men of character in Quebec," he said, "and that cog can be removed."

She eyed him sharply, and when she heard his words, with a smile she bade him good-by. With a dark look, she saw him leave the room. Then she put on a cloak and hat and went to the Intendant's palace.

It was a huge building, once a brewery built by Talon, and had been a center of intrigue and evil, and here Madame Ranard came to plot with this good-looking, dark and able cavalier. He was the slave of his passion, and, now that her husband was away, she could go more freely to him. She arrived at the palace in about a half an hour and was at once shown into the office of Duchesneau. She accepted his embrace, and said: "We have work to do, my Jacques. La Salle has returned to Quebec." He started.

"My secret service lack precision. Who has seen him?"

"Tuke Darois saw him and came straight to me. La Salle went at once to the Château, less than an hour

ago. He is there with Frontenac. The two can do bad
work."

"They cannot put La Salle back where he was. He is
financially ruined; his day is over."

"Not over. If he had not come to Quebec—yes; but he
is here and he gets what he wants, as he did at Versailles
with so much against him—with you and the Jesuits and
myself against him. Yet he triumphed in a big way."

Her foot beat the floor angrily, her eyes flashed fire, her
face took on the look of one who would ruin the world for
her own dark purposes. "Oh, I could tear my eyes out when
I think of it, and even Frontenac's wife insulted me. The
female Mephisto!"

Duchesneau almost laughed. It was so strange to see this
clever, beautiful woman in a rage. "Yes, he beat us all there,
but he cannot do it here, for we have the whip hand. All—
nearly all merchants are against him. I see no chance for
him."

She had the brains of a born diplomatist, the heart of
a vulture, yet her lips were like rose leaves, and her eyes
like lights of heaven. She said:

"Be not so sure. Do not think him of no account. Something in him gets what he wants in the end. Somehow—
somehow—" She shivered, for it seemed, no matter what
was done, he conquered. She had set Jolycœur to poison
him, she had incited Darois to get Duplessis to kill him, she
had arranged again for him to be poisoned by an evil
huntsman, and yet he had come through it all with no ill
results. Somehow he baffled her, and she showed perturba-
tion now. This great Intendant had not defeated him. He
controlled finance and justice, and was the big policeman of
the country, and yet was beaten. She wished she was in
the Intendant's place, and yet what could she do? It did not
matter that they were acting against the best interests of

the country. They did not think of that. It was each for himself, and the devil take the rest!

"Somehow he arrives," she said, with despairing malice.

"Do not yield like that," said Duchesneau. "We have work to do. We shall beat him even with Frontenac behind him. Frontenac is with him for gain's sake, for naught else, and together they work for money, not for France."

"But they are two clever men together!"

"Aren't you and I as clever as they?" he asked, almost sullenly.

She looked him in the eyes. "Yes, we are—almost, but not quite, for they are concentrated and work in one mind—two powerful factors toiling as one. We are powerful, but we are concentrated in *ourselves* and that makes all the difference. We are less powerful because we love, and they do not love each other, but they love what they do!"

"And we only think of the state!" Duchesneau said with a hoarse laugh, for he had a sense of humor, and was only small because he was in the hands of this creature who would imperil the biggest man that ever lived. "Only the state!" he repeated.

She flushed with anger. "Only the state—only that which would make the state better than it is. But if it were only the state we should never be successful."

"We get nowhere just the same," he said, sententiously.

"Let us plan to get somewhere while La Salle is in Quebec. He thinks of one thing ever. We are not bound to one idea for every hour in our days."

"Yes, we are bound to one idea always," he said—"you and I. From that we shall win what we will."

A little later she laid her hands on his shoulders. She said with irony: "My friend, while we play he works, and we must act now, if we are to win. France is at stake, and we

[151]

should think of her and of Canada, which would be lost to France if this man has his way."

Duchesneau laughed softly. "France—yes, we think of her always; and are working against King, Minister, and Governor to save this child of France from everlasting perdition. Now what shall we do first?"

For long they sat and talked with ominous look; their hands came close together and they nodded and affirmed.

Meanwhile in another home a girl was learning from her father that La Salle was in Quebec.

"What do you mean to do?" she asked, with trouble in her eyes.

"It is not for me to do aught," he said.

"Only for the Intendant and Madame Ranard!" Lya replied, and from his face she knew that she had guessed right—in a way.

Chapter XXII: "SPY OF THE HUDSON'S BAY COMPANY—GO!"

NEXT day all Quebec was excited by the news that La Salle had returned. He had a bitter interview with his brother, the Abbé, who sharply told him that his misfortunes were due to his own lack of judgment.

"Brother Abbé," said La Salle, "you have not yet lost by me, and you never shall. I have been struck hard before, yet I have won, and I shall win again. I turn my face to each blow, and you see it determined still. You never wholly believed in me—never!"

The Abbé twisted in his chair, and his thin, ascetic face wrinkled, for he had not the great control of his brother—priest though he was—and he said, acidly: "I have always believed in your will and purposes, but not always in your way of doing things. You see far for this country, but you spoil all by mistaken ways."

"Mistaken ways? Abbé, how can you judge? You don't see my daily life, and you would not wholly understand it—I know not why. At times you have helped me, as when I came from France last, but again you obstruct me. The world is not blind, and when a brother is not upheld by brother, that shakes their faith. I have been hard hit of late, but it does not break me. I go on."

He got to his feet and held out his hands in appeal. "I never *beg* assistance, yet here now I beg you to stand by me. You shall lose naught. I can pay you back all I owe you, and will before I leave Quebec. I want more than your money. I want your faith, your love, your outstretched hand. I live a life that bears scrutiny. I am sober, honest, and clean in spirit. Never have my foes proved a single bad act on my past. Jean—Jean, stand by me, and give me your blessing."

His eyes were hot, his face was shining with rapt faith, his body was tense with feeling, and even the Abbé's small soul was impressed. He had some temperament, he felt the force of all La Salle said. His hand suddenly came out in blessing, and he said with feeling:

"Yes, I will have faith. The great thing is in you. God be good to you and give you success in this world and peace in the next."

The shoulders of La Salle straightened, his face grew brighter, his lips pressed firmly together, and his inner life was shown, for he said in almost broken tones:

"You give me greater faith in myself than I have ever known. I feel I am at one of the turning points of my fate. Something will happen before I leave Quebec to put me right—something!"

His eyes were looking far beyond his brother and this room. The Abbé's eyes were moist, and they were seldom moist with feeling, and he said: "You have much against you, but you have that which conquers all. What can I do to help you?"

La Salle smiled softly. "You have helped me. You are with me, and that is the great thing. I do not fear the future. My work will live when I am done with life and time."

Soon after they parted, and the Abbé watched him go with the first stirring of real affection he had ever had. As the door closed behind La Salle, he said: "Robert, you have the soul of a pioneer and a martyr, of a soldier and a poet—of a patriot, first and last!"

Hardly had La Salle left his brother's door when he was met by a messenger from the Intendant, who brought a note with a flourish. La Salle looked at the vain messenger with inimical eyes—he saw behind the insolent face the harsh face of his master.

He took the note, read it, and said: "Go tell his honor that I shall wait upon him presently—and go quickly," he added, sharply, as he saw the man moving slowly away. The messenger saw La Salle's stern eyes and gave haste to his footsteps.

La Salle sought his lodgings first, and took therefrom papers of Fort Frontenac and the West that he wished to show the Intendant; then he went to the palace. On the way he met men he knew and they saluted him, some mockingly, some in a half-friendly way, and one or two in doubtful courtesy; but on the way he met Barrois, the secretary of the Governor. He asked him to tell Count Frontenac whither he was going. Barrois' eyes showed the faith he had in La Salle, and a curious hard smile played at his lips.

"The Intendant will try to overcome you—but at least you will leave the palace safe!"

La Salle smiled. "If I can deal with the master, I can, I hope, deal with him. Colbert is his master!"

When La Salle entered the palace, he saw leaving by another door Tuke Darois, and he said to himself, "Here's what wants heeding."

In the Intendant's office he was met with courtesy and sly satire. "Ah, M. de la Salle, we find you in Quebec again, bringing reports of your doings in the West, I suppose. I wished to see you before you went among your friends here. I ask you to give up your work in the West. It comes to naught—to naught."

La Salle shrugged a shoulder and said, bitingly: "The Governor wishes me to continue the work which the Grand

[155]

Monarch gave me to do. Shall I heed words against the commands of those above you, Your Honor?"

"I have never believed in your work, as you know, and your late mishaps prove I am right."

"Right! And so you detain my men come from France, and seize my property and my furs, and—"

"*Your* furs! The furs of the King whose laws you break, you and the Governor. You have done illegal things, but, now you have come, I shall release your men. I detained them, for they are sons of France whose lives should be spared the fate awaiting them with you."

La Salle drew from his pocket a report. "I have had this made out for Your Honor. It gives my doings since I left Quebec last. I shall leave it with you, for naught can be said till you have all the facts. Those you receive from the Jesuit fathers are not correct."

"Have you then seen them—eh?"

"I have not seen *them*, but I know the Jesuit fathers, and all they say is tinctured by their hate of me. Perhaps they do not mean to deceive, but they do."

"Those are hard sayings. I have asked you here, Sieur de la Salle, to make you an offer. I have long valued your ability and zeal, and if you will abandon Fort Frontenac and the West I will give you a post under myself here where you will win high place and be a blessing to France."

La Salle grimly looked the Intendant in the eyes. "If it is to abandon the work given me by the King to do, you have grossly mistaken me. No obstruction and no mishap prevents me."

"Your *Griffon* was lost and nearly all else, and you have no hope, no chance!"

"I have hope that in the end my name will live in the story of Canada when yours may be forgotten save as my foe," was the stern reply of La Salle. "But I beg you to read my report, and I will come again if you wish, Your Honor."

"I may not wish you to come again, but I will read your report. Do you expect to get money in Quebec to put you on your feet again? Do you?"

"It is all in the hands of God, and so far God has been with me."

"Well, well, we shall see—we shall see!"

"Yes, we shall see," was La Salle's response, and there was that in the reply of the Intendant which La Salle did not like. He recalled Tuke Darois at the door.

With all due courtesy La Salle left the Intendant and busied himself in the city, trying to get money for his purposes—and failing. He had seen old friends, and they all declined to help him, and men to whom he owed money were unfriendly at first. Yet the calm will of the man impressed them, and their anger became less insistent as he talked. Somehow the bigness of his purposes influenced them.

In the distance La Salle had seen Madame Ranard, and she was more radiant than ever, and he had also seen going into her father's office Lya Darois, buoyant and entrancing. His heart gave a great leap for this was what came nearer to La Salle's inner life than aught he had known. He did not wish to speak with her, and though she knew he was in Quebec, she did not wish to speak with him, she knew not why. She was perplexed, for her father was strangely set in manner, and she felt it had to do with La Salle. She knew he had been at the Intendant's palace, and she was now going to his office to discover why, if possible. She was in a sore position and it vexed her.

That night at ten o'clock La Salle was going to his lodgings, when he was met by two masked men who blocked his way and then set upon him with swords. Two to one and a bright moon and a lonely street. For five minutes they fought hard and La Salle knew he was against men who used the sword skilfully. Behind them, not far, were two other figures that came no nearer, but watched the fight. At length La Salle knew that one of the men attacking him was Tuke Darois. By a brilliant stroke he brought one of his foes to the ground, and then he fought Tuke Darois. Now a small crowd began to gather, and La Salle fought on. At last the mask dropped from the face of Tuke Darois, and La Salle pressed him hard. This man must die. He was a traitor, a spy and a rogue, and the truth must now be known. At last he had his foe at his mercy, and with a sudden deft stroke he struck him to the heart with the words,

"Spy of the Hudson's Bay Company—go!" and Darois fell with a cry.

" 'Spy of the Hudson's Bay Company!' Was that the work of Tuke Darois?" The few people present murmured these words, and they stared at the dead men.

"I was set upon by two of them, and both are done for," La Salle said.

At this moment a figure came forward. It was that of Duchesneau, the Intendant. He knelt beside Darois. "Speak," he said to the dying man. "Is it true? Are you a Hudson's Bay Company spy?"

Darois raised himself slightly on his elbow. "Yes, a spy —God forgive," and he dropped back dead.

Duchesneau turned to La Salle. "You have done good work for France to-day, Sieur de la Salle. You have taken the life of a foe of France. In France's name I thank you."

"Yet he was in your employ, Your Honor. You did not know, but I suspected at Fort Frontenac, and I did not speak."

"Not speak—why?" The Intendant's face was disturbed.

"What good? I was far away. I thought you knew, and yet I could not understand it. Had it happened in Quebec, I would have exposed him, but the only one who knew the truth was his daughter, who came to Fort Frontenac to warn me—he had not told her he was going there—and she came back as a watch upon him. I cannot tell how she came to know. Why he hated me I could not tell at first, but when I guessed he was a spy of the Hudson's Bay Company, I understood."

"The truth must be told now," said the Intendant in anxiety, for he had employed this man.

"Quebec knows it at his death," said La Salle, pointing to the few men.

"Take up the bodies and bear them to their homes," said the Intendant.

The bodies were lifted and carried slowly away, and La Salle followed that of Darois to his home. The Intendant went heavily to his palace and La Salle knocked at the door of Darois' house. The old French servant came to the door, and behind her was Lya.

In the moonlight the picture was a grim one. Lya saw the body and ran forward.

"Mademoiselle, you have lost your father," said La Salle. "He with another attacked me and I killed him. To the Intendant he said he was a spy, after I had accused him."

The girl's face was set. "The Intendant was there?"

"Yes, there."

"Then I know who drove my father to attack you, monsieur!"

"And so do I, mademoiselle."

"Bring the body into the house," she said, and the men laid it on a couch in a downstairs room.

She looked at La Salle with half-blinded eyes of misery.

"You killed my father!" she said.

"He would have killed me. What else to do?"

In his eyes was the bitter truth that now and forever all was over between them. He had killed her father, and while they lived they could never be aught to each other save friends.

Chapter XXIII: LA SALLE SEES LIGHT

THE next day all Quebec knew that La Salle had been set upon by Tuke Darois and his friend, and had killed them both. It showed that La Salle was an accomplished swordsman, and the killing of a spy was published by Count Frontenac as patriotism of which Canada could not be too grateful. No one supposed the Intendant or the Ranards knew of his being a spy of the Hudson's Bay Company. They did not, but they used the spy for their own dark designs, and the Intendant set Darois and his friend on La Salle on the suggestion of the Ranards, and Ranard was with the Intendant when the attack took place.

On the night of the killing, Duchesneau, Ranard, and Madame Ranard met at the palace, and Madame Ranard, with fierce anger, said: "That pest La Salle has skill with the sword given to few, and now in the eyes of Canada he will be a bigger man than he has ever been."

"He killed a spy—Darois was a spy of the Hudson's Bay Company," said the Intendant.

"I did not know that when I engaged him," said Ranard. "It is the most damnable luck, and now La Salle will return to his work with money and with glory."

Barbe spoke. "We shall do well to applaud meanwhile, and you will make your statement about Darois at once, else folk will say you hired a spy of the foes of New France!"

"His daughter—did she not know he was a spy?" asked Ranard.

"Who knows? She is a pretty vixen, and she plays her

part well," said the Intendant. "Somehow, I don't think she knew the truth."

Barbe shrugged a shoulder. "You are too gentle-minded, Intendant. She is bad to her last inch, and so Quebec will believe. She cannot live here now. No. The world will be against her."

The Intendant nodded, yet after a moment said: "But wait. La Salle will say something. He knows why she followed her father to Fort Frontenac. We must wait for La Salle to speak. He has a dark spirit, but he is able."

"If he *knew*, and did not expose Darois at once, he was as guilty as Darois," said Madame Ranard, keenly. Her eyes lighted, her fingers twisted.

"He could not know unless the girl told him," said the Intendant.

"She would not betray her father," was the alert reply. "She can have no home in Quebec. She should go to prison, and you will do well to place her there, Intendant."

"I will see how the wind blows," was the reply. "She has not yet spoken. Wait till Darois is buried."

The day was bright and glowing, and the river, big and splendid, seemed like a conscious spectator, for it gently rippled, as though with laughter, and on its broad bosom Indian canoes and little ships moved softly.

In the palace of Bishop Laval was a stern judge of events. La Salle was not loved by the Bishop or by the Jesuits, but he had done a fine piece of work. As for Darois, he did not deserve Christian burial; he must be put in unconsecrated ground, with the sparsest ceremonies. Also he must be buried that very day. None could say no to Laval's decisions in such things. He sent his chaplain to Darois' house, and gave orders for the body to be placed at once in a coffin and buried before sunset.

When the chaplain arrived he found the undertaker there, and Lya stood like one over whom there hung an ugly cloud. Her eyes were sad, her face was drawn, yet it had sincerity and honesty. She bowed her head to the order the chaplain brought, for she knew her father had cruelly earned his disgrace.

The chaplain said to her: "My daughter, have you naught to say?"

"Naught, but this—the Bishop must be obeyed. My heart and conscience are clear before God. I have not sinned against France or Canada. I am the friend of both, and my father earned his wicked end. There is no more to say. For me there is no future."

The chaplain was moved. His thin lips quivered slightly as he said: "Your future is in the hands of God, and He knows your heart. Have no fear, the Church will be your friend. I will report to Monsieur de Quebec."

When he had gone, Lya said: "The Church will be my friend! No, never that. Death were easier than that."

She did not see La Salle until the burial came. He had been received by his old friends in much applause, and the Governor had sent word that he would have him dine that night at the Château. Meanwhile La Salle raised the money he wished for his purposes, and not at too high a rate of interest, and was ready for his work in the West again. One man, the greatest merchant in the city, Charles Le Moyne, who had gallant sons, D'Iberville, Bienville, St. Helene, and Longueil, said:

"You have much against you, yet you always win—and this last deed brings you close to all of us. What you need for your work you can have—you have placed us all in your debt!"

So, it was that as the coffin of Darois was carried to his grave, the only mourner was Lya; some of the population followed in curiosity. With Lya was the old Frenchwoman who had brought her up. She gave no thought to anyone else, but saw his coffin lowered, with meager rites and scant formality, in unconsecrated ground. She knew that while she lived she must bear her father's shame and must ever suffer. Strangely enough, La Salle stood not far from the grave when Darois was lowered, and her heart went out in gratitude. He had killed her father, who had tried to ruin and kill him, yet he came to see him put away so darkly, with many near who did not grasp the spirit of his chivalry. He was bigger than any of them knew, but the girl understood. He did not speak to her, and she knew that feeling was high against her, but that did not shake her. Besides, here was a true and honest friend, Luce Hontard, who knew her life as no one else knew it and who would have given every drop of blood in her fat body to shield this girl.

The priest said but one word to her when he had ended his brief ceremony, and it was, "Peace!"

He could have said naught so comforting to her, and she turned from the grave of dishonor with a heaving heart, but with a spirit that would not be daunted. She would face whatever might be with valor.

La Salle saw her go with pain and a sorrow that would be with him while he lived, for he had sunk an everlasting chasm between them. She left with head erect and body firm, but with woe dragging her footsteps, and she knew that no one dared show her kindness—yet.

That night at six o'clock La Salle sat at the Governor's table, and the dinner served was delicate and plentiful. Frontenac had a good cook and he had a gift for entertainment as for administration. He raised his glass to La Salle soon after they were seated.

"I drink to my friend, Robert, Sieur de la Salle, and may his work prosper!"

La Salle drank with glowing eyes. "All is well with me now, Excellency, but is it so with all here? I have been loaned money to-day, and I shall leave soon, for my work calls. But the daughter of Tuke Darois is alone and disgraced and poor. What of her?"

Frontenac smiled: "Think you I forget these things? I know what the Intendant and others will try to do, but I have faith in the girl. She is as straight as the candle and burns as pure a flame. She shall not suffer."

La Salle shook his head. "She will have the Intendant and the Jesuits against her, and they are powerful. She lives alone with old Luce Hontard. I fear for her."

Frontenac laughed and his face showed a sense of triumph. "Suppose she came to live at this Château!"

La Salle put down his knife and fork: "Came—to live here!" he said, in dismay.

"Why not! Madame Louvigny, a cousin of mine, lives here now, and she likes the girl and has ever done so."

La Salle could scarcely believe his ears. "What will the Intendant and the people of Quebec say—do you not see, Your Excellency?"

"I see, but what difference can it make! The Intendant would put the girl in prison if she did not live at the Château; but he dare not arrest one who has the protection of the Governor's house. Can you not see?"

"I see. Good God, how strange! To live here—But suppose she will not come. Suppose she sees the danger of it—?"

"Danger—to whom?" Frontenac gazed, surprised, at La Salle.

"Danger to you, Excellency! If the Intendant reports the fact to the King, or Colbert, how will it seem to them?"

"But if I report that the Intendant and Darois tried to murder you, and that they used consciously a spy of the

Hudson's Bay Company, how would that strike the great men in France! Am I so blind?"

La Salle saw that Frontenac would strike ruthlessly at the Intendant if need be. "Excellency, you are bigger than any of these folks and they cannot defeat you, and mademoiselle will be safe from the Intendant. A proud position for a girl so badly born. Even the people of Quebec cannot question what the Governor does, when they know that the girl came to Fort Frontenac to circumvent her father. She did not tell me this, but I guessed it, and so did Tonty; and she prevented him in so far as she could."

"It was not wholly good," said the Governor, "but it cannot be helped, and she was not with him. People will say she should have denounced him, but shall you ask a girl to destroy her own father? The girl shall live here as a ward of mine, and who shall fight me on the point? I am free from stain. I have no axes to grind, save one, and we will grind it together. While we dine here, Madame Louvigny has gone to Tuke Darois' home, and before dinner is over we may know whether the girl will come."

An hour passed and there came a soft knocking at the door. Frontenac gave the order to enter, and Madame Louvigny came forward smiling:

"Excellency," she said, "I have good news. The girl consents."

Frontenac and La Salle rose at her entrance.

"Good! good! Be seated, madame," said Frontenac.

"No, not yet. She would not at first listen to me—save in thanks, but when I said it was for her own safety and that she could not refuse the Governor, she said sadly, yet proudly, she would come. Her tears of gratitude wet my hand. So she came, and even as we left with old Luce Hontard, a soldier came from M. Duchesneau to summon her to the palace. I said the Intendant would find her at the Château, and she is here."

"Here now at the Château! That's as it should be," exclaimed Frontenac.

"Here now—Excellency—outside," said the sweet-faced woman.

"Here now!" said La Salle, and his heart gave a leap, then seemed to stop beating.

"Bring her in, please," said Frontenac, and Madame Louvigny vanished for a moment.

Presently the door opened again. Madame Louvigny entered, and with her was Lya Darois, who stood with steadfast, wondering eyes, looking at Frontenac.

TONTY had been left to make good foothold in the Illinois at Fort Crèvecœur. He had fifteen men, smiths, ship carpenters, housewrights, and soldiers, with l'Esperance and Friar Membré and the gentle and devoted Father Gabriel de la Rabourde. After work for some time on a new boat, Tonty went to fortify a cliff not far away. The day after he had gone the men mutinied—ten only remained faithful. They destroyed the fort, stole all the lead, provisions, and furs, inscribed on the small vessel *"We are all savages,"* and took to the woods.

Thus in one day was the work of weeks destroyed, and La Salle injured by those who served him. It was beautiful weather and the spot was lovely, but the men were off-scourings, and, with La Salle and Tonty absent, gave themselves the freedom of pirates.

The opposition of the faithful ten nearly lost them their lives, but they had courage and adroitness and escaped before the worst was done and the mutineers had left. They made their way under great hardship to Tonty, and the rebels completed their work of destruction. That such things could be done is a sign of the vast spirit of evil in a beautiful new world. These men shared no joys of discovery or settlement; they saw naught save the hour in which they lived, the food which they ate, the furs got by hunting. To them life was daily toil and struggle, and ended with the day, but they were capable of enthusiasm and great braveries.

Here was a fort at the start of the Mississippi adventure, broken by those who helped to build it, here was the ship on which they had labored inscribed with the cynical comment, *"We are all savages."* They were not far removed from the primitive debauchery and cruelty of the Iroquois, but they had no gifts of organization which made that body so successful. These men had no Long House like the Iroquois—sometimes five hundred feet long and containing many fires and great numbers of savages. These Iroquois watched women prepare great kettles of food while themselves played with cherry stones, games of chance, at times bartering all they had, or made arrowheads, or smoked, or sat with girls, making love in silence, or quarreled, or slept, or slapped the bare bodies of children who crawled round.

Life in the Long House was like that of a university, where men live in—the spirit of the tribe holds all, and one house becomes a center of tribal spirit. The Long House was the most powerful thing among the Iroquois, for, while there were innumerable small quarrels, these were overcome by the general tribal feeling. Looking through the Long House, one was conscious of organized life in which dark things might be done, but all was held by the strong circle of visible being.

It was like the court at Versailles—huge, with small rooms, where all met. Union, concentration, were the pervading influences. Louis lived an open life like the chief in the Long House. There was little privacy at Versailles; there was little privacy at the Long House, but in France it turned a series of duchies into a great kingdom, and it was as successful as with the Iroquois. Versailles was more than a palace, it was a nation. In it the nobles were under the eye of the King, and if he said of those he never saw, "I do not know them," their life was over. It was France concentrated.

In Canada two systems were working, and the one bound
to last was struggling for life. History says which was
greater, Frontenac or those who opposed him, La Salle or
his foes. This was the period, more than at any other, when
the fate of Canada was in the scales. With the discovery
of the Mississippi to its mouth, with the establishment of
Louisiana, was to come the building of an empire. And
this period after La Salle had triumphed at Quebec was
the most acute in his whole history and in that of Canada.

When word came to Tonty of the mutiny he sent
four men, two by one route and two by another, to find
La Salle. Boisrondet and l'Esperance, a youth called Renault, and one hired man, and the friars remained with him.
They lodged in the empty town of the Illinois until the
spring, when thousands of natives returned and life became
perilous. The Iroquois had started strife between the
Miamis and the Illinois. All summer Tonty waited, and La
Salle did not come. At last after vain efforts to convert the
Illinois, the two friars withdrew to a lodge a league away,
and the remaining Frenchmen did what they could to pass
away the time.

At last a Shawanoe Indian, who had been visiting and was
returning home, reappeared and gave word that the Iroquois army was near. There was immediate excitement
and natives threatened Tonty. They threw into the river
the tools of the French, greased their bodies, painted their
faces, befeathered their heads, and shook their hatchets to
work up their courage. With morning came the Iroquois.
They were over five hundred with one hundred Miamis.

It was a strange sight, tall, naked warriors, some in buffalo robes, some with shirts of deerskins fringed with dyed
porcupine quills, with clubs and quivers with stone-headed
arrows. Some were armed with guns, pistols, and swords;
others had bucklers of wood or rawhide and wore corse-

lets of rough twigs. The scouts declared they had seen a
Jesuit among the Iroquois, and it would seem that the
French and the Iroquois were working together. Tonty's
life hung by a hair, but when he said he and his men would
fight the Iroquois the danger lessened.

The fight began and Tonty saw it would all end in disaster, so with the assent of the Illinois he would mediate.
He took a wampum belt and holding it up walked forward
to meet the savage multitude. Soon he was in the midst of
the furious warriors and the guns of the Iroquois were still
firing. It was an odious sight—the writhing bodies, the
fiendish yells, every passion of an Indian war at work.
Tonty was dressed half savagely, and a young Indian
stabbed him, but the blade struck a rib, and then a chief
said he was a Frenchman, for his ears were not pierced!
The wounded Tonty told them the Illinois were twelve hundred and that there were sixty Frenchmen to help them.
So, at last they let Tonty go back with a flag of truce. Then
the Illinois sent a young Indian with Tonty, but this youth
nearly proved the ruin of the negotiation, for he betrayed
the weakness in number of the Illinois. Tonty, however, by
skill, address, and coolness, was able to complete the treaty.
But the Iroquois grew hourly more jealous of Tonty and
would have killed him, but it was not their policy to fight the
French at the moment. At last they called a council, and
Tonty and Membré were bidden to it. With six packs of
beaver skins, it was made clear that the Illinois should not
be fought; then came plaster to heal Tonty's wound, and
sunflower oil to anoint him; and they would strike camp
and go home. All seemed well. But now some of the Iroquois shouted they would eat Illinois flesh before they went
home!

Then Tonty at once kicked away the pledges in rejec-
tion and the chiefs, in rage, drove them from the lodge. In

the morning, after a night of alarm, they left, followed by the curses of the Iroquois. They went in a leaky canoe and paddled about five leagues, then landed to dry their baggage and repair their canoe, and the noble Father Rabourde landed and wandered across the meadows with his breviary. He never returned. He was captured by Indians and scalped; and so another son of a great Burgundian house gave his life for his cause in an age of vice and virtue and chivalry.

In the Illinois town dreadful things were seen. The fury of the Iroquois was spent upon the dead. They ravaged the graveyards, burned and threw bodies to the dogs, placed skulls on stakes as trophies, and some of the hideous remains they ate. Then, later, when the Illinois broke up into their several tribes, the Tamaroas remaining near the mouth of the Illinois were assailed. The men fled, but seven hundred women and children were captured, and revolting torture and lust took place. At length they passed with hosts of captives, triumphing over women, children, and the dead.

Tonty and his men went on and gathered acorns and roots for food. They lacked ammunition and Boisrondet melted a pewter dish for musket balls, and they made moccasins of the leather mantle of Father Rabourde. They abandoned their canoe and set out on foot for Lake Michigan. The cold was intense, and they grubbed up wild onions from the frozen ground to prevent starvation. They reached the bay and patched up an old canoe, but again they had to leave it in a great storm. Etienne Renault was taken ill from eating a piece of an Indian rawhide shield. And this was their salvation, for the next day a party of Kickapoo Indians came upon them. These they welcomed how gladly! After this they passed through matted forests where the squirrels chattered. At night, after passing far-reaching sheets of water and grassy heights and crags, they smoked pipes by the fire and slept at peace beneath the stars. They were carried at last to an Indian village of the Pottawattamies, who were under a chief friendly to La Salle. They were given to eat, in birch-bark dishes, wild rice with dried whortleberries.

Here there was naught to do but wait for the coming of La Salle. Tonty was sure La Salle would at last find them. Among the Kickapoo Indians they were safe and at peace, but Tonty kept the men building huts and making moccasins and mantles. The Indians came and went, and they sang their native monotonous chants and more than once arranged a war dance in which the latent furies of primeval life had play—tattooed and painted and feathered, and pagan in their gestures and language as they were. They also had other dances, and these they did with a curious fantastic grace, and even their squaws and girls were permitted to join them—the women almost naked, oiled, and rankly perfumed—in their grotesque gyrations.

Then they asked the Frenchmen to sing to them, and this they did with consummate point, for the squaws shook with laughter and the girls hung their heads or peeped through their fingers. This was one of the songs:

> "Who will buy from us,
>   These skins of cat, of she-goat, of hare,
>   Ah, who will take them—
>   I have skins of dog, of she-goat, of cat.
> When you marry,
>   My advice is that you take them,
> Taking them young,
>   The cuckoos will sing.
> Taking them old,
>   It will already have sung—
>   Laire, laire, la, la lon laire, laire, laire, lainderira."

[173]

This song was sung in their own language in a translation made by Boisrondet and it was most popular, for life among these Indians was free and vicious, and they well knew what the song meant. Even the young girls made suggestive motions and the eyes of the older ones glowed viciously. So the weeks wore on, and again at a catch of fish in the lake, this song the explorers sang to the assembled Indians to applause:

"In the water the fish frisks about,
    Who will catch it?
       Ladera?
In the water the fish frisks about,
    Who will catch it?
You the young girl
    They will love you!
       Ladera!
You the young girl,
    They will love you!"

By such primitive ways with friendly Indians they held their own and waited for La Salle. Their food was plentiful of its kind and there were plantations of beans and corn for which they paid by presents of knives, hatchets, sweetmeats, and crude utensils, but ever there was the danger of hostile Indian attack. It was a cold and raw region, but when the sun shone it gave their spirits impulse, and there was sun in plenty now and rain but seldom. Tonty was most successful with Indians, and while he was impatient he had a feeling that all would be better when La Salle arrived.

Chapter XXV: THE LIGHT FROM THE RUINS

WHEN La Salle left Quebec after killing Darois and getting money from those who had before refused him, he went again to Fort Frontenac where La Forest was in charge, and, taking a surgeon, ship carpenters, joiners, masons, soldiers, voyageurs, and laborers—twenty-five in all—needed for the outfit of a vessel, he at length reached Michillimackinac, and was again faced by hostility. He went forward with six Frenchmen and an Indian. If the Iroquois had invaded the land of the Illinois it would be ill. In all his travels he had met with discouragement, but difficulty only braved his spirit. When at last he made the journey all was lonely, now all was life to the full. The plains were alive with buffalo, and they killed buffalo and deer, geese and swans. They cut the meat into flakes and dried it. The men were in good fettle and they looked forward to seeing Tonty. They passed the cliff called the Rock of St. Louis where Tonty had been ordered to build his stronghold, but it had no signs of life. No work had been done on it. They gazed on a scene of desolation—ashes, charred poles, human skulls, wolves, crows and buzzards, open graves, bones, mangled corpses. The contents of the caches—store of corn—were scattered and cornfields burned.

As La Salle gazed on the terrible scene, a vast comet appeared. It was the largest and most lurid in recorded history and came nearer to the earth than any other. Many believed it a portent against the earth, but not La Salle; it had for him only scientific interest. For days he watched it and marveled at the excitement of the Frenchmen and the Indians. To him, if aught, it was a beacon to march forward.

There was an abandoned camp of the Iroquois. One hundred and thirteen huts stood in the meadow, and the trees were covered with their insignia, and marks of Illinois killed or captured, but none showing that Frenchmen had been slain. At last they came to Fort St. Louis and found it a ruin and a hideous scene, and with horror La Salle and his men descended the broad current and at length reached the Mississippi, the lode-star of his dreams and hopes.

Who can say what were his feelings then? The blazing comet was only a token of better days to come. It awoke in his firm breast a deeper faith than he had ever known. It was the sign from Heaven that all would be well with his schemes. The glowing sky above was the glamour of his dreams come true. He raised his head, and invoked it with the persistent faith of the zealot and the pioneer. It was like a hand beckoning him. Then they turned back toward Lake Michigan to find Tonty.

Hardships followed. Snow fell in vast quantities for nearly three weeks, and through forty leagues of open country they fought their way. Furious winds blew, and the snow was so light they could not wear their snowshoes, so La Salle went ahead, pushing his way through drifts, and at length they reached Fort Miami, but no news had come of Tonty, and all they could do was to wait.

He spent the winter at Fort Miami by the borders of Lake Michigan. He knew his foes in Quebec city had leagued with the Iroquois, and he planned to bring together the tribes of the West and colonize them at this fort in the valley of the Illinois. There were friends and allies near—

refugees from Virginia and Maine, Abenakis and Mohegans —they were of a hero-worshiping clan. Also Ouiatenons, Kickapoos, Mascoutins, Kilaticas. These swore to follow him, no matter what the perils or hardships. Then came new allies—Shawanoes from the valley of the Ohio, and La Salle urged them to come also, and planned to negotiate with the Miamis and the Illinois, for the Iroquois had murdered a band of Miamis and had intrenched themselves in rush forts in the Miami country.

La Salle set out to negotiate, and reached the prairies where at a camp of Outagamis, he got news that Tonty was with the Pottawattamies. This news made La Salle's heart sing. He met bands of Illinois whom he placated and won, and then he went to the Miamis. Three Iroquois warriors had been among these traducing the explorer, but La Salle confronted them and said they dared not repeat in his presence what they had said behind his back. They were silent and confounded, and secretly left the town in the night.

At last at Michillimackinac La Salle found Tonty and told tales of disaster, and listened to tales of woe that would have overcome lesser men, but they were not of the lesser kind, and they paddled their canoes for a thousand miles south. At last La Salle determined to lead his men to the mouth of the Mississippi.

So they started in fine weather and with cheerful hearts. They passed through a wonderful country where was now plenty of game, and Nika, ever silent and watchful, was busy directing the skinning and drying of the flesh of deer and buffalo, and all seemed going well.

One day as the canoes went swiftly, there came a song from a canoe which was at last taken up by them all, and it floated over the shining waters:

[177]

"My father married me to
  Petite Jeannete, glon, glon,
And knowing nothing except
  To guard the house,
To the sound of the bigournoise
  Sound of nuts and apples,
Of figs and strawberries,
  These are the steps of la glon, glon, glon,
Gloria de la ladereta,
De la bigournoise, o gai,
  L'espoir, c'est de la bigournoise."

It was a happy and exciting song, and La Salle and Tonty listened, and Tonty joined in it. La Salle's lips murmured with the rest, and he waved a hand towards the south:

"It is there—I know all is coming now, Tonty—to the sound of the bigournoise. I hear the steps of la glon, glon, glon!"

He laughed softly, and Tonty nodded.

"The hope, it is bigournoise," he said.

The days went on.

So it was that at last with a hundred Shawanoes and others, and thirty Frenchmen, with Tonty he drew up his canoes on the shore.

Chapter XXVI: A VISITOR FROM FRANCE

SOON after La Salle left Quebec there arrived his cousin, François Plet, whom he had asked to come. He had high character and much vigor, middle aged, strong, and reliable, a brain not easily turned, and a patriot. He had lent La Salle money when in France; no one had yet done so, and his confident faith brought other sums to La Salle. La Salle had, in truth, no head for commercial enterprises, and in a letter written to one of his creditors he begs his correspondent to send out an agent of his own:

"He need not be very *savant,* but he must be faithful, patient of labor, and fond neither of gambling nor women, nor good cheer, for he will find none of these things with me." He further adds, "I have neither the habit nor the inclination to keep books, nor have I anybody with me who knows how." Elsewhere he says:

The twenty-two men who deserted and robbed me are not to be believed on their word, deserters and thieves as they are. . . . It needs as unjust a judge as the Intendant to prompt such rascals to enter complaint against a person to whom he had given a warrant to arrest them. . . . Those who remain with me are the first I had, and they have been with me for six years. . . . I do not know what you mean by having popular manners. There is nothing special in my food or clothing, which are all the same for me and my men. . . . You do not know the men one must employ out here, when you exhort me to make merry with them. They are incapable of that; for they are never pleased unless we give free rein to their drunkenness and debauchery and other vices. If that is what you call unpopular manners, neither honor nor inclination would let me stoop to gain their favor in a way so disreputable; and besides, the consequence would be dangerous, and they would have the same contempt for me that they have for all who treat them in this fashion. . . . As for what you say about my looks and manner, I confess that you are not far from right. But *naturem espellas* and if I am wanting in impassiveness and show of feeling towards those with whom I associate, *it is only through a timidity which is natural to me, and which has made me leave various employments where without it I could have succeeded.* . . . Abbé Renaudot knows with what repugnance I had the honor to appear before Monseigneur de Conti, and sometimes it takes me a week to make up my mind to go to an audience. . . . It is a defect of which I shall never rid myself as long as I live, often as it spites me against myself, and often as I quarrel with myself about it.

This was La Salle's picture of himself, and it explained some of his failures, for his mind was shadowed by great timidity. He could inspire respect always, but only those who came near him loved him, yet he could influence men high and low, from the accomplished Louis himself, and Colbert and Seignelay to the poorest Indian in the West. The note in his life counting most was character, and that he had in unmatched degree. Self-concentration gave him powerful steadiness, and he kept his head up where most men would fail. He was first in any hard work with his men; he marched at their head; he took the worst of the blows; and he stands a magnificent figure in the early history of the land he did so much to create. Like all great men, he could get nearer to the primitive mind than most others; he could sway Indians where none but Frontenac could do so.

When François Plet came to Canada he was at once received by Frontenac at dinner, and said he had come at La Salle's request to take charge of trade at Fort Frontenac. To this Frontenac replied:

"Your cousin I have always upheld, for he is the true pioneer and explorer, but he has, alas! small gifts for merchanting. He has made money enough to pay all his debts over and over again, but he has not the great trader's caution, and he has had bad luck—heavy losses with boats and furs. He has powerful foes, but he will succeed. He has the soul and the face of a majestic dreamer."

François Plet inclined his head. "Excellency, he not only dreams, he acts, and his acts approved by Count Frontenac shall be upheld by the King."

Frontenac smiled, then laughed outright: "I saw what was in him from the first, and so did his foes. He has won his way in spite of them."

Then he told of Darois and his daughter and the plot, and how La Salle killed both men, and had gone West with fresh loans got by his killing of a Hudson's Bay Company spy.

At that moment Barrois, the secretary, came with a letter, giving it to Plet, who opened it and presently said to Barrois: "Say that I will go to the palace within the hour, if you please."

He added to Frontenac: "It is from the Intendant. He wishes to see me. It was taken to my lodgings and brought on to me here."

Frontenac nodded. "He will try to influence you. He has a gift of tongue, but he is too clever. He is the foe of La Salle."

At the Intendant's palace there was a party and guests were dancing and playing cards. Among them were new arrivals from France who had come in the same ship as François Plet, and they were mixing with local guests, flaunting their ribbons and laces as though they owned New France.

The whole atmosphere was different from that of the Châetau St. Louis. It was more frivolous and buoyant; it had an air of garish splendor, a kind of gayety in keeping with the gorgeous candelabra that hung from the ceiling. It was vivacious and gay in a vicious sort, and because of that was dangerous. Here the pleasure-loving folk came, and here was bred the spirit which had made Madame Ranard the mistress of the Intendant—it was the air of the place. Here men and women played with the sober realities of life, and gave cause for anxiety to the Bishop and the priests. In shadowed corners could be seen careless triflers caressing each other, and girls receiving gifts of jewelry as was the custom of the time. No girl was ashamed to receive gifts, for what was done at Versailles could be done in Quebec, and yet there was little grave immorality in the city, for girls married so young and there were fewer maids than men. It all had not the splendor of furniture, paintings, and sculpture of Versailles, but there was light and decoration and good music, and influence deadly to perfect civil life.

At one card table sat Rojet Ranard and a seigneur and two ladies; they were playing at high stakes with happy turmoil. When François Plet passed through the room, Ranard whispered to the seigneur and watched him till he disappeared. The eyes of many followed Plet, for all knew him as a cousin of La Salle. They had heard this after the ship, the *Carcassone,* arrived, and yet few had seen him until now. His name passed from lip to lip, and heads nodded, for they guessed what the Intendant meant to do, and a very few of them hoped that Plet would remain true to La Salle.

A moment later François Plet entered the Intendant's room, and Duchesneau came forward from the table, laying down a pen as though he had been at work. He shook hands cordially.

"Ah, Monsieur Plet, I welcome you to Quebec. I only knew of your arrival just before I wrote. You have come, monsieur, to do business at Fort Frontenac for the intrepid La Salle."

"I have come to take charge of Fort Frontenac, and trade in his name for a time. He is as just a man as belongs to France."

"He has reputation for fairness and honesty, and yet he has not succeeded. He cannot succeed unless I hold out a hand to help, for he has no business instinct. I would not lend him money—no—for the chance of getting it back is small."

"My own view is the chance is excellent!"

"Excellent? Excellent? Is that why you are here?"

"That is why. Nothing will be lost by any who loans to La Salle. He may not have great gifts for making money, but none has yet lost by him."

"That is because I have given him my support, for I am head of finance and the law in this province."

"I cannot think your support is so great as that of Count Frontenac, the Governor, who is over you and is head of all."

"Count Frontenac is not over me in aught," said the Intendant, sharply.

"Excuse me, Your Honor, yours is the mechanism, but his the policy. Working together, you can do much—apart, his policy counts—he can do all needed to make this land worthy of its origin."

Monsieur Plet had touched the Intendant on the raw, and had done it purposely. He hit hard when he hit.

"You have not the turn of it all, monsieur. The late Intendant Talon built this palace as a brewery, and he had policy of commercial development which did Canada great good. He controlled commerce, shipping, and the policy of trade. He built great industries—he taught trades—he explored the West—through him the Mississippi was discovered—and he even opened up trade with the West Indies.

It was more than mechanism, it was policy, and I, and not Frontenac, am responsible for the commercial welfare of the province. In my field I am supreme."

"I see. I see. But you and Count Frontenac work together, then, and you both would advance La Salle's interests. That is great news. I had heard that Frontenac had ever been with my cousin, and you when it pleased you!"

"I have never been with him as Count Frontenac has been—never, for his plans would not bear faithful scrutiny."

"They are the King's plans."

The Intendant bristled. "Not the King's plans! They are his own, and the King assented to them, because he did not fully understand them, but he is doing so now."

"Your Honor keeps the King and his Minister informed, of course?"

"As is my duty. I am a friend of La Salle, but he will not succeed in the end; he has too much against him—the Church, the merchants, and the spirit of the community. We all believe in trade, but are not with him in his methods."

"You are one in policy, but opposed in administration—is that it?"

"That is it. If there is too much settlement in the West and South, the difficulties of government are increased. Do you see?"

"Yet the King gave La Salle right to trade in the farther West, and to build forts and so on. I do not understand."

Monsieur Plet looked dumfounded, but he was a good actor, and he knew he was in the presence of one who was a great comedian—a tragic comedian. Now that he had got the true measure of the man, he played with one object only—to protect La Salle's interests.

"The King was at Versailles and La Salle was there. Had

I been there, the King would not, I think, have given La
Salle so many concessions. It was a grevious error."

"But now that La Salle is in the work, you would not
have him withdraw yet—not immediately, perhaps."

"That is it—I would have him withdraw, but not at once.
I hope you will get what is due you at Fort Frontenac."

"I am glad of your approval. I am not going for myself
only, but for all of La Salle's creditors. I will only take my
fair share. That is all."

The Intendant was astounded. Here was a really honest
man, who would work for others as well as for himself! If
he could work with this man he might himself get profit out
of La Salle. With enthusiasm he said:

"You are the kind of man Canada needs. Can you and
I not work together—eh?"

François Plet was in a quandary. He could not work with
Frontenac and this man also, and yet he wished to save La
Salle from attack. So he said, calmly: "I told Count Fron-
tenac I would work for La Salle, with his support, and I
will gladly work for La Salle with Your Honor's support.
We all shall be working for the same thing."

"Not quite, for the Governor approves of La Salle's
methods, and I do not. Yet that we should work in har-
mony for a while is good. Change of method, that is the
thing, and when you get to Fort Frontenac you will see
what I mean. I will send a man with you. You will need
help."

"Your Honor, do not send your man till I give you word
—I would like to start the work alone. When I have
mastered the present methods of trade I will send for your
man, if I may."

In agitation well hidden the Intendant bowed his head.
"It shall be as you say."

Then they left the library and passed into the great ball-

[185]

room. It was all revelry and gayety, and through clouds of tobacco smoke could be seen dancers holding each other close, and eyes of sensual heat looking over broad shoulders, while loose folds of linen showed breasts beating with the excitement of the hour. Behind her husband, who had been losing heavily, stood Barbe Ranard. She was brilliant with color and she dropped a curtsy as the Intendant with Monsieur Plet appeared. Plet observed her closely. At the door of the salon the Intendant said good-by to him.

As Plet left the palace he shook his head. "An able and a dangerous man. This fight demands every atom of resource. He tried to win me, and to perdition with him! That woman, Ranard, is the devil's own dam. She has gifts and a soul of shame."

As he walked on alone the wonderful air crept into his bones. The moonlight was like a silver fire, the stars like tender far-off friends, the St. Lawrence a broad path of radiance, the Laurentian Hills the coverts of great souls, the home of everlasting hopes, the place where men could go to hide their failures or recall their glories. They belonged to the everlasting history of the seventeenth century. His eyes lighted.

Chapter XXVII: THE END OF THE DAY

IN the black days of late November, La Salle, Tonty, and D'Autray, and Abenakis and Mohegan allies—eighteen in all, with wives of ten Indians whom La Salle did not wish to take, and twenty-three Frenchmen, among whom were Friar Membré and Pierre Prudhomme—making fifty-four altogether—started from Fort St. Louis for the Mississippi. La Salle had abandoned building a vessel, and they made the journey in canoes. Yet with canoes he could not carry enough furs and produce to repay his creditors.

At the beginning of the journey Tonty said to him: "It is in my bones that this time you will succeed. I am only sorry we have not a ship. It would impress the natives, it would carry furs and goods—but to impress the natives is the chief thing."

La Salle replied: "You are right, but I cannot wait to build a vessel. My needs are urgent. To find the mouth of the Mississippi will be the reply to my foes and it will secure me with my creditors. Even Count Frontenac could not see ahead at first. He is powerful, but he cannot do all, he can only help when I have opened up the way."

Tonty nodded. "Next to news of the money, what you told me about Lya Darois was the best you brought."

La Salle saw the gleam in Tonty's eye, and it pleased him, for between himself and the girl was now an impassable barrier.

"She is a true friend of this great land. She can make

[187]

all believe in her that do not wish to hurt her. At the Château St. Louis she is safe."

"But this courageous act of Frontenac may make feeling against him at Versailles."

La Salle shook his head somberly. "I thought of that, but it would need much more to influence King Louis. They are big men and Frontenac's wife is a good agent. He is better served by his wife than if she were here. She is more powerful because she does not go to court."

Tonty smiled. "It is said that Louis was once in love with Madame la Comtesse, and it may be so. But women do not influence him. He makes up his own mind. He has broken the power of the nobles and built up that of the middle class, and his generals, Condé, Turenne, Vauban, Villars, and Luxembourg are masters of war."

La Salle nodded. "He sees for himself and he works like a slave."

He threw back his head and laughed softly. Then he grasped Tonty by the arm. "We are not old friends, Tonty, as time goes, but we come nearer than do those I have known all my life. Time is not all. I seem to have known you always, and I never feel shy in talking to you—yes, I am a shy man, Tonty."

Tonty smiled. "You are a combination of shyness and bigness—as big as any man this land has known, and as shy as a child—Goliath and Garonne!"

La Salle laughed again. "Certainly not David and Delilah!"

He was thinking of Barbe Ranard. Then he pointed towards the Gulf of Mexico. "My goal! There must be no delay. Yonder is my land of promise. I see the reward of all our toil and misery. Ours is the biggest enterprise this land has known. I have no fear now, whatever lies between."

They stood in silence and looked towards the south. To both came happy prescience and melancholy. Their bodies were tense, their eyes were alight, but their faces had a strange pensiveness. Long afterwards, when strange things happened, Tonty remembered it.

They moved on down the Illinois, and at last in February came to the dark and tumbling waters of the Mississippi.

They built camp fires in the forest on the banks, and next morning, after singing hymns and a "Te Deum" and listening to the words of Friar Membré, they set canoes again on the muddy rushing stream, and further on found a deserted town of the Tamaroas. Then a fortnight later they came upon three Chickasaw towns. Here Pierre Prudhomme, one of the company, was lost, and for days they hunted him without avail, but at last Prudhomme appeared, to their great joy. La Salle hastily built a fort here and called it Fort Prudhomme.

Three weeks later they found themselves in a thick fog. When it cleared they saw Indians on the far bank of the river. The Indians were excited, but La Salle sent a Frenchman with a calumet decorated with ribbons to meet them. They all were warmly welcomed to the town of Kappa of the Arkansas Indians, who were of great civility and handsomeness. La Salle and his company had heard the throb of the war drum and the sounds of an Indian war dance, but that was because the Indians did not know the purpose of these strangers. Dances and functions were held; La Salle, Tonty, and their followers marched to the center of the town, a hymn was sung, *Vive le Roi!* was shouted, and La Salle in Louis' name took possession of the country. La Salle drew from the chief fealty to Louis, and a gayer, kinder, more companionable lot of Indians La Salle had never seen. When they left it was with cheers of good will following them.

As they rowed down the river, moving swiftly, one of the company, a Frenchman, who had been a cook in France, started a kind of chanson doggerel, making it up as they went on, and his friends joined in with him, and the river rang with it:

> "He who made
>   This jolly song,
> This jolly song,
>   Who came from Lyons,
> Cook in the galley,
>   And handled the oar,
> Always in great misery,
>   *Hélas!* always in great misery—
> Because he was a slave.
>   But now he is free in a free land,
> And out of his great misery.
>   Tra la, tra la, tra la,
> Tra la, tra la, tra la,
>   Tra la for the Sun King!"

La Salle in the same canoe as Tonty said: "That's the spirit, my friend. In France he was a slave, and here he is free. In France it was *Hélas! Hélas!* Here it is tra la, tra la!"

Tonty nodded: "They feel success at last in their bones. How could it be otherwise in this sweet, smooth air, in this exquisite land? Yet though the air is soft it stings with life! Even the Indians hereabouts are quieter, more civilized. Those we have just visited are the finest we have seen. They have better homes, better food, and they have a religion that lifts them up."

La Salle nodded. "None of the Indians of Canada are as far advanced as these. These"—he motioned backwards—"are a progressive people and this is a beautiful land."

They were floating down through lovely prairie where

game was in plenty and birds innumerable sang, and flowers bloomed in profusion. Even a snake ten feet long hanging from the branch of a tree on the bank seemed out of place. La Salle nodded towards the reptile.

"Yet everywhere the tongue of evil shows. There's a Jesuit even here Tonty."

Tonty laughed. "But its head hangs down!"

"Yet if you were beneath it and it— See!"

The snake dropped from the tree, a loathsome, wriggling thing.

"No, it is not a Jesuit," said La Salle. "No Jesuit is ugly. He is as taking as he is deadly, and he is a blessing, not a curse—save to me."

About three hundred miles below the town of the Arkansas, they stopped by the edge of a swamp. Here, as their two guides told them, was a path that led to the great town of the Taensas. Tonty and Membré and others were sent to visit it. Their men shouldered the birch canoe through the swamp and launched it on a lake which had once been of the channel of the river. At length they reached the town, and Tonty had seen naught like it— large square brick buildings with dome-shaped roofs. Two of them were very large. One was the home of the chief and the other was a Temple or House of the Sun.

Tonty and Membré visited this Chief. His tribe was the Taensas, and they were affable, distinguished in bearing, and hospitable. They were received in the Chief's lodge. The Chief was seated with three of his wives at his side, and sixty old men in white cloaks of mulberry bark made his court. He received their gifts, treated them with high honor, and addressed them graciously.

Tonty made brief reply, for he wished La Salle to speak to them and he said so. His master would presently pay his respects—he was a friend of the King of France, the greatest country in the world. In numbers it had fifty times the population of the whole American continent, and had vast cities, while this of the Taensas, though grand, was but the head of a pin to a kettle; and yet this was the finest native town, and the people the most advanced he or his friends had seen.

Then Tonty and Membré went to visit the Temple, where were kept the bones of dead chiefs, and it was built like the royal lodge. The inside was crude, yet there was a sort of altar in the center, and before it burned a fire that never died, and two old men always watched it. The place was full of smoke and there were dark, forbidden recesses. They held the riches of this people—pearls from the Gulf and other jewels.

At the entrance were three wooden eagles faced towards the east, and a mud wall with stakes on which were hung skulls of foes sacrificed to the sun, and at the door was a block of wood in a shell decorated with the hair of the victims. It was impressive and powerful.

The next day the Chief came to La Salle's camp at the river-side, in great pomp for a native. He was preceded by a master of ceremonies and six attendants to clear the path for him, and carried an awning to shield him from the sun. He was clothed in a white robe, preceded by two men with fans of white plumes, and a third carried before him two plates of bright copper.

Then ensued a scene of beauty and friendliness. La Salle spoke eloquently, and the Chief with great dignity and force replied, and concluded by saying: "We give you our hearts and our love. We bury the hatchet of war. We are brothers. We are at peace." They all feasted and La Salle gave presents, and they embraced at last and said farewell.

Then La Salle and his people visited the Coroas, were threatened by the Quinipissas, a troublesome tribe of these south lands behind the canebrakes, found the village of Tangibao, and three lodges filled with corpses—a sack of their foes a few days before.

Moving on, happy that there had been no bloodshed, La Salle looked back at the country they had visited, from which they had only kindness in spite of the gloomy predictions of the Illinois, the Miamis, and the Iroquois, and his heart swelled with pride. The brine of the sea came to his nostrils, and his eyes shone. They were in a land all sun and warmth, all goodness to the sense, a land like none they had ever seen—glorious in its softness and fertility. His heart swelled within him. He stretched out a hand, looking back.

"I have come from darkness to light; I have beaten the evil thing; I am content. God is with us." He made the sign of the cross. "Thanks be to Him."

Early in April they came upon three broad channels. La Salle took one, Tonty another, and D'Autray a third. As they drifted down between the low marshy shores, the brackish water changed to brine. Then at last came the broad bosom of the Gulf, and La Salle saw for the first time the waters destined to be the center of tragedy and the source of sorrow and happiness and immortality. On its restless surface was shown the strife of the undercurrents, which were to destroy not the dreams of his life but the value of his great discovery to France for the moment. They had come a journey which could be made from the Atlantic Ocean up the St. Lawrence to the Great Lakes and the Illinois and the Mississippi to the Southern Sea—a journey of thousands of miles—and all by canoe! It was marvelous, and at last La Salle and Tonty and the rest met on a spot of dry ground not far from the mouth of the river. There they erected a column bearing the arms of France and inscribed:

Louis the Great, King of France and of Navarre, Reigns:
the Ninth of April, 1682.

Under arms the Frenchmen stood, the Indians looked on in silence. They chanted now the "Te Deum," the "Exaudiat," and the "Domine salvum fac Regem." Then came volleys of musketry, shouts of "Live the King!" and La Salle, standing near the column, read in a loud voice the proclamation naming the new country Louisiana, and taking in all the nations, peoples, provinces, cities, towns, villages, mines, minerals, fisheries, streams. The territory should extend from the mouth of the Ohio along the Mississippi to the Gulf of Mexico. He declared they were the first Europeans to descend the River Colbert, or Mississippi, and protested against any nation invading these lands. Then a cross was planted beside the column, and a leaden plate with the arms of France and in Latin the inscription, *Louis the Great Reigns*. Then they all sang the grand hymn "Vexilla Regis":

"The banners of Heaven's King advance,
"The mystery of the cross shines forth."

ONE day Frontenac received a letter from La Salle. It told of the discovery of the mouth of the Mississippi. Here is the letter in part:

Excellency, at last I have found our goal. A canoe can come from the Gulf of the St. Lawrence thousands of miles to the Gulf of Mexico, and it passes through a land rich and fertile, with vast opportunities for furs, farming, and ranching, and with the hope of a great future. Nothing can stop me now, save only if you should be taken from this land. Then I could not count on getting arms and goods to keep my work going along the Mississippi.

I was seized with illness and for months I lay near to death's door at Fort Prudhomme, then I recovered slowly, came to Fort St. Louis, or Starved Rock, and here I have a wonderful settlement. I have Indians of many tribes, Shawanoes, Abenakis, Miamis, Illinois, in all near four thousand warriors, and they live at peace with each other and with me. From my high fort at Starved Rock I look on a marvelous country, and here I am founding a colony of French and Indians as a bulwark against the Iroquois, and as a storage of furs. These furs will go down the Mississippi to its mouth. I will found a fort there, and they can be sent direct by ship to France. I know they try to rouse the Iroquois against us, and they may succeed. That is why it is good to have at this fort so many brave men combined against our common foe. I should go to Quebec at once, but if I do, and the Iroquois should attack, it would be said I had led the Indians into a trap. Tonty and I have built here a fort which, with proper supplies, cannot be taken, for it can be mounted only at one side and then one man at a time and with great difficulty, and we have here stores and dwellings, and have encircled the summit with a palisade. This fort will hold some of the French settlers and with the Indians combined at the bottom, and with proper armament, it cannot be taken. It is small at the

[195]

top, but with Fort Frontenac, and Michillimackinac, and this fort
as distributing centers, all capable of good defense, a way may be
found for building here a great granary for France, and a fur trade
which the King will applaud.

All I ask is that I be furnished with arms and goods, and even
with the Intendant against me that is possible. With you behind me,
Excellency, I have no fear. So I shall stay here till I have made
the post secure. I see no chance of getting to Quebec till next
autumn. Meanwhile, may I beg you, Excellency, to present my
discovery to the Minister of the Navy, Seignelay, and to King Louis.
I am writing to Marquis de Seignelay, but if you will permit me,
your official report should uphold what I say.

When Frontenac in pride read the letter he decided to go
to Fort Frontenac, and have La Salle meet him there, even
though it would give a freer hand to Duchesneau and his
friends. Frontenac shrank not from any course he thought
his duty: but he called in Louvigny before he made his
plans.

He spoke with elation. "Louvigny, La Salle has reached
the mouth of the Mississippi, as we had heard in rumor,
and he is building a fort on the Illinois, and gathering forces
which will be a center of resistance to the Iroquois. I have
decided to go to the far West. I should give strength to his
hands. What think you?"

Louvigny shook his head. "You should not leave Quebec
now, Excellency. Your foes are hard at work. They may
influence the King. Your protection of Mademoiselle Darois
gave them a point of fresh attack. You are far from the
center."

After a frown had come to his face, Frontenac smiled.
He felt that Louvigny was right.

"Very well, Louvigny, but I shall see that La Salle has the
arms and goods he needs. No evil shall befall him—not
while I am here."

At that moment there was at the Intendant's palace a

scene full of portent for Frontenac and La Salle. A voyageur had arrived and had gone at once to the palace. He was admitted to the Intendant, for he was a servant of the Intendant's office. With the Intendant was Madame Ranard, and the face of the voyageur was excited. When he entered, the Intendant and his favorite saw there was great news.

"Your Honor, I have sailed swiftly in my small boat, for I bring word you have triumphed in France. Within four hours there will arrive a ship, the *Narbonne,* and she brings the dismissal of Count Frontenac!"

Madame Ranard's hand went swiftly to her breast in agitation. This was news indeed. Her brilliant face even turned pale.

"How do you know?" asked the Intendant.

"I went on board with the pilot, and the captain told me. He showed me the envelope to Count Frontenac, and one to yourself, and there can be no doubt."

"But sometimes the Intendant as well as the Governor goes. That has been." There was great excitement in the Intendant's face.

The man nodded. "The captain said he was told by Monseigneur Seignelay, that Your Honor was to remain and that Frontenac was to go, and that La Salle's discoveries were no longer agreeable to the Grand Monarch."

"What—all—all—like that!" said Madame Ranard, in excitement. "It is too splendid to be true."

"It is true, gracious madame, as people will know soon. I slipped from the *Narbonne* when she was anchored for repairs, and in my little boat reached here but now."

The Intendant opened his purse. "You have brought great news, Marsolet, so take this gift from the state." He placed some of the contents in Marsolet's hands. With many words of gratitude the man received the gift, but ere he left the Intendant said:

"You are not to speak of this to anyone, Marsolet. You think the Governor does not know?"

"Who is to tell him, Your Honor? I only know."

"Good—most good!"

When the man had gone, the Intendant and Barbe were so elated they could scarcely speak. "It has come—it has come at last. Heaven be praised!" said Barbe.

"My letter about the Darois girl had much to do with it, I'm sure. He played into my hands when he took the daughter of the spy into the Château St. Louis. That is the kind of mad thing he does."

"You can arrest the girl when he goes—yes?"

"He may take her to France."

Barbe shook her head. "He is no such fool. Besides, the girl is too clever to go. Her head is better than that of most. She is as straight as her father was crooked, and she has deepened Frontenac's friendship for La Salle. I loathe her. She is a curse to our country."

Duchesneau laughed, and his creased cheek showed his evil spirit. "She will have short shrift with me. I will imprison her—at once."

"But that will depend upon Bishop Laval, beloved."

The Intendant tossed his head. "If I have defeated Frontenac, I will defeat the Bishop—yet."

"But not you alone have defeated Frontenac; it is the Bishop and his friends. They are powerful in France. You have not all the kudos, but you have the bulk of it!"

With a deprecating gesture the Intendant said:

"I wonder who is the new Governor—some one not in sympathy with La Salle, I'm sure. La Salle troubles Church and State, and it is good the King sees at last."

Madame Ranard was a woman of intelligence and vision.

"Somehow, I do not feel so positively sure. The trouble is Frontenac has a clever wife, and he has friends at Court. He is a man of power—that, at least, or he could not have fought us all so long."

"He has no such power as will save him from fresh defeat. Once a man is recalled by the Grand Monarch, he ceases to exist."

He opened and shut his hand with anger. "I—I—have fought him always, and at last I have spoiled him. And now La Salle shall fail completely. He shall not explore and administer beyond this year. I have provoked the Iroquois against him; I have said they might take his life and that France will not object, and if the new Governor says the same—and he will soon be here—what can he do? Naught —naught!"

"Yet when we had him in just such a net before, he escaped," said Barbe sagely.

"Ah, but Frontenac was behind him, and Frontenac is no more! La Salle found the mouth of the Mississippi. That's big, yet Frontenac is recalled, and La Salle is done— forever!"

Four and a half hours later, the bells of the Jesuit College and the cathedral rang, and there was the boom of big guns, for the *Narbonne* was entering the harbor of Quebec, and word had been passed by Frontenac to welcome the ship. He did not know it contained the record of his removal, but when the letter from Seignelay was brought inclosing a brief one from King Louis, his breath came in quick gasps, his eyes went hard and fiery, he stamped his foot, he burst into oaths which came from a tortured mind. He had been defeated by lesser men—the Intendant and others. It struck him where he was tender—it was his one drawback, but he had always been vain from a child, and his heart was strong against defeat. He had ever proved himself of un-

flinching courage and of inflexible will. This blow was a
sad stroke to his pride, but after a short time he calmed
himself and he would face the population calmly. They
should not see he had been struck in a vital spot. They
should respect him to the last, yet to his immense credit
in his own beaten state, he said in bitter regret:

"La Salle—poor La Salle!"

That was the man. For an instant his mind dwelt upon
La Salle, then he returned to his own affairs. He called his
secretary, and Barrois came.

"Barrois, I have been recalled by the King, and our work
together is at an end," he said, quietly.

Barrois' face turned pale. "Oh, Excellency! Excellency!
That they should be able to do it—God torture them!"

"God does not torture, Barrois, he does justice, and out
of this will come justice to me. I see myself once more
Governor of Canada. When I get to France—"

"When you get to France the King and Monseigneur
Seignelay will take a new view of you and your work. They
will miss things here—"

"Yes, there will be war with the Iroquois and those who
play with them now will pay a bitter price for their folly
and crime. You cannot play with such two-edged tools. They
can never be trusted. I would wipe them from the earth.
They bring only evil with them. They are powerful because they are well organized. When our foes try to work
them for their evil ends, they cut off their own heads."

Frontenac dropped a hand on Barrois' shoulder. "We
shall await composedly the coming of the new Governor.
He is not a strong man or they would not recall me. What
lies they have told I know not, but the King's letter says
I have not lived at peace with the Intendant and the
Church and the merchants; and so they reap the ugly
harvest—my recall! Live at peace—who could live at

peace here who does right? I love the land with my whole heart, and I'd give my life for it, and that *they* would not do. They are honest—the Jesuits—but Duchesneau is not honest." He paused, then a curious look came into his eyes.

"Barrois, no man can do well in his office, who is moved by a woman. She plays him, and he pays—he pays!"

Chapter XXIX: THE NEW GOVERNOR

A MONTH later a ship, the *Boulogne*, arrived bringing the new Governor, Lefebre de la Barre, an ex-naval officer, and Frontenac received him with good will and all display at the shore of the St. Lawrence. There were present militia and officers and soldiers of France who had come years before—of the Carignan-Sallières Regiment and of Bearne, and gentlemen of his court in uniform and laces and colors, and many local gentlemen and their families, and among them were Madame Louvigny and Lya Darois, quietly dressed. Some women looked at them adversely, for they were of Frontenac's household, and Frontenac was hated by many—not because of himself, but because of what he did. They admired his splendid appearance, his undeniable courage, his power of administration, but that turned them against him; they were influenced by men folk who thought him evil to the country's best interests, and they believed it for the moment.

Yet when they saw who succeeded him they turned to Frontenac with a sense of loss; for Frontenac had presence and great character, and their new man, in splendid uniform and laces, had neither character nor dignity. None would turn to look at him twice, and even Bishop Laval, no friend of Frontenac, shrank from the hopeless figure. He had no distinction and seemed narrow and fussy and petty. Even Duchesneau, who had presence, saw in him a tool.

Frontenac saluted La Barre with elaborate courtesy, then they embraced, and the Intendant and the Bishop were presented, and a few others, and Frontenac saw what gave him sorrow—the thin character of the man, his pompous vanity, his unreliable soul.

Frontenac said: "Your Excellency, I greet you in the name of the dominions now extending to the Gulf of Mexico and west beyond to the Great Lakes; you will find it a good and a true land. It will bring wealth to the Crown. We all love it, as you will do, and we serve it with whole-hearted love, as will you. You will have great problems to solve, but we pray your stay here may be for the good of Canada."

The new Governor cleared his throat, and with uneasy eyes and a fluttering hand replied—his body restless, his legs rigid, his face without intellect—fierce with a passion he could not have explained.

"I have no words for what is in my heart, Count Frontenac. I will do my duty, remembering His Majesty's commands—to keep a steady, conciliatory course. Yes, yes, the King must be obeyed, and I shall approach all questions carefully after consulting with the Intendant, the Bishop and the Council, and local men of influence!"

Frontenac's eyes did not show disdain, but he glanced at Duchesneau and Monsieur de Quebec, and saw satisfaction in their faces, and disdain in that of the Bishop. He escorted the new Governor to the Château St. Louis and gave up the books of office, and before he left, five days later, he handed over La Salle's letter, and asked for him due help and men and goods, that his great discovery should be supported by the Government. La Barre said he would give it all serious thought, but he was not sure these discoveries were for the good of the Province of France, and he would no doubt hear from the Minister upon the matter.

"Meanwhile, what is to become of Sieur de la Salle, Excellency? He is at Fort St. Louis and needs men and stores, and before you can hear from France he may be wholly ruined. I beg Your Excellency not to delay sending succor. The King gave him title of nobility and his commission."

"I will give it all most careful thought," said La Barre, conventionally.

Frontenac was enraged, but protest could do no good. It would only, maybe, make things worse, so he held his peace, but he said to Barrois:

"There is no hope for La Salle from the new Governor, but I will see Seignelay. It is all so grave, so tragic, so critical for France and Canada!"

Madame Louvigny was not going to France. Her husband still stayed—on the staff of the Governor—but she no longer lived at the Château, and Lya still was with her.

At her new home Frontenac saw Lya. He said:

"Madame Louvigny will be good to you. These are dark days, I fear. The future of La Salle is in the hands of God. The new Governor is not friendly, and dark things may be done, but not so dark that Heaven cannot make them bright. All will be well with La Salle in the end." After a moment's silence he added, "I would ask you to come to France, but it might not be understood."

"Excellency," replied Lya, modestly, "here is my place at present. The great man, La Salle, was not born to fail—no."

He looked at her with satisfaction, and smiled.

"You will have trials—one cannot know what the new Governor and the Intendant may do, but you will surmount all dangers—and we shall meet again."

Frontenac left Quebec with little show of farewell, save for the booming of the guns that La Barre had ordered, and the hoisting of the fleur-de-lys on the Château.

Frontenac had scarcely left the harbor of Quebec when the Intendant summoned Lya to the Château, and, though Madame Louvigny opposed it, Lya said: "I shall go, though he means no good. God has kept me in the past; he will keep me now."

On the way to the palace she saw Bishop Laval in the distance. "He is not cruel, he is sincere, and I would not fear him. He is not small," she said.

At the palace she was shown into the Intendant's office. She wore a dress most plainly cut, but it suited her figure, and her fine face was full of expression. Her eyes were steady and her forehead clear of lines. Her hair hung loose about her neck, as was the custom of the time.

His eyes absorbed her with the look of one that desired women. There were none in Quebec with a figure like hers, save one, and this girl was much younger, and no one had yet had her love—or so he thought. He smiled at her.

"You have a new home, mademoiselle—yes?"

She inclined her head. "Since Count Frontenac left the Château St. Louis, yes. I am with Madame Louvigny, as Your Honor knows."

The Intendant motioned her to a chair. "Will you not sit? You will be more at ease."

Lya did not like his eyes. She kept her head, however, for what could he do? She sat in a big low-backed chair, and leaned her arms on the sides of it. There was determination in her face, and her eyes bravely met his. He could not read her, clever though he was. To him all women were alike, to be got at a price high or low, and he was in power now far greater than when Frontenac was in Quebec. The new man had no will to follow in Frontenac's footsteps.

"I have asked you here, mademoiselle, to say that for your father's crime you must be kept in prison. I never shared Frontenac's view that you were wholly innocent. You hid his crime, enjoyed his immunity and the salary of his office. You had too much liberty under Frontenac."

The girl's face flushed with anger and her eyes grew

brighter. "Count Frontenac had means of judging my guilt, Your Honor, and so had Bishop Laval. Do you think the Governor would shelter a criminal against the land he loved so well?"

The Intendant smiled. Her anger pleased him. He knew she was innocent and that she had only done what any woman would have done for a criminal father, but that was naught to him. He observed how fine her hands were, how delicate her ankles, how radiant was the air about her. She had the gift of radiance. She was like a planet with an aureole of her own, and all who met her felt it, though they loved or hated her. She had an atmosphere as definite as her person.

"Whatever knowledge Count Frontenac had, I, as head of the law, have better. Sieur de la Salle gave your father his deserved end—a good act done by one who is no savior of this land. He hurts it. Although he killed your father, you are his friend—eh?"

She bowed her head. "My father and his comrade meant to kill him. He did what any man would do. I have thought, Your Honor, that there was behind my father a great figure in this land."

Duchesneau got slowly to his feet. The challenge had been bold, and she had courage to face him so. He frowned, his eyes glistened with malice. Did she think she could say such things? She had more than courage, she had rashness. He spoke with control:

"All men in high places are slandered. I need not answer your mad challenge. Do you think I would put myself behind a traitor? Am I that sort of man—the Intendant who has triumphed over its Governor? Is it thought I was behind your damnable father?"

Her reply was quiet: "I do not work things out by logic; they come through my soul. You have prevailed—over Count Frontenac, by what means I know not, but when he comes again you will not be here, Your Honor! The land will be better for it."

The Intendant laughed sarcastically: "Well, well, you are bold, mademoiselle, and you take risks, for I shall have you imprisoned. The new Governor will not prevent it, and the Church will not defend you."

"I will not accept the protection of the Church. I am a good Catholic, but I must be free from such control. No one can point to crime of mine to warrant prison. One can live but once, and I will live in my own way in so far as I can. You cannot prevent that I know."

Duchesneau delighted in her noble courage, and she was so enticing, this orphan girl. He did not reply at once. He walked to the window and looked out over the great St. Lawrence River to the Levis shore, and he wondered what to do or say next. The girl was worth many risks; she was beautiful, valiant, and clever. She was here in his palace, and he could do what he would. Suppose she should cry out? Well, and if she should, how would that affect him! No one would come. Somehow Lya felt what was passing in his mind. She had in her dim way expected it, and it did not frighten her. At last he turned from the window.

Coming slowly back towards her chair, he said: "Very well, you shall be put in confinement here in Quebec."

He was behind her now, and he suddenly stopped, caught her head back quickly, and before she could prevent it kissed her mouth again and again. She sprang to her feet, and her eyes loathed him.

"You are my prisoner in just that kind of way," he laughed. "Your lips are honey, your person is as sweet as your mind is reckless. Did you think I would hear all you said and not reply? You drove me to it. No, no, you need not go to the door, for I will put you at once in prison!"

"Your Honor has played a devilish part," she said, with

low anger. "Do you think you can make that kind of prisoner of me? In your mind am I so low as that?"

"You are the most perfect girl on all this continent, and you can be a great figure here in Quebec, as my friend and confidante. You have the gifts. You can be to me what—"

"Yes, what Madame Ranard is! You may be a great Intendant, but your kisses were blotches of mud in my face. You are not for me—no—never!"

"Very well, mademoiselle, you shall go to prison. I am head of the law in this country."

She waved an angry hand. "I shall be free to tell the world what you did to-day, and to turn against you Madame Ranard. If you imprison me, I, a girl of the people, will fight you to the end. You are high, and I am low, but right will be with me and I shall win."

"You will win—at the price of all you hold most dear. It will be when I have drunk your sweetness. You think you can influence Madame Ranard? Try it. She will know you stooped to slander to gain your ends."

He came nearer her, but she did not move. She simply said: "If you touch me again, I will kill you—not now, for I have no weapon, but before you are much older. You are base and bad, and should not be in power here."

He laughed. "You will not kill me, and you shall taste solitary confinement."

"Oh, that is what you would do! You would give me freedom if I went to your arms; if not, you will imprison me. You want my body, and if you cannot get it you do what Indians do, you torture. That is how the man who fought Frontenac would win. Give me your prison cell, but remember there is one above all ministers on earth—One who controls the world for its own good—who is a friend to the helpless!"

He felt he had gone too far. He must retract, for she was unlike any woman he had ever known. She had overwhelmed him by her innocence and grace; she was the very heart of purity. He could not fight her and win—not yet! She was too dangerous to play with, for she had brains and character. He admired her as she stood with cheeks glowing, breast heaving, fingers clenched.

His tone changed. "Mademoiselle, I have spoken thus and acted so to try you, and I find you perfect in goodness. I do not regret, for you have won with flying flags. You have a soul of heavenly make, a heart of singular goodness. I know the Governor did well in trusting you."

His face was soft and alluring, and his manner was that of a born actor. For so clever a man, he had been reckless, and he was wise in his present attitude. He civilly waved her to a seat. He had not convinced her in the least; but it was well to allow him retreat, for he had power and could defeat her with the people ready to hear evil of her. She veiled her real feelings.

Her face was still pale, her eyes flashed, her hands were tense, but she said: "It is not the custom to go so far and it is dangerous. What is it you would have me do?"

He swiftly had changed his method. He smiled. "You shall not go to prison yet. You shall be free to live your own life. You are in good care—with Madame Louvigny. If you and she would help me as you helped Frontenac, it would be for the good of Canada. Will you?"

"We did not knowingly help Count Frontenac, though madame acted as hostess. We cannot do that for Your Honor."

"And why?"

"It would not be understood."

"By whom, dear mademoiselle?"

"By the public and by Madame Ranard!"

He frowned. "Leave Madame Ranard's name out of it. You think Madame Louvigny would not help me?"

"Never, Your Honor. She does not believe in you. She knows what a foe you were to Count Frontenac—that through you he was recalled."

Duchesneau preened himself. "That is correct, mademoiselle. I did it, and for the good of the land."

She bristled up. "You think the new Governor compares with Count Frontenac?"

"In no sense, but he will do what the Bishop and I ask him, and the Bishop and I agree in most things concerning Canada."

"You tried to ruin Count Frontenac, and you would ruin Sieur de la Salle; that is your purpose, and as Madame Louvigny believed in La Salle as she believed in Frontenac, she cannot work with you."

"You speak for Madame Louvigny assuredly."

"I think I know her mind, Your Honor."

Duchesneau rose to his feet. "If not with me, you will not work against me—eh?"

"I cannot speak for Madame Louvigny in that."

"Only for yourself! Well, so be it. I cannot complain. you have a patriotic mind, destined for high places."

He went courteously to the door and slowly opened it, smiling, and so they parted, admiration and black passion in his being.

As she left the palace, every vein in her body tingled with hatred. She understood him. She knew his malice would still go on—that he had tried to deceive her—that his change of manner was only due to caution. She had waked him in two things—a desire for her, and a devilish purpose to do her harm in all ways, if she did not come to him. He knew no such thing as loyalty even to Madame Ranard. She should be his or he would destroy her if he could.

When she left the palace he paced up and down in anger. "God, she was clever, and she was skilful! She will not give me away now—no. I did not foresee how she would twist things. She is an artist. I must go carefully with her."

At last he was roused by a knock on the door, and there entered on him Madame Ranard, her face was shining, her eyes were brilliant.

Chapter XXX: LA SALLE STRUCK HARD

AT Fort St. Louis things came to a climax with La Salle. There were signs of an attack by the Iroquois, and he had not enough arms or soldiers to resist them fully. He said to Tonty: "I doubt the new Governor, La Barre, means well by us. He sends naught for which I ask. I have scarce a hundred pounds of powder here."

Tonty nodded, but his face was cheerful. "You stay here yet, lest the Illinois should think you were not their friend, and if the Iroquois strike it would be bad. Yet it would be well to go to Quebec, and from Quebec to France, and meet your foes and fight them."

La Salle's face showed his perplexity. "It is a knot hard to untie, but it will unravel."

It unraveled that very day, and La Salle decided to go to France.

There came from Fort Frontenac news that it had been seized by Le Chesnaye and Le Ber in the name of the Governor, La Barre, and they had sold for their own profit the provisions sent by the King, had lived on La Salle's stores and had turned cattle to graze on the growing crops. La Forest, in command, was told he might stay if he joined those against La Salle, but declined to do so, and with the excellent François Plet, who had been successful, started for France after having written La Salle at Fort St. Louis:

I have not asked your permission, beloved Sieur, but you will understand. We will go at once to Paris. Count Frontenac will be

[212]

there and we shall prepare the way for you. That you will come to Paris now, there can be no doubt. You have been vilely used—vilely!

Reaching Quebec, they at once set sail for France in a ship that had brought strange news. They declined invitations to the houses of people of Quebec, for they trusted none save the Louvignys, and there they supped and were well received. Louvigny had lost his place with the Governor, but he had interests in trade; he was well-to-do and had weight with some people. His name was above reproach, and that he was a cousin of Du Lhut, the famous *coureur de bois,* was to his advantage, for *he* was a man whom all admired, even though detested by the merchants from whom he took trade.

They were not invited to the Château or the Intendant's palace, because La Barre and Duchesneau did not wish to hear what had been done at Fort Frontenac. Their own agents had brought word, and they had accurate record of all the two did in Quebec. They knew that at the house of Louvigny they had met the Abbé Cavelier.

The Abbé was as thin as ever, and as difficult of temper, and François Plet did not like him, cousin though he was. But the Abbé had invested cash in his brother, and he was keen to get it back.

"You are coming to France to help Robert?" asked François Plet.

"That is my one desire," replied the Abbé, with set lips, but he could not have told truthfully what was in his own mind.

"FIRE! Fire! Fire! Name of God, Fire!"

This was the cry that rang out one night in the Lower Town of Quebec, and at once the tocsin began to ring and people to assemble, though many Lower Town folk were away at Montreal on affairs of business. It began in the home of Esteere Blanchon and, consuming it, seized that of Philippe Nepsert and destroyed it.

Chartier de Lotbinière, Lieutenant-General, summoned carpenters and hastened to the scene of the fire, down the one precipitous street from the Château St. Louis, where dwelt the new Governor, La Barre, the obtuse and obdurate tool of Monsieur de Quebec and the Intendant. He hastened to the fire, but De Lotbinière and the Intendant were already there and were in control. Besides, it was the business of the Intendant to control in such an event, though Frontenac would at once have commanded all.

There were present, among many others, Duquet de la Chesnaye, public prosecutor; M. de Pstray, councilor of the Supreme Court; M. de Louvigny, M. de La Moyne with two of his sons, and many others. The Lieutenant-General had ordered the carpenters to pull down the small home of De Saintre and that of the Sieur de L'Espeires to try to stop the fire, but to no purpose. In increased in great volume and had covered the street and attacked shops of merchandise and at last was to *attack* the shop of the Jesuit fathers.

And here at the fire was La Salle. Madame Louvigny and Lya Darois were also there, and had withdrawn to the great square, though they worked hard to help poor people, half mad with terror, to save some of their belongings. Two-thirds of Lower Town had already been destroyed and the road to the Upper Town was made almost impassable by subsidence of rock and earth, and even the palace of the Intendant caught fire. The Intendant left the square, followed by the Ranards, and hastened to the big house which was the pretentious rival of the Château St. Louis.

La Salle would not go to the Intendant's palace; he stayed in Lower Town and saw it the victim of the destroying force. Even the carpenters could do little to resist the hellish sword of flame which cut wide swathes even upon the waters of the river and lighted up the shores of Levis opposite. Many people took refuge in the square and watched the engulfing flood of fire until between fifty and sixty buildings had been destroyed.

Meanwhile the tocsin still sounded at intervals, and Bishop Laval encouraged the people to increase their efforts to save Lower Town from complete ruin. The heat was great, the excitement immense, and Laval said sadly to La Salle, "Who shall increase when God says decrease?"

"Monsieur de Quebec, none—but has God said decrease?"

The Bishop frowned and waved a hand towards the smoking ruins, and at that moment the Jesuit shop, which so far had escaped destruction, caught fire. Priests and others ran forward to enter the building, and could not at first, but at length two entered, and one, scorched badly, brought out books of account; but the other did not come. The first arrived stumbling into the square. The building was now all aflame and the face of the aged Bishop turned pale, for he had human sympathy and great natural heroism. To go himself—he was ready to do that—but he had little physical strength, and the priest would have to be carried. He looked round among the priests who were near him, but none moved. It was too dangerous. At that instant La Salle rushed forward into the sink of flame.

In the square the Bishop and all others watched with deepest anxiety, but most concerned of all was Lya Darois. It was not alone La Salle's life, but what would happen to his work of life. It had entered deeply into her soul. It was her daily thought, her exquisite indirect ambition. He was on his way to France, he had come, discouraged, from the far West, through innumerable dangers, safe; would he come through this? The hand of Madame Louvigny found hers, and for two minutes, which seemed like ten years, they stood and watched; the girl grew rigid with intense feeling, her heart panting like a rock-drill, her face grown haggard. Even Monsieur de Quebec's face showed anxiety, and all men and women stared in hopelessness and murmurs ran through the unhappy crowd. Even La Barre, the Governor, was nervous and agitated and his eyes were blazing with a fire that could burn naught.

At last from the flaming mass there emerged La Salle, carrying the unconscious Jesuit. His clothing was aflame, but he staggered forward till men ran out, among them Monsieur de Quebec, put out the flames, and took the priest from his arms. The courageous priest had fainted in the heat and would have been lost forever had it not been for La Salle.

Monsieur de Quebec raised his hand above La Salle:

"God be good to you, my son," he said.

La Salle, badly but not dangerously burned, replied, "But God did not say 'decrease,' Monsieur de Quebec. Your priest lives and I live."

Laval felt the sting of the reproof. "You are near, then, to God, Sieur de la Salle?" His voice was friendly.

"I hope I am not far, Monsieur de Quebec."

Louvigny said: "Come, La Salle, come with us." He took La Salle's arm. La Salle's hands and face were scorched.

"Thank you, I can walk to my lodgings," La Salle said, and he slowly climbed the steep road with Louvigny, Lya Darois, and Governor La Barre close behind.

"Plenty of courage at least," said the Governor.

"At least that," said the girl.

Behind in the square, the Bishop, turning from the now recovered priest to watch La Salle and the Governor climb the steep hill, shook his head mournfully.

"La Salle is a mistaken gentleman. He has no fear, and helps his foes. Duchesneau thinks only of himself; and the Governor—pah!" He looked at the ruins of Lower Town. He sighed. He was a patriot. "It will take long to rebuild—and we are poor." Then he looked towards the Intendant's palace, where the fire had been stayed.

"The Intendant and the Ranard—oh, my beloved Quebec!"

He saw the futile Governor from the heights looking down. Laval shook his head somberly as De Lotbinière drew near to him.

As Duchesneau was sitting down to dinner, days after the fire, his secretary brought a letter just sent from a ship arrived from France.

It had a royal crest and it came from King Louis. As Duchesneau read it, his face went white.

Your usefulness as Intendant is at an end, and you will return to France by the next boat leaving Quebec. You have made me see where Count Frontenac erred, and now I see where you erred—grievously— in making La Salle's path too hard. Sieur de la La Salle has been wrong in much, but you—in far more. So, forthwith return to France.

Duchesneau could scarcely believe. Here after these long years he was master of Canada, and he was recalled by the King, beaten at his own game—by himself. La Salle had been wrong in much, but he, Duchesneau, in far more. That was his fate—to be cast aside when his work was finding true fruition!

As he walked up and down in angry agitation he knew that he had been his own undoing. He had fought Frontenac and had prevailed; he had fought La Salle and had prevailed: and yet had not prevailed; for at his feet lay his own career—a base and useless thing.

An hour later Madame Ranard came to him, summoned by a message. When she saw his face she felt ill had come. "What is it—oh, what is it?"

He gave her King Louis' letter. She read it with trembling fingers and a tumultuous heart.

"Good God—good God—after all these years!" she said, in anguish.

"After all I have done for Canada—this!"

She pulled herself together. "One thing is to do. Get Bishop Laval to help you. I, too, will go to France, and together we will put things right."

Duchesneau's face had anger and despair. "The Bishop will not help, after the fire. La Salle saved his priest. No help will come from there. Yes, come to France, but that devil, La Salle, may prevail again. He, too, will come to France."

Barbe went to the window and looked down in the moonlight to ruined Lower Town. She shuddered and came back.

"All goes against La Salle, but he reappears. This is our last effort, Jacques. Let us make it invincible. We will restore you to the good will of the King, and you shall have another post. But you shall—you shall!"

She kept her head up, but furtive tears were in her eyes.

"NO, no, Monsieur l'Abbé, I am come not in defeat, but in victory. I found the mouth of the Mississippi, with Tonty, the best friend man ever had, and, after dark dangers, reached my goal. This was my commission from King Louis, and I was proud of it."

He paused, and the Abbé Renaudot said: "You have forced success over bad dangers, and your way may be dark now, but you will succeed again. Frontenac is here, La Forest and François Plet are here, and Prince Conti is your friend."

La Salle looked at the Abbé with glowing eyes. "Frontenac, the best Governor Canada ever had, is in disgrace. He was my true friend in Canada. Where is he now?"

"He is not in Paris. The King would not see him, and Seignelay would only give him a cold reception; and the big man, fierce and insistent as ever, spoke angrily to Seignelay, which was not for his good."

La Salle shook his head with a smile. "That is Frontenac. They shall know his sharp tongue is the most honest thing France has at the moment. They will know it in good time. La Barre has slandered me, has robbed my Fort Frontenac of its provisions and its furs, and has turned cattle on the growing crops. He is a malicious machine, with little brain and a hateful heart. I shall never forget the day I left my fort on the Illinois. I looked down on a big valley, once a place of massacre of the Iroquois, and there were gathered four thousand Illinois, Shawanoes and Abenakis,

[219]

Ouiatenons, Nation du Feus, Killaticas, Chaouanons, Kickapoos and Miamis, and many others, all under my control against the Iroquois. Here was a colony at peace which had been at war; here is the center of a new life for Canada. Here when I looked back I saw the nucleus of a new empire—Fort Frontenac, Michillimackinac, Fort St. Louis, thousands of miles apart, and with the mouth of the Mississippi, making vast links in the chain of territories of the King. All this had been done with the help of Count Frontenac."

He got slowly to his feet and stretched an arm, while his handsome eyes glowed. "My God, I see out there a tremendous power. It will make for France a new home for millions of her subjects; it will be a profitable heritage for all time. It is the work to which I give myself and all that I am. It is my life's love!"

"My life's love!" Did thought of Lya come to his mind then? Did her face shine between? His eyes took on a weird, determined look, and he knew that for him there was no love as men know love, for he had killed the father of the only woman who had ever moved him in his adventurous life. He put her endless distance from him, and yet she would always be with him, an inspiring force, a friend and only a friend—forever!

The Abbé's heart was filled with pride. Here was a man of men, on whom could be placed all reliance and in whom was all hope. La Salle stood like a pioneer prophet, with one idea—the glory and development of France. No Jesuit was ever more concentrated than he, no saint more absorbed in the one thing to do. He was a religious man, but religion was not the first and last thing with him; he had left its active forces for wider, more active forces. To him the fear of death was naught. He had seen the terrible end of life's activities, how often! All motion, all vitality, all vigorous movements suddenly stopped forever, and all that man did immersed in the sea of inactivity. The man himself became a rigid, cold, and emotionless thing; he was engulfed in Time's blankness: and yet Personality went on forever. To the eyes of the mortal who does not see the invisible activities that never die a man's work might be arrested. Personality is memory, and memory is the biggest thing that comes to life. It never dies. All the great men that ever lived go on in the memory of mankind, and from Adam until now are in the world's archives. Christ, Moses, and all the prophets, if their active mortal life is apparently stayed, that which they were goes on. Time is the friend of all, it is the solace for all ills, the chain which binds all men together in the workings of the world. There is no disappearance; it is only transformation.

The Abbé said: "My son, you have the unconquerable soul. You shall not fail. There are those who can help you, and they will. But it is yourself that helps you most, for you can make people believe in you even when they are warned against you. Frontenac and La Forest and François Plet as expert witnesses stand beside you."

La Salle smiled, for he knew these men could do naught by themselves. He had not yet seen either, for La Forest was away at his father's home, and François Plet of the Rue St. Martin had been ill, and they had not yet talked together.

"They are all good men—Frontenac great—and they will play their part, but they have no power to open gates—none. They can do little alone. Duchesneau, the Intendant, is here, and the woman, his mistress, but Duchesneau is in disgrace like Frontenac, and the woman is the only vital spirit in the group. She is able and persistent and pernicious, and she is at work now, we may be sure. Her husband is still an officer of the Government of Canada, and she has entrance to official quarters here. She is more powerful than them all, but—" He paused.

Then the Abbé said: "But even she shall not prevail. She did not before, and she shall not now. She has the Abbé Potin, who was the confessor of De Montespan, and the Jesuit influence with her. That she was the mistress of Duchesneau does not count, for such women have nine lives to their lover's one. In France women are powerful, but not with King Louis. No one influences him, not even De Maintenon, who brought up the children of De Montespan and is now the secret wife of the King. She was the widow of the dissolute poet Scarron, and has risen to highest place. The beautiful De Montespan was capricious and difficult, and De Maintenon is of smooth, placid temper and gradually got a hold upon King Louis. She reconciled him to his Queen, and the Queen was grateful, and De Maintenon's place is forever secure."

La Salle nodded. "She has supplanted the woman whose children she raised! She is not ambitious, Abbé?"

"Ambitious? Yes, but in a wholesome way. She would not bear all she has suffered if not ambitious. Her ambition is the good of France. She is not like De Montespan or others who were playing their own hands always. We priests see, we understand."

The Abbé paused a moment, then rose and laid a hand on La Salle's shoulder. He looked in his eyes long and earnestly. "You are experienced, La Salle, but you have little worldly wisdom. I, a priest, have more. The obvious things are not for you. You forget that men are won as much by diplomacy as by character. Like all great men, you are a child—yes, a child!"

La Salle's lips took on a whimsical look. "I am as Heaven made me."

While this scene went on between the Abbé Renaudot and La Salle, at the Hôtel des Invalides, Madam Ranard was talking to the Abbé Potin, the confessor of the deposed De Montespan. It was through her he had been made the clerical head of the new Invalides, and he did his work well. They were in a room of the vast building which had all the details of noble surroundings. Not far away was the big tomb with its chapels, all empty as yet, save for one where was the last resting-place of a great general of King Louis. From above and from the side windows the sun beat down with soft power. Of the soldiers who had fought for Louis, numbers were in the rooms and grounds, and they wandered about with faces that knew no want, for they were well cared for, were the pride of the nation. Louis kept his army faithful, and the people faithful to the army.

The myriad life of the vast hospital gave a new turn to the splendid career of Louis. It marked the period when he put old things behind and turned his face to quiet work and the fulfillment of great ambitions. When he buried his Queen he showed real grief, and he said the only tears she had ever made him shed was when she left him forever.

The Invalides was a monument to Louis' vision and patiotism, and it stands now as a hospital and a tomb and memorial—national and imperialistic. He had made De Montespan a duchess, put her into a convent, parted from her peaceably, had listened to her request to do something for the Abbé Potin, and so had made him Superior here.

Into the room where was a bust of Louis, and a crucifix, and shelves of books and heavy curtains of purple, and an air of piety, Madame Ranard was shown. Through the shaded windows there came the low rumbling sounds of the life of the vast place; it was like a soft and vivid overture to the drama which would presently be played. Barbe's eyes fell on the crucifix and she made the sacred gesture, for she had a superstitious element, and in her crooked way she was a devout Jesuit. Then she turned to the bust of Louis and she shook her head, for he did not inspire her. To her he was a hard machine that would not beat time to her song of life—a great man of whom she had a wholesome fear. Even as she sat in this big handsome room she shivered, for he had seemed to her a personal danger, yet she knew not why.

Her hand went to her eyes with a sudden start of anxiety, and at the moment the Abbé Potin entered, quiet, smooth, dignified, yet with a stealthiness which was part of his equipment. He had brains and no real religion. His faith was the business of his life and valuable only in what it did to advance his interests. His most striking features were his eyes, which had a look of imagination and dominance, and yet the rest of his face was an oil of gladness that soothed the tyrannical glance falling from them. He had a sense of humor and cynicism not natural to a priest.

"So you are again to France, and your friend the Intendant, once so powerful in Canada, has come too."

She bowed low and kissed his fingers. "We have come to see if justice can still be got from the court of France. *You* have got it, Abbé!"

He smiled. I am well placed here, but I miss the life at court. Since De Montespan has gone I am naught there."

"But you must still be much nearer the throne. Surely that is so, dear Abbé?"

He reached out slim fingers and raised her chin. "Look at me. I had naught save influence with De Montespan. The Grand Monarch has done well by me. I am master here and it is comfortable—and interesting, but I am naught at court." His fingers strayed from her chin to her cheek, and in his eyes was what should not be in the eyes of a priest. She saw the look and, great actress and hypocrite as she was, she suddenly rose, wrapped her arms round his neck, burst into tears, and her lips found his.

"Oh, I cannot bear it, I cannot bear it! I have no power now in Quebec—and none in Paris, but I felt you could help me, dear Abbé; I felt that. Can you not help me—please say!"

His face was flushed, his heart beating hard, but after a moment of rapture he drew back and controlled himself. She was beautiful, she was enticing, her touch was so magnetic, her luxuriance so thrilling, and yet he must not! "You should not kiss me," he said, in a husky voice. "It is not what I can bear—no. But I will try to help you." He stepped back from her. "You work for our Church and that means much even in Paris. Now what wish you to do at court? What?"

"To let me talk with Marquis Seignelay. The Queen is dead and De Maintenon is now the wife of Louis, is it not so?"

The Abbé nodded. "It is so, and she has vast power, but in a quiet way. I am told that at conferences with his Ministers Louis turns to her and says: 'And what does your Solidity think of it?' He pays no attention to ladies of the court, is set only on his work. Life is still brilliant at court, it always will be so while Louis lives, but not in the old dazzling way—its gorgeousness and licentiousness. I have no weight now with De Montespan gone. I have no power. Yet I know Seignelay well, and in times past have been of service to him. I can perhaps help you to see him. You did not influence him before!"

She nodded: "But I have seen enough life to know that to-day's *No* may be to-morrow's *Yes*."

The Abbé smiled, and a hand went up in amused protest. "You have much wisdom for one so young."

Her face was that of a child as she glanced up roguishly

at him. "I am as old as all the hills, and as young as the flowers in your garden, Abbé. Make it possible for me to meet Seignelay. I will try again."

He looked with eyes that saw far, and he realized that she was able, resolute, and very bad, but she was a good agent of the Jesuits and that was enough for him. "You shall see him—in good time. I will arrange it."

Her eyes gleamed; she would have kissed him again, but he gave no help in this, for he did not wish to give her any power over him. He had no virtues, yet he had tact and a subtle mind. He looked at her handsome face, at her exquisite figure, at her fluttering breasts, and he knew she was ready to give him what he would, but for him not yet, and not now. She must await events.

"You will go now," he said, gently but firmly, "and you will hear from me when I have seen Seignelay."

He drew himself up with pious austerity and held out his hand. She was quick to understand. No more emotion. She kissed his fingers, and her hot lips thrilled them and his veins, but he had the gift of self-control.

He gravely opened the door for her, and she looked at him with eager feeling in her eyes, but his face was calm.

After she had gone he sat down in a chair meditatively. After a time he said:

"She has greater gifts than De Maintenon or any of them. She is the everlasting Sibyl!"

Chapter XXXIII: OLD FRIENDS MEET

COMTESSE FRONTENAC lived at an apartment in the old Arsenal, the gift of a French general, Duc de Lude, with Mademoiselle Outrelaise, and together they were called "The Divines," and this name had been given to the Illinois by La Salle, but mademoiselle was now visiting her family and the Comtesse was alone. She and Frontenac had not lived together for many years, yet she was proud of him and had in these later times the wish to help him in all ways. She had come of a good family, the daughter of La Grange Trianon Sieur de Nouville, and she had run away with him to be married at the little church St. Pierre aux Bœufs, which could unite couples without the consent of their parents.

This was in 1648, when Frontenac was a brigadier-general at twenty-six. Their married happiness was short, for she was witty and brilliant and self-willed, and Frontenac was masterful and vain and loved display, and, though not of the highest rank, his position was an enviable one, for he had been a close friend of Louis XIII. They had fallen apart, but the years went on. She had been popular at court, and had at last retired, having little money. She and Mademoiselle Outrelaise, who never went near the court, still played a great part in Parisian life, and after Frontenac went to Canada from the Venetian Embassy where French troops had been under his command, she who knew now his prodigious worth helped him all she could, but would not go with him. They were again the closest friends.

[227]

La Salle visited the Comtesse de Frontenac at her home by appointment, and there he met the returned ruler, who gave him a hand of warm welcome. The stalwart, self-possessed ex-Governor was no older; his face was more seamed, but his virile voice rang.

"La Barre did not help you—hurt you every way, and despoiled our fort, and used you like carrion. He has the soul of a beetle—no more, La Salle."

La Salle smiled and turned to the Comtesse. "Your great husband has the soul of a lion—and more!"

"They do not lionize him now," she replied, "but I do not fear the end. So much was made against Frontenac because he housed the daughter of the spy."

Frontenac laughed. "There will be trouble again with the Iroquois, and La Barre cannot long resist. I have told all to Seignelay, and he said he would speak to the King, who will not see me—yet. These are bad days!"

"You found the mouth of the Mississippi," said the Comtesse, "and that should influence Louis. There is trouble with Spain, and the Gulf of Mexico can be used for attack."

Frontenac nodded grimly and his eyes became somber. "But there is a Count Penalossa here, born in Peru, who was Governor in Mexico, quarreled with the Inquisition, and came to France. He has seen Seignelay, and offers to attack Mexico."

La Salle's lips set sternly. "A Frenchman should lead Frenchmen, and I hope M. Seignelay does not encourage him."

"Penalossa knows the country, but he should not be employed by France against his own people. Seignelay takes a wiser view of things in Canada now, but all moves slowly here, and our foes work. They are deadly and resourceful. I can do little. But La Forest and François Plet must see Seignelay, and, if possible, the King. The way seemed clear—the Mississippi mouth was found by you, and the way was open to big things in New France—and then came my fall and your temporary ruin!"

"Both temporary," said Madame la Comtesse.

Frontenac shook his head with an ironical smile. "I cannot see far ahead. That fiend, Madame Ranard, is here. She has the subtle skill of her accomplished kind. She was seen at the Invalides—the Abbé Potin—and she influences those much bigger than herself." He laughed sharply. "A daughter of Satan, surely."

They talked no further, for there came knocking at the door and a servant entered. "Two ladies to see Count Frontenac," he said. "They will not give their names, but they know Count Frontenac well. They come from Canada."

All three started; the eyes of Frontenac grew bright and he understood who they were.

"Admit them," said the Comtesse.

La Salle's perceptions were not so swift as those of Frontenac, save with exploration, and he was astounded to see Madame Louvigny and Lya Darois enter.

"Good God!" he said under his breath.

Lya was composed and quiet, yet in her shining eyes was a light of purpose and high character. The vivid North was in her spirit, something unlike the artificial ways of Canada and France—something mysterious, original; but she had no Indian blood—it was the far North, the everlasting pulses of life.

After the Comtesse and Frontenac had kissed Madame Louvigny and warmly received Lya, and La Salle had cordially greeted them, Frontenac said, "May I ask why this descent on France?"

Madame Louvigny replied:

"Things are bad in Canada. The Governor and the Intendant, Muelles, work with the Jesuits and all goes ill. I thought it well to bring mademoiselle here. There is a tale she must tell Seignelay and the King, concerning the late Intendant. Writing is not sufficient. The evidence and the presence of mademoiselle are important to you and to the Sieur la Salle. Words are good, but personality more."

The eyes of the three listeners grew deeply interested, and Frontenac brought his hand down on his knee with an ejaculation of emotion. "Well said, madame! For myself I am glad." He turned to La Salle. "You, La Salle, agree?"

The eyes of La Salle looked at Frontenac, then turned gravely to Lya Darois.

"It is good they have come. Mademoiselle can do most to show what kind of man defeated the great Governor."

The Comtesse Frontenac smiled and said: "Not defeated, tricked, and the trick shall not succeed." She looked at Madame Louvigny. "By what vessel did you come?"

"The *Anticosti*," said Madame Louvigny. "She was not expected; she came with cargo from the West Indies. We decided quickly, and came by her. So we are in France—at the court of the King!"

Frontenac nodded. "And now perhaps mademoiselle will tell us of her meeting with Duchesneau."

There was an instant's hesitation on the part of Lya Darois, and tears came to her eyes, due to the presence of La Salle. As La Salle looked at Lya there came to his mind one of the old chansons of Canada he had heard sung on the great rivers. It rang in his ears now:

> "It was a frigate,
> My pretty heart of rose,
> But, oh, why do you weep so,
> My pretty heart of rose?"

Flushing first, and then turning a little pale, Lya said: "I will tell all that happened at the Intendant's palace," and exactly all she told—quietly, yet with a restrained emotion which stirred them all. She kept her eyes on those of Count Frontenac and more than once his hand clenched and fierce resentment came to his face.

When she finished there was profound silence for a moment. Then Frontenac got to his feet. "The black-souled rogue!" he said, fiercely. "Ranard was not enough, but he must pursue an innocent, parentless girl!"

He and La Salle looked into each other's eyes with the anger of clean-minded men, and La Salle stood up.

They said naught at first, but their hands grasped, and at last Frontenac said: "For Canada's sake, for France's sake, we must fight it through!"

In La Salle's face was the old, indomitable look. He turned to the Comtesse Frontenac. "Madame, I have faith. There is much to do. We have many foes. The way is dark, but dawn is breaking."

Lya slowly rose to her feet, a strange mystic look in her shining face.

"The day will come, in God's name!" she said.

Tears dimmed her eyes, for she felt herself with two great men, whose names would live throughout the history of France and it touched her deeply—Frontenac greater, because of his past office and his imperial work; La Salle great in a different way. He loved his country as Frontenac loved it. He felt the stirrings of the future awaiting this vast new empire reaching from the far north to the mouth of the Mississippi, and in him were forces that would provide for him a glorious immortality. Lya was the daughter of a spy, but her work would play its part in the life of a vast continent.

"The day will come, in God's name," she had said.

[231]

> "Grand Dieu, sauvez le Roi
> Grand Dieu, vengez le Roi
> Vive le Roi.
>
> Qu'à jamais glorieux
> Louis Victorieux
> Voye ses ennemis
> Toujours soumis."

THESE were the words by which the Grand Monarch was awakened from his sleep at Versailles.

The bedchamber of Louis had white-and-gold blinds, mantels of bluish marble and large mirrors, richly carved cornices; the west wall hung with crimson velvet bordered with gold, and his bed was on an estrade under a high canopy adorned with white plumes. As a rule the first valet de chambre, Bontemps, woke him. Then a garçon came to light the fire, and others opened the blinds and removed the night lamp.

Then came the *entrée familière*—Monseigneur the Grand Dauphin, his sons, the King's brother, and Louis' illegitimate sons. The Grand Dauphin was fat and good-looking, but the Prince de Conti had broken his nose when young, and it a little disfigured him. He had a fine fair complexion, a face of a healthy red, handsome legs, delicate feet, was fond of the table, avaricious, idle, with little discernment, and would have made a pernicious King. Few understood him.

[232]

When he looked good-humored he was angry; when he seemed amicable he was ill-tempered; and yet he was no fool.

Louis, knowing his bad qualities, was not fond of him, yet he had given him the best of tutors—Bossuet, who became Bishop of Meux, and Montausieur, and Blondel, and for him Louis wrote his incomparable memoirs; and all pains were taken to prepare him for his great responsibilities; but it was of no avail. He had married the Dauphine of Bavaria and was good to his family, however great his faults, and they were many.

When he entered the chamber this morning, bedecked with laces and ribbons as was his wont, the King said: "You have the air of a chanticleer and the gayety of the morning. Listen to that singing. It gives me good spirit for the day."

The Dauphin, ever respectful to his father, bowed, smiled, and said, "The spirit of the Sun King, Sire!"

The King nodded, pleased. Then the nurse who had been with Louis from childhood came, and she kissed him. With her was admitted the Grand Chamberlain, M. d'Aumont, first gentleman of the chamber, and Doctor Fagan and the surgeon who rubbed him—for he sweated much—and changed his shirt.

Next to Louis' bedchamber was the Oeil de Bœuf, the grand antechamber, and here were gathered the great people who were privileged to be at the second entrée. Among them this morning were, Louis' chaplain, Père la Chaise; the Prince de Lorraine; the Duc de Guiche; the Marquis de Seignelay; Louvois, Minister of War; Turenne, the great general; Chamillart, the chancellor; Molière, who was to breakfast with Louis; Pelletier, who succeeded Colbert; Duc de Chartres; the Prince de Joinville; Marquis de Dangeau; Duc de Vendome; Maréchal de Loges; La Comte de Brienne, and many others.

After the choice of wigs for the day came the King's prayers, and Louis shaved himself every other day with a mirror held before him by Quentin, his barber. Upon arising Louis had taken two glasses of sage and veronica, and always on going to bed he had glasses of water with orange flowers in them. Fully two hundred people saw him dress, and after dressing he breakfasted simply on the fare provided by La Quintinie, his cook, after due trial of the food had been made. This food was always tasted by three people before Louis ate, and this morning he had Molière to breakfast with him, autocrat monarch though he was. So it was that princes and nobles saw Louis at table, while beside him sat a man of the people whose plays he had helped to make successful, and who with Racine came as close to Louis as man ever did. Quinault and Lulli, composers, were praised and encouraged by Louis, and in his time France rose to greater heights than she had ever done in war, in literature, in art, and in trade and commerce. Besides, Molière, and Racine were Corneille, La Fontaine, Lebrun, Claud Lorraine, Le Nôtre, Mansart, Massilon, Girardon, Fenelon, Bourdaloue, and very many others. There was no foppery in Louis. He was simply dressed, with slight embroidery, sometimes with naught save a gold button. His vest was of cloth, or red, blue, or green satin. He wore no ring, no jewels except buckles on his shoes. Yet he ever wore the *cordon bleu* over his coat.

Every morning after prayers Louis went to his cabinet, and there for a few moments he played with the dogs of whom he was fond—Diane, Nonne, Folle, Nitte, Blonde, and the rest. He talked to them as though they were children, and showed his intensely human character, so much obscured by the conventions and duties of court life. No king had ever such outer control. His intense suffering as a youth when in the Fronde rebellion he and his mother had to flee from Paris influenced greatly his mind. He had endured cold and hunger and lack of a good bed, and it made an ineffaceable effect. All he fought for he held, most that he tried to do he did. Europe fought him as it fought Napoleon. He was forty-six when he married De Maintenon, and from that day for thirty years no other woman entered his life. One must think of him not as of to-day. He was of his time. As Napoleon was hated, so was Louis hated, but the Revolution which was said to come from his extravagance, eighty-five years after his death—after Louis XV, who reigned sixty years, a bad King, and Louis XVI, who was stupid, had other origin. Had the Duke of Burgundy, son of the Dauphin, a brilliant, moral, clear-headed boy, lived, there would have been no Revolution.

As Louis and Molière sat at breakfast, there was little talking. With the Grand Monarch, "voices were silent; with Louis XV men whispered; and with Louis XVI they shouted!" During breakfast two sounds came through the windows, the fountains in the vast gardens with their fourteen hundred jets of water, and the voice of a woman singing:

> "Lovely dragon coming back from the war,
> Lovely dragon, ran pata, pata plan,
> Lovely dragon coming back from the war!"

Louis, smiling sedately, said: "Such singing goes well with the tune of the water jets in my gardens, yes?"

Molière replied, "Sire, it is the throat of France that sings." Then there floated in another song:

> "Out there on the prairie,
> I hear my love singing.
> Out there on the prairie,
> I hear my love singing.
> Out there on the prairie,
> I hear Nanon singing."

[235]

Louis smiled again. "A soldier of my army who has been to Canada—the prairie and Nanon! Well, well, our explorer La Salle is from the prairie—yes, yet he has no Nanon there, I hear."

After breakfast the captain of the bodyguard said in a loud voice, "Gentlemen, the King!"

On his way to chapel anyone who wished could speak with Louis. The work of the day was ever carefully planned. So long as he lived, this small but impressive figure worked as few men worked then or now. His own Prime Minister, the head of all departments, his own Foreign Minister, writing or dictating letters to ambassadors, and every detail of domestic political economy was at his finger's ends. Little escaped his notice, little happened that he did not realize, for his observers were everywhere. Vanity he had, but the vanity of a trained, precise, observant mind, without vast temperament, but with the imagination of the French people which lifts its owner out of the commonplace—the dust, the ditch, and the stable-yard of life. Bolingbroke, the great English ambassador of Charles, said, "If King Louis was not the greatest King that ever lived, he was the best actor of majesty, at least, that ever filled a throne."

Two days after the meeting at the house of the Comtesse Frontenac, King Louis was closeted with his Minister, Seignelay, and near by sat Madame de Maintenon. De Maintenon, the widow of Scarron, the poet, born a lady, had seen the entry into Paris of King Louis in 1660 on the occasion of his marriage with Marie Thérèse; had admired him then and had served him ever since, directly and indirectly.

No one knows whether De Maintenon had planned for dominance in his inner life over Louis, but slowly, surely, she had come through a series of hateful attacks and cruel crises to the time when in the third of the four phases of his life he needed her most—if he needed anyone. Her friendship with De Montespan had founded her fortune. Even her title and estate were got on the effort of De Montespan. At first Louis had not liked her, but her letters to De Montespan converted him, they were so well expressed and interesting. De Montespan's capricious ill-humor at length alienated the King, and Louis turned to Maintenon more and more.

Then he fell in love with her, but she acted the coquette and wore her garb of piety, and fascinated and evaded him. And so it was that in June, 1684, De Maintenon was married to Louis in the Chapel of Versailles at night. Père la Chaise said mass at the altar prepared by Bontemps, the King's first valet, and Archbishop Harley of Paris read the service, and Louvois and Montchevreuil were witnesses.

At length De Montespan came to pay her respects to De Maintenon, the wife of King Louis. All her friends—the Mortemarts, the Thianges, the Rochehouarts—her own family—and the Maréchal de Vivonne urged her to pay homage.

So in a robe of gold and silver she went, and De Maintenon sat in a chair of rich brocade. Louis was present and De Maintenon did not rise, but after some talk while Louis worked, told the still beautiful De Montespan what was intended for *"Our* Duc de Maine," De Montespan's own child by Louis, and other plans for Montespan's children, the Count of Toulouse, Madamoiselle de Blois, Louise of Bourbon, and François of Bourbon, all of whom had been legitimatized by Louis!

On her stool the humiliated but proud De Montespan saw De Maintenon whom she had made, at the head of all, though not declared Queen, and she never was, though

Louvois, who influenced the King against the formal declaration, was never forgiven by De Maintenon.

As De Montespan left Maintenon's presence, the latter said, "Do not let us cease to love each other, I implore you."

Among those who waited outside to see the fallen favorite were the astute and able Duc de Saint-Simon, the insufferable Princesse d'Harcourt, tall, fat, ugly and gluttonous, Duc and Duchesse de Beauvilliers, Duc de Coislin, and Prince Salm, who pressed her hand tenderly and said, "You are flushed and I can well understand why."

Ere long the pensive but bitter Montespan was to retire, spend her last days in a convent, and hold a kind of court, receiving in sumptuous style.

After the chief business of the day had been settled, Seignelay spoke to the King about La Salle, of his strife with the Church in Quebec, of his finding the mouth of the Mississippi, and of his proposal to settle it with Frenchmen. He would later bring down from the North Indians to invade and conquer Mexico, and provide a port to which trading vessels could sail the year round as they could not do in the St. Laurence.

At the mention of Mexico, Louis' eyes lighted. He grew at once interested. "Mexico—Mexico—yes! Things go ill in Canada," he said. "Much trouble falls there."

Seignelay shook his head. "De la Barre has destroyed Fort Frontenac, stolen its stores, and ordered your supplies to be scattered, and lets the Indians destroy the crops."

Louis' brows knitted. "Destruction, eh! Evacuation, theft. Come, come, La Barre! Who brings this to us?"

"De la Forest, in late control, and François Plet, who loaned La Salle money and was asked to go to Fort Frontenac and administer its finance, because La Salle has little gift that way, but has genius for exploration and settlement.

For a moment there was silence. Then Louis shook his head.

"It was folly to recall Frontenac. As for Duchesneau, he is the cause of all. He lied, I suppose, about that girl, the daughter of the spy. Frontenac sheltered her at the Château St. Louis, although her father was a traitor. That influenced my mind, yet who could tell! Frontenac was bitter, quarrelsome, and difficult."

Seignelay quietly said: "Sire, the girl has come to France with Madame Louvigny, who cared for her after she went to the Château, and she, Lya, I hear, has that to tell of the Intendant which may affect your policy in Canada."

Louis looked up sharply. "Where is she?"

Seignelay glanced at his watch. "She should be in the palace now, Sire. At the request of Prince Conti I consented to see her."

"Oh, good, good! Bring her to me here."

Seignelay seemed astounded. "You wish to see her here, Sire?"

The King laughed. "Even as I said—if her Solidity makes no objection—here."

Madame De Maintenon, who had not spoken, smiled and inclined her head.

"Then bring her, Seignelay. I would see her—and one moment, I would see La Salle also."

Seignelay was pleased. "I fear, Sire, I could not reach La Salle at once, but within the day, at your will, he shall be brought."

Louis nodded. "Then the girl at once."

Seignelay rose. A moment later a messenger was on the way to Lya Darois.

Louis turned to Madame de Maintenon: "Since La Salle found the mouth of the Mississippi it is a vast estate I have yonder. I could put in it provinces of France and have enough left for ten Englands and twenty Belgiums. I see now clearly this New France which Cartier, Champlain, Maisonneuve and La Salle have made possible to my France. Yes, yes, I see. What will come of it? Who knows?"

After an instant De Maintenon carefully said: "Sire, you know. It all is yours, your fate, your destiny. What you do will be right, Sire. You are France."

He stretched himself proudly to his brief height, but there was greatness in him from first to last. As a child of ten he had said to his mother at Fontainebleu, "I will govern now," and from that time to the day when, his work done, he sent De Maintenon to the convent of St. Cyr and closed his eyes to the pomps and vanities, the powers and achievements of his great time—he governed.

"Then I must obey the soul of France, and that soul says, 'Be just, be generous to Canada.' "

Whereupon he sat down and worked silently. De Maintenon, handsome, quiet, with beautiful eyes, watching—watching. No time of hers was her own. She was the galley slave of state from the moment of her waking till Louis bade her good night. Even her meals were interrupted. If physically unfit, it made no difference. She paid the heavy price for what she was.

At last the door opened. With Seignelay, Lya Darois entered the presence. Her face was pale, but her eyes shone, she trembled slightly. Seeing the King, she bowed her head, dropped to her knees, and kissed his outstretched hand. She did not dare look up. Much honor had been done her. No lady had ever before been admitted to the workshop of Louis XIV. With self-control she remained kneeling.

If there was one on earth who understood the human heart in a vague yet certain way, it was King Louis. Her humility touched him. Her curious beauty, so unlike that of any woman he had ever seen, impressed him. His words to De

Maintenon: "I am France, the soul of France," came to his mind now, and he said to her, "Arise and look at me."

She got to her feet slowly, looked him in the eyes, and, as she looked, a strange, passionate simplicity and beauty filled them, but it was all joined to such modesty, to such demure dignity, that Louis gently said: "Mademoiselle, tell me why you came to France? I will understand."

She could not speak instantly, but after a moment she told him of her stay at the Château St. Louis, of all that Frontenac had done for her, of the shame and disgrace of her parentage, of her faith in and her admiration for the man who had killed her father. Then she told of the visit to Duchesneau at the palace and all that happened there.

When she had finished in tears and her lips trembling, Louis said: "The low dog! So he influenced us, eh! Before God, I will attend to him. The woman, Ranard, she is here too, Seignelay?"

Seignelay bowed his head: "She also is here, Sire, and is a friend of the Abbé Potin. She has seen him."

Louis smiled grimly: "Potin! Potin! whom I put at the head of the Invalides. Not a good man, but an able abbé— reward for useful service. He confessed one who was once" —he glanced curiously towards De Maintenon—"in a post of some importance."

Chapter XXXV: POINT TO POINT

A FEW hours later Seignelay was visited by the Abbé Potin, who came to influence him against La Salle. They were both astute men, but Seignelay was far the bigger in character and in intellect, and he was without prejudice against La Salle—and now without prejudice against Frontenac. His face showed little emotion. It was calm, powerful, implacable, determined. He was handsomer than his father Colbert, and nearly as able. He had the greater spirit of France conceived by Richelieu, developed by Mazarin, and continued by Colbert with Louis XIV.

As the Abbé approached the palace, full of sophistry and subtlety, his whole being alert, he heard a young woman singing:

> "Ah, if I had a round penny,
> Ah, if I had a round penny,
> I could buy a white lamb,
> La verdi, la verdon,
> Et loupe, sautez, donc, la verdon."

The Abbé's attention was arrested. He knew the song. It was of Touraine, where he was born, and he had heard it as a child. The girl was a Touranian. She was comely and joyous, yet there was sadness in her voice. She would buy a white lamb, would she? Buy a white lamb! There flashed to his mind the Lamb of Calvary, and so it had seemed to him in his youthful days before he decided to become a priest. The Lamb of Calvary—and he was on his way to belie all his earlier hopes to waste his naturally big soul in a pernicious cause. He watched this girl till she disappeared, and then, shaking his head, went on his way. He was touched somehow by this quaint doggerel ballad, for he sighed and a somber look came to his eyes.

When he entered Seignelay's room, the glimmer of a smile played at the Minister's lips, for he knew there would now come contest between the Church as represented by the Jesuit body and Abbé Potin, and the King as represented by himself. The immediate issue might not be immense, but the principle at stake was as big as France itself and greater than France itself.

There they were, Seignelay soberly but elegantly dressed —though not so gorgeous as many of his confrères—with ribbons and color and bright lapels and soft lace, and above all a head with long hair, vigorous, powerful, and resolute. The glitter below was as naught to the quiet dignity above. That was France under Louis XIV. There was great ceremony and color and swords and ribbons and laces, and the outer flamboyance of life and society, but above all was firm unshaking purpose.

Opposite was the lean, clean-shaven, handsome, sensuously ascetic face of the representative of the Church, in his plain cassock and plain black belt, lightened by the glimmer of white collar at the throat. The Abbé Potin represented the austerity of the Roman Church, but behind this austerity was the same glitter and show which marked the court and the social life of France. Richelieu, Mazarin, both cardinals, lived in magnificence, and the Palais Royale, next to Versailles the greatest building in the French Empire, was the home of Richelieu and Mazarin, and now a palace of the King.

Never in history had there been such state power in France; never such power of the Church as was to be seen at Notre Dame and in the great cathedrals. Money, the Church had as much as the state. Power, it was world-wide. Purpose, it was touched, how terribly, by ambition to control. All these things were in the mind of Seignelay as he looked at this quiet, self-assured, ingratiating figure before him.

"Well, Abbé, how like you your new office at the Invalides? Well, I hope."

The Abbé bowed and smiled. "The honor is great, the duties are many. I can but regret it has no higher governor than the poor Abbé who comes to you to-day."

Irony was in the face of Seignelay as he said: "Time works in all development, but it cannot tarnish the present ruler of France." His eyes lighted. "Far beyond our dear land, on that vast continent of America, the state—with the Church—plays its prodigious part. Missionaries—the Recollets, the Sulpitians, and the Jesuits—have proved that France is not the slave of luxury, expenditure, and vapid social life."

Seignelay said these things not with his tongue in his cheek, but preparing for the encounter to come. "Listen, Abbé," he continued, "everywhere in Europe, France is at the head. We have the greatest generals the modern world has known. As for our navy, my father built it up from fifty ships to its present force of three hundred men-of-war. France is now at her greatest period in literature, in art, in sculpture. Trade flourishes and will flourish more and more, because the Sieur de la Salle has opened the way to the conquest of Mexico, and the increase of our trade and commerce."

The Abbé bowed and his face flushed a little. "That has brought me here, Monseigneur. Is Sieur La Salle then to form settlements near the mouth of the Mississippi? Is that the purpose of His Majesty of France?"

"No one knows the purpose of France until he himself has spoken. What I know I do not know. What I think I do not think. It is not the duty of a Minister to declare the high master's will until commanded to do so."

A sly, sardonic smile touched his lips. "The Church is no friend of La Salle, Abbé," he said. "It has pursued and defeated him where possible, tried indirectly to poison him, destroyed his ships, captured his men, wasted his goods — No, no, no, do not object. What I say can be said to all the world, but I do not choose to do so."

The Abbé's eyes flashed and indignation touched his lips. "The Church has been true to the policy of the King, and that our missionaries gave their lives after torture is best proof of the fidelity, honor and piety of our Church."

"But not best proof of its imperial wisdom, no. You would convert the Indians, but make them always the servants of the Church. It is not white settlement you want in the West and the South. It is native settlement which the Church would forever control."

He got slowly to his feet. "And there can be no question of who shall control within the territories of Louis XIV, none. His policy prevails. Pope or priest are as naught to him when it is a question which shall be the final power where his flag flies. The fleur-de-lys always, before all else —always. Also Christ and his Church always, but not to control the state. No, no, Abbé, be sure of this—New France with all its magnificent possibility belongs to the people of France, and the people of France are the rulers of France. You wish to influence His Majesty against La Salle through me. To be frank, enough of that influence has been shown. Through it Frontenac and the Intendant have been recalled— the one a good great man, the other a low bad man. The Intendant lied to me and to the King. We know the truth.

While the world stands, Duchesneau shall never again represent France in any part of her dominions. Frontenac is, and has always been, an honest man; La Salle, one of the best of the King's loyal subjects. No, Abbé, come not here against La Salle."

The face of the Abbé Potin was white and rigid. "I came because it was my duty. I am faithful to my Church and to my vows. The Church has naught against La Salle. It only opposes his mad policy, which was against the policy of the King, who told us he wished no settlement on the Mississippi."

Seignelay smiled. "Then Kings may not change their minds and alter their policies? Greatness lies in the power to change the mind and have a masterly retreat if necessary; but there is no retreat! King Louis does not retreat or retract. He restrains those who fight him; he develops those who march with him. La Salle is marching with him."

"I am nobody," replied the Abbé Potin, bitterly. "I came because you have known me long and well and to plead with you."

"Yes, I know you well, Abbé, and while I would work with you, I would never let your influence touch my judgment. I used you years ago concerning the Abbé Renaudot, and you did well. You have your reward—the Invalides. There is naught more to say. I trust your Church will not oppose La Salle, for it is to oppose France. Did you ever think how poor La Salle is? He is vastly in debt, and yet he can get money. Is that one in whom confidence may not be placed?" Seignelay came forward and held out his hand: "Say not more, Abbé, but bid me *au revoir*. You will have no place for me at the Hôtel des Invalides. I am no soldier and no general, and shall have no monument there, so be content that in death I shall not disturb your peace."

The grim humor of the Minister overcame, for a moment, the anger of the Abbé Potin.

"You have never disturbed my peace in life, and could not in death, monsieur," and in the note of the Abbé's voice was also a touch of satire.

Chapter XXXVI: AGAIN RANARD

THAT night late, La Salle was walking to his apartments. The street was narrow, deserted, and unlighted, though a faint moon was showing. He had spent the evening with the Abbé Renaudot after visiting the Prince de Conti, where with La Forest and François Plet he had made a convincing statement to Conti. He had been told of the visit of Lya Darois to King Louis and of her triumph there, and somehow hope, faith, and a new ambition stirred deeply in him.

With a spring in his step he neared his apartments. At about fifteen feet from the door, with the instinct of the trained woodsman, he felt stealthy steps behind him and swung round. As he did so a lariat flew over his head and would have garroted him, but his hand shot up to the leathern rope. Then two men sprang towards him. With one swift, prodigious kick he struck one of his assailants well below the belt, and with a shriek of pain, the man fell backwards and writhed on the ground, and the other he caught by the throat. The struggle was fierce, for the man was strong and a trained murderer, but La Salle had the gifts of an Indian fighter, and he freed the rope from the hand of the garroter, swung him to the ground, and buried powerful fingers in his throat. The murderer's tongue came out of his mouth, his face turned purple, his struggle became fiercer, and then suddenly relaxed, and he was gone. La Salle sprang to the other man, whose agony was still great, and said:

"Tell me who sent you, or you shall die also. Speak—my hands are at your throat!"

Still twisted with pain, the murderer said, "Madame Ranard!"

So this was her last attempt to drive him from the field. She had heard of Lya Darois' success with King Louis, and now would put him out of the battle by garroting. Taking a small whistle from his pocket, he blew it. Presently he saw running to him through the street three gendarmes. He pointed to the two men and to the lariat, and said: "They tried to garrot me. The one I killed, the other is there injured. I am the Sieur de la Salle, explorer from Canada."

The gendarme in command looked closely at the faces of the two men on the ground. "I know them," he said; "they are notorious. You have a strong arm, Sieur de la Salle. Two men at once is immense. Why did they attack you?"

La Salle was about to reply, when the man on the ground still in agony, said: "We were paid by Madame Ranard. We know not why."

With a firm voice La Salle said: "My address"—he pointed to the door—"is this. Come when you have disposed of these men and I will explain. Will you?"

The gendarme looked him up and down, smiled grimly, and said, "Yes, m'sieu', I will come." He turned to his comrades and they lifted the dead man and carried him, while the chief gendarme gave his attention to the living criminal, and La Salle entered his rooms.

Seated in the small salon dimly lighted, La Salle considered his position. Surely God had been good to him, for again and again his life had been attempted, and yet he had escaped. Every pulse was beating hard and his heart was high. He believed he was now on the road to definite success. The odds against him had been innumerable, but here he was at the foot of the throne, waiting the final judgment of the ruler of France, for the new commission which would send him to lay the foundation of a great empire of the South.

As he sat, the three mouths of the Mississippi were before him, and the broad water and the tang and the smell of the Gulf of Mexico. Once again he saw the clear blue sky, the bright sun, the everlasting sea. He stood up, and slowly paced the room with elation and resolute will. He could not exactly forecast what the State would do, but it was clear it meant good to him or Barbe Ranard would not have sent these criminals to drive him from the field.

At last there came a tapping at the outer door. Presently there entered the gendarme who was in some ways a cut above his business. He had a face of intelligence, though a tongue that did not speak good French and a heart that would not do bad things. He doffed his head-gear and would not be seated until La Salle motioned to a chair. In it he sat like some uncouth baron of an uncouth county, but with a far-seeing eye.

He had not yet opened his mouth. He waited. They measured each other. The judgment on both sides was good. At last La Salle said: "My life is of value to myself, but it is also of value to our nation—I have discovered the mouth of the Mississippi!"

"The mouth of the Mississippi!" said the gendarme. "The mouth of the Mississippi! Think of that! I had a brother who served under Du Lhut in the Western country. The mouth of the Mississippi! Oh, *bidemme!*"

"I discovered it, and I see a vast field of settlement, but I have bitter foes. The Jesuits are against me, and Madame Ranard, the mistress of the late Intendant, Duchesneau, is their tool. Now you know why I have been attacked to-night. My foes stop at nothing."

"You don't think the Jesuits ordered this attack, m'sieu'. But no, eh?"

"They order no attacks, but they have agents, and the agents do as Madame Ranard tried to do more than once to me in Canada. I tell you because I do not wish this man to be tried in public. If he is tried the truth must be told, and at this moment I do not wish France to know that behind this woman was the Church, and yet that truth must be told at the trial."

The gendarme frowned. "The woman should die, m'sieu'. She had not courage to kill, but she got hireling beasts to do it. It is vile, so."

"I know how vile, but I know what is best. That is why I tell you the whole truth."

"God knows I like the truth!" said the gendarme. "There is too little truth in France. Yes, *par le baptême!* I like the truth."

La Salle thought for a minute, then he said: "It will be enough to get power from the King to continue my work. I am willing this man should escape, if you can permit it, and that the woman shall not be punished. If I get the rights I seek, she cannot touch me again. The Intendant is gone from Quebec, and I am told the King has no will to give him place again, but may send him to the Bastille."

"The woman is foul; she should die—but yes!" said the gendarme.

La Salle did not speak at once; he poured out a goblet of wine and gave it to the gendarme, then poured one for himself. They drank, and La Salle filled the gendarme's goblet again.

"The woman is foul, as you say, but she gets punishment in the failure of her plans, which is a torture to her. I ask that this man shall escape, and the woman be free from state reprisal."

"By the Lord, one would think you loved her, m'sieu'!" said the gendarme, bluntly.

A grim smile played at La Salle's lips. "She is beautiful —she is young—she has the grace of a great lady, but love her! It would be ruin."

The gendarme frowned. "Then why in God's name should she go free, I ask you?"

"It is clear I have told you badly, for you don't understand. Will you give me word that you will let this man escape and not inform on the woman?"

There was something communistic in the gendarme. He had no love for beautiful ladies of society, nor for society itself. His one passion was doing his duty—a rare thing in corrupt but imperishable France.

The gendarme did not at once reply, but moved his head from side to side in cogitation, but at last he thumped his knee: "Very well. It shall be so. But I am not alone. My comrades heard what that murderer said, and they may talk. I cannot clinch their tongues, but no!"

"Good!" said La Salle. "Good! We must take our chances on that. I do not like to offer—"

The gendarme looked up quickly. "Offer naught, m'sieu'. Do not try to buy a gendarme of France. That's too ugly in an ugly world! I'm not for sale, *nom de chien!*"

La Salle smiled: "I would not try to buy you, my friend, yet I beg you to accept now, since you have promised, this small gift from a poor man who wishes—for France's sake —he had riches."

He pressed a purse into the hand of the gendarme.

The gendarme's face was now a study. "Well, if you had offered it before I'd promised, I'd have thrown it at your feet, m'sieu', but I'll take it now because you have not tried to buy me."

"Well done, well done!" said La Salle. "Give me your name and address. I shall care to meet you again before I start my long journey to the mouth of the Mississippi."

A moment later he had the address on a slip of paper, and presently the gendarme was gone with these words:

"M'sieu', but, m'sieu', I could follow you—to hell!"

Chapter XXXVII: "FORTY STRIPES"

THE gendarme who had promised La Salle was right. Before he could arrange the escape of the prisoner, one of his comrades had told a spy of Seignelay that La Salle had been set upon by two garroters paid for by Madame Ranard. He did not discover this until he learned that Barbe had been arrested secretly by command of the Ministers. It was too late to do aught. He could not find La Salle and tell him.

La Salle's anxiety was great. His big heart was against harsh punishment to the woman. She deserved the worst that might be, as Nicolas Perrot, the explorer, had done, but he had forgiven Jolycœur, behind whom she was. It was little to conquer the violence of one of the weaker but subtler, more dangerous and more bitter sex. She was as bad as any woman had been in the history of France, but he hoped for fresh commission for settlement at the mouth of the Mississippi, and this dark incident might prevent its fulfillment.

In confinement, Barbe Ranard, with the vigor of mind which had not yet deserted her, thought that if she might reach the cathedral of Notre Dame she would be safe. *There* was sanctuary, as Cardinal Retz in the early part of Louis' reign had found. She had much money with her, and she arranged to bribe one of her guards. He was a man of dissolute habits and of polluted soul, and she was ever a master of such men.

She smiled at him, and with a graciousness for which she had a reputation said, "This is no place for a lady, my friend."

He twisted a leg. "Ladies come here just the same!"

"But never a lady like me."

He nodded. "None so beautiful, maybe."

"Then why should I remain? It is the evening, and all is dark. Why should I remain here?"

"Because King Louis says so, madame."

"I cannot buy King Louis!" she replied, meaningly.

His face took on an acquisitive look, for he had no cash, and he was thirsty and poor, and his nature was carnal and selfish, and he had no sense of duty. He had risked his life often, and had escaped, and he could risk his life again if it was worth while.

"It would take more cash than anyone has to buy him, madame. Not all the gold in France buys him. He is France, he buys. He has bought other kings and rulers and bishops, yes."

She came close to him, so near that the perfume of her clothes came to him, and, oh, but she was ravishing, and perhaps it was intended to behead her—this exquisite creature!

She said: "No, I could not buy King Louis, but is your price so high?"

The gendarme drew his hand across his mouth. "I ain't got any price—but no. I'm a soldier on duty."

"Then I will name the price, soldier: A kiss, and—" She whispered to him.

His face grew inflamed. "So much? What proof!"

"Here is the kiss," she said, and she kissed him with a smile—his big fat, preposterous mouth. Then she drew from her bosom a silk purse and thrust it into his hand. "There is a fortune for you, my friend!"

His eyes blinked. "I could take this and not do you service, madame."

"But you will, for I have kissed you? You will set me free—is it not so?"

He sniffed, looked at the purse in his hand, then said, "I take bad risks, madame, but yes." He looked into the purse. "Here is enough for many a year. See—in ten minutes or so we take you to another prison *en route* to Notre Dame! On the way there you will escape—and we will follow you. You will not be bound, for we are armed and you have no weapons. There—if that may suit you, madame!"

Ten minutes later she was taken from this cell and was marched through the streets and, thank God, towards Notre Dame. Suddenly, when they were not far from the great cathedral, she jumped and ran. The gendarmes did not fire, for they had no such orders, but they followed through the dimly lighted streets, her own gendarme purposely leading his comrades away from her. As she ran swiftly, for she was fleet of foot, she heard a voice in the street shouting after her:

> "When Marion goes out,
> When Marion goes out,
> She never walks, she always runs,
> Deriron, bah, bah, derirette,
>
> Gai, gai, oh, gai, gai,
> Derirette!
> And I am the shepherdess of all,
> And I am the shepherdess of all,
> I will give her to the wolf,
> Derirette!"

So that was it—and the wolf might get her. She ran. She was now near Notre Dame, and people watched excitedly the flying criminal. The dark walls of the great church came up before her eyes. She rushed for them and reached them, ran up the steps, but now behind her she heard swift feet, and the doors of the church were shut. She beat on them with her frenzied hands, crying:

"Sanctuary! Sanctuary! O God, Sanctuary!"

But before the doors were opened the gendarmes were upon her, and even as they swung back to the hands of a priest they came between. She was captured again, and she fell fainting in the arms of the gendarmes, among whom, vastly perturbed, was the man who had helped her. He had in vain tried to misdirect them.

"Oh, Heaven and Hell!" he said, bitterly.

La Salle arrived at the court-room, and he learned that at the suggestion of King Louis, before whom it had all been put by Seignelay, Barbe Ranard was to be branded on the shoulder with the broad arrow. The branding was to take place at once. There was no chance to go to the Minister or to invoke the assistance of the Prince de Conti or anyone.

Through the permission of the captain of the gendarmes, with whom La Salle's gendarme had influence, La Salle was admitted to the branding by the white-hot iron.

To the hour of his death La Salle could never forget the woman's face. It was distorted, pale as death, her eyes staring in terror.

La Salle felt ill, and a sense of degradation entered his soul. He could only do one thing. He could plead with the captain of the gendarmes to wait until he has seen the Minister, Seignelay.

Forgetful of his own safety or the peril to himself in going against the command of the monarch, which he did not fully realize, to the captain of the gendarmes, he said: "In God's name wait, monsieur. This crime was against me, the Sieur de la Salle. I wish to beg the Minister of the King to remit this sentence. One day, one day only!"

Until his eyes closed on life and time he could never forget the woman's face as he made this appeal. In it were amazement and remorse. Something divine had struck at the farthest corner of her nature. It soothed her horror.

The captain of the gendarmes shook his head sternly and said: "Not one day, nor one hour. You have no right to speak here. It is not a question of wrong to you, but to the state of France. Punishment shall be according to the King's command. You show a spirit which commends itself to all who feel, but there is something deeper."

La Salle broke in: "I know, but the deepest thing of all is not France, but the eternal spirit behind France, behind all the world. In the name of God, wait!"

The face of the captain of the gendarmes hardened. "I will not wait. The garrotte is a Spanish means of death, and her attempt to bring Spanish crime into France which angered our King. Sieur de la Salle, be still."

La Salle knew the man was right. "I will not stay to see it done," he said, in horror. "No, I cannot stay."

His eyes met those of Barbe Ranard, and she said to him, not in words, "Go, and because you have done this I shall bear my punishment better." Her head sank upon her breast.

La Salle, shaken to the innermost, left the room, and as the door closed he heard the voice of the captain of the gendarmes:

"Now!"

Within an hour the knowledge of these events came to Seignelay, whose duty it was to explain all to the King. He was fearful of the result to La Salle, but when next day he met the King, he told him quietly of what had happened. He did not wish to prejudice His Majesty against La Salle, but he feared the result.

The usually immobile face of King Louis flushed slightly. His hand clenched.

"And who dare intervene between me and my will? The man's a madman and a fool. By God, he shall be branded too!"

Seignelay's reply was calm. "Sire, with all respect, he was neither madman nor fool. It was the Sieur de la Salle! He said to the captain of the gendarmes who declared it was France and the spirit of France that imposed the punishment, that there was a greater spirit behind the spirit of France—the eternal spirit. Sire, it is not for me, your faithful servant, to suggest what judgment Your Majesty should impose, but I beg you assent to one thing."

He paused. With an impatient gesture, Louis said: "Before God, La Salle! La Salle!

"What is it then?"

"I have sent for La Salle to meet me in the palace here to-day. No doubt he is come. I ask but this; that Your Majesty will hear the talk between La Salle and myself, seated behind that screen, and impose your judgment, Sire, after you have heard. The judgment of the God of all the world is like that; He does not refuse to hear. The King of France represents that eternal judgment. Will he refuse to hear?"

If there was one thing that impressed Louis in his Minister, it was the calmness of his logic, and himself had the logician's spirit. He did not analyze the astuteness of his Minister's request. After an instant he said:

"So be it. My judgment will be afterwards."

Seignelay was too trained a diplomatist to smile; he bowed his head humbly. "Sire, Sire," he said, and that was all.

Soon, with the King behind the screen, this conversation took place between Seignelay and La Salle.

"Sieur de la Salle, you sought to change the judgment of France upon Madame Ranard."

"No, no, Monseigneur, not that. Crime had been committed against me. I have seen torture without end in my explorations on the far continent. I only sought to say some things to you which might perhaps induce the Grand Monarch to lessen the punishment. Three times I have been poisoned in New France; twice I have known my poisoners and have forgiven them."

Seignelay interrupted. "You have forgiven because it was a matter between you and the criminal, but behind you both was the State, and the question was whether the State should forgive, not whether you should forgive."

Behind the screen, King Louis, with ears intent, rubbed his palms together.

"Yes, Monsieur, but should the agonies of torture such as Jesuits have endured be imposed by the State? Let me speak from the depths of my soul. The Jesuits have persecuted me, tortured me, not directly, but indirectly, have destroyed my ships and would have destroyed my life. You say that behind the criminals is the spirit of the State. I say that behind this criminal is the spirit of the Jesuits. If the King of Kings must punish, then let him punish the spirit of the Jesuits, of whom this woman is one."

Seignelay smiled inwardly. It was the very reply he hoped La Salle would make. "It is the tool that is punished so often, not the hand behind the tool. I say to you that France is bitter against you. Who are you? You come of a good burgher family—you were at a Jesuit school—you were educated for a Jesuit priest—the King gave you a title of nobility—you are one among the millions of the subjects of France. Why should you step between the executioner and the criminal?"

"I did not step between. I am naught but a faithful

servant whose life, since I was among the Jesuits, has been given for the good of my native land and of my King. But I have something of the spirit of France, that spirit which is King Louis. God above! I have offered my life, risked it again and again for France. It was the soul of France in me made me ask that this woman, who has pursued me for years, should not suffer the hot iron on her shoulder. I beg you, try to know what I sought to do. I have one love, one love only—the love of my native land; for that I have striven; for that I am here. I ask that he who is the spirit of France shall understand me. That is all."

Seignelay rose to his feet. "I think you will realize, Sieur de la Salle, that I can promise nothing. You have offended the head of France."

Shaken, but powerful, and with his head up, La Salle turned to go. Seignelay followed him and said:

"You are coming to the gala at the palace to-night, are you not?"

"As the servant of my sovereign, I shall be there," said La Salle.

Chapter XXXVIII: THE DAY OF FATE

IT was a day of sunshine, freshness, and gayety of nature in France. Good news had come to Louis of his armies and never had his heart been lighter or his faith in France greater. The courtyards of the Palace of Versailles held many people. He had returned from the chapel, with a company of bodyguards, preceded by pages of the court, all gentlemen of birth, and all ambitious and good-looking. It was their duty to carry candles before the King at night and to attend him on all his appearances in public.

This was a great day at court for there was to be an embassy from Siam, and the people of Paris, and the nobility, and the "camp-followers" had gathered. When Louis had entered the palace, followed by members of his family, and nobles among whom were his Ministers, the Duc d'Alba, M. d'Aumont, first gentleman of the Chamber, Duc de Grammonet, Comte de Brionne, Maréchal Bellefonds, Duc de Fronsac, Marquis Sourdes, Marquis de Torcy, Maréchals de Vauban and Turenne, and many others. La Salle entered the courtyard. He was not in high feather; he was depressed and lonely. With him was the Abbé de Renaudot, his faithful friend. As they stood in the resplendent crowd, nobles and gentry being carried in sedan chairs to the entrance of the palace, there passed a company of grenadiers in handsome uniforms, and near the two, three young girls, daughters of men employed at the palace, sang:

> "There is the beauty who sleeps,
> Oger! Oger!

The Day of Fate

There is the beauty who sleeps,
Oger!   Oger!"

This "Oger!" "Oger!" was ever the greeting to the cavaliers. The cavaliers bowed their heads and laughed, and
the girls tossed a scarf towards them. They were pretty,
naïve, buoyant, like the day, and yet La Salle was heavy
with gloom.

Then one of the girls began to sing again, looking after
the cavaliers, and presently the others joined in softly.
Their voices were very little raised. They were wholesome,
healthy girls, with knowledge of life:

"When I go to the garden, garden of love,
I think I hear steps—
I would fly and dare not.
Here is the end of the day,
I fear and I hesitate,
My heart beats wildly,
When I go to the garden, garden of love."

They did not realize the full significance of the words. It
was only happy youth in them that sang. None of them
was over twenty, and they were dressed in gay colors and
had aigrettes in their hair, and white stomachers and frilled
dresses. La Salle, looking at them, thought of Lya Darois.
She was like them, comprehending and yet not comprehending, naïve, true, wise, with all nature alive in her, and yet
had made friends by her exquisite uprightness and charm.
These girls were like her, but in many ways so infinitely
less. He shook his head sadly, then drew himself together.

They had heard the great cheering as Louis entered his
palace, they had seen the fluttering of handkerchiefs and
scarfs, of saluting hands, and it was as though France stood
still to see the Sun King shine. They were to see stranger
things before the day was over. They must watch the vast

crowd until the reception of the King, to which La Salle looked forward with moroseness.

The Abbé Renaudot understood, and he did what he could to cheer him by quiet ascetic remarks on people they saw, and the troops of soldiers in the vast courtyards. For one who had mingled so sparsely with the world, the Abbé had some wit.

"This is more than tinsel, it is the cake itself. This is the gay music of the august opera of France, which Lulli or Quinault could not compose. It is France as Louis has made it."

La Salle looked at Renaudot with resolute eyes, but did not speak. Renaudot continued. "Every petty German prince tries to build a Versailles, and our language is spoken in all the courts of Europe now."

Now La Salle spoke: "King Louis is like the comet of four years ago. He lightens up the world. It is only of its day. Its day passes, and the world is no longer dazzled."

The Abbé laid a hand on La Salle's arm. "No, the light is permanent, it will not pass. King Louis is for all time. He is France."

La Salle stood silent for a moment, then he gave one of his rare smiles and nodded. "Abbé, you are right. It will not pass, this light. It is the way of toil and torture, and happiness and peace." All at once his eyes lighted and a new spirit entered into him.

Inside the palace King Louis went towards the salon where he would dine, and in passing spoke to Comte de Brionne, the master of his stables, where two horses gay with ribbons for him to ride were kept, and where one hundred English hunters—the amaze and wonder of the world— were housed; to Grammonville, the great diplomatist; and to Duc de Saint-Aignan, First Gentleman of the Chamber, who passed the word that the dinner of the Grand Monarch was to be served. Then Louis stopped and spoke to Maréchals de Boufflers and Duras; to the Duc de Guise, his old boyhood friend; to M. de Chamillard, Secretary of State; then to an architect, Coyzevox, and a painter like Lebrun; to the Comtesse de Bethune, Princesse de Carignan, Duchesse de Toscane, Madame Sévigné, the accomplished writer, and friendly to his most severe but admiring critic, the Duc de Saint-Simon. No face of note escaped him, and all his salutations were marked by the way he touched or raised his hat. To each a greeting with his hat according to rank, and to ladies he took off his hat and held it in his hand while he spoke to them. It was the nature of the man, not affectation or pretense.

This day Louis had four plates of soup, a whole pheasant, partridge, a large plate of salad, mutton *au jus,* two big slices of ham, a whole plateful of pastry and fruit and hard-boiled eggs. It was a meal which in these days would quickly send the stoutest constitution to Vichy or Plombières. The King was over an hour eating it, and meanwhile he eyed his courtiers with benign austerity and talked sparingly with the Dauphin.

When the meal was finished, Louis rose and summoned Seignelay and Louvois, his Ministers. "Messieurs," he said, with a finger tossed towards the gardens where the people and his soldiers were singing and people of Paris were assembling, "all this means well. We are at the summit of my reign. We have made peace with the Dutch, with the Duke of Brunswick, Luxembourg, and the Bishop of Munster, and with Sweden. Now Frederick William of Brandenburg and Charles II of England and Bishop Francis Egon of Furstenburg are in our pay. Genoa has almost been destroyed, the Spaniards have been compelled to agree to my terms. All goes well with us, messieurs. We flourish."

They bowed, and he carried his head in pride.

They were going to the Throne Room, the King wearing a gold-laced coat with large diamonds, which was his way on such great occasions, and he was now to receive two ambassadors of Phra-Narai, the King of Siam. It was a scene of unparalleled splendor. Louis, in his silk stockings and shoes with red high heels and a long cane, walked as though he were the master of the world. His long hair was brown and curling on his shoulders, and in his face was the lofty look of one who counted himself France.

Now as he came to his silver throne he bowed to right and left and took his seat.

As Louis had said, he was at the apogee of his power and influence. While he waited for the ambassadors of Siam in the salon of Apollo—he talked to the Prince de Conti.

As he had walked he had seen Rose, his Secretary, who for long years did him service. Rose was neither fat nor lean and had a taking face and radiantly clever black eyes. He had art, too, and a real literary touch. He wore a little cloak, a smooth collar, and satin skull cap over his graying hairs, and was a great judge of men. Rose wrote many letters for the King, but Louis revised them all, and his choice of words was worthy of the time when France had vast distinction in art and letters. To them who served him well Louis was gracious, and now he summoned Rose and in the presence of his Court said kind words which were acknowledged with humble dignity.

Behind his throne was Père la Chaise, his confessor, and near was Harley, the Archbishop of Paris, who had married him to De Maintenon. Near the throne stood Madame de Maintenon, richly dressed and looking not more than thirty-five, though she was forty-eight—three years older than Louis—whose marriage was never formally acknowledged, yet was fully recognized. She was ever addressed as Madame by members of the Court. Her face was agreeable. she had a beautiful forehead, eloquent eyes, and a more graceful carriage than any other lady present. It was a winning personality, though a little too imposing, but alleviated by her smile, which was entrancing. She had great purpose, and gave her life to turning Louis from domestic infelicities. She had influence on his character, but none upon his policy. Charlotte Elizabeth, Duchess of Orléans, who stood not far from her, whispered to a friend, "All the Ministers have placed themselves under the heel of this woman!"

Among the many guests at the palace were General Du Quesne, and Liebniz, who had urged Louis to take Egypt; and if he had done so, the fate of the world would have been different. Napoleon understood this, but he failed, and Louis had succeeded. Also there was there the Marquis de Soyecourt, who had been the dear friend of the infamous but beautiful Lenclos; Despréaux, the poet; Girardon, the sculptor; Princesse de Montbazon and Mademoiselle Nantes, the Comtesse de Fiesque. These were all not far from De Maintenon, and near her stood the Grand Mademoiselle, the King's cousin, whom he had never forgiven for turning the guns of the Bastille on his troops long ago. She was able and powerful in her way, but had been more than once exiled and now lived at the Luxembourg in great splendor. She, like the Duchesse d'Orléans, was clever and pointed, and in spite of all had her way with King Louis in much. She had no love for De Maintenon and now said to her:

"France has gone far and not stumbled. When will she stumble?"

De Maintenon, who foresaw the revocation of the Edict of Nantes, though she had dared to speak against it, said:

"The Grand Monarch does not stumble. He is France. If stumbling comes, it will be those near him."

"Well said, old Maintenon," declared Duchesse Charlotte in a whisper to Cardinal Bouillon of Nantes.

At last the Siamese ambassadors appeared, and there were murmurs of excitement at seeing these representatives of Phra-Narai in their long robes of silk and glittering swords and peaked hats, slowly approaching the throne. On being presented they remained so long upon their knees that Louis, growing impatient, asked his chancellor, in an undertone if they were never going to rise.

The Abbé Lyonne interpreted the speeches. Standing up at last, they said that Phra-Narai had been greatly touched by the letter from Louis with his miniature. They spoke of commercial privileges and begged that a French embassy should be sent to Siam.

Louis welcomed the delegates warmly and said they had done well to come; that never had France been so powerful. He had an army of 400,000 defended by a hundred fortresses; a huge navy and wealth greater than that of any other power in the world. He bade the ambassadors look round and see in this circle of magnificence the overwhelming character of France. He was pleased that Siam wished treaty, and he asked if their king would accept the Christian religion. The chief mandarin, replying, said it would be difficult for Siam to discard a religion she had held for over two thousand years, but this was not for him. It belonged to the King of Siam himself.

Louis then said France's greatness had come under the Christian religion and no doubt his good brother, the King of Siam, would sign a treaty to make Siam the greatest country in the Oriental world.

He bade the mandarins study France and see its vast cathedrals, and above all Notre Dame; to visit the Louvre and the Tuileries and the Palais Royale, and his last great work for France, the Hôtel des Invalides, where the soldiers of France were cared for when their fighting was done. He bade them see the vast fortifications everywhere, the institutions he had founded for the benefit of France. His ships went to the farthest seas, to the West Indies, where France owned San Domingo, Martinique, Guadaloupe, Tabago, Granada, and the Barbados; to America, Africa, Asia and Siam.

Through the windows of the huge Throne Room came from the splendid gardens of Versailles a song which softly sounded in the ears of all:

> "This is the day of France,
> The day of France, the day of France,
> This is the day of France,
> Oh, gai, vive le Roi—
> Oh, gai, vive le Roi!"

When the ambassadors had again made obeisance and retired, Louis said to Seignelay, "La Salle has come?"

Seignelay bowed. "Sire, I will send for him."

King Louis beckoned to Harlay, the Archbishop of Paris, who drew near with anxious eye.

"Archbishop," said King Louis, "the progress of our Faith in France is slow, but it reaches far?"

"The Church progresses with you, Sire, its head—as far as God permits."

"Well said, Archbishop, but that is within our borders here. I am not sure that overseas the Church acts always with its King."

The words of Louis filtered through the vast audience as a kind of subtle irritant. Men and women looked at one another and murmured. Nobles thrust heads forward, listening intently.

Seignelay's messenger found La Salle in the gardens with the Abbé Renaudot. He was summoned to the Presence, and with a nod he looked curiously at the Abbé and moved quickly toward the palace. As they went a lame soldier who had done duty for a quarter of a century and had but one leg, sang softly—for he had come from the Invalides ruled over by the astute Abbé Potin.

> "Brave Captain,
> Coming from the war,
> Searches for his honors—
> He has searched so far,
> Searched so long,
> Searched with no reward,
> That now he bows his head
> And goes with boding tread—
> Oh! Brave Captain,
> Coming from the war!"

With the Abbé Renaudot not far behind, La Salle, with the sad song still in his ears, went forward, brooding but composed.

In the palace La Salle walked behind Seignelay, with head erect, but with despair in his eyes. He knew not why he had been summoned. All seemed ill to him. He was pale, almost haggard, and yet he bore himself with that spirit which had made France the greatest factor in the world of struggle, strife, exploration, conquest, and civilization.

La Salle was conscious of the excited spirit of the great crowd, but as he neared the throne he bowed low. Then as he came closer he bowed once more and stood still. In Seignelay's face there was naught of hope. Seignelay had learned immobility.

There was deep silence for a moment, and then Louis said: "Sieur de la Salle, you have come again to my court after years have passed. You have been on a far continent working for France. After toil, anxiety, and danger you have discovered the mouth of the Mississippi. Is it not so?"

La Salle's face did not change its look, but in his eyes was amazement, for Louis' tone was kind. "When France speaks, who shall gainsay?"

Internally the King smiled, for these words gave naught, sought naught, revealed naught, save an astute and comprehensive mind. Louis' voice came again, clear and strong:

"They have destroyed your forts, monsieur, and that against my will!"

La Salle's eyes startled, looked at Louis with a new sense.

"At Fort St. Louis," continued the King, "you have gathered thousands of Indians faithful to you and to that behind you, the will of France. Come nearer, Sieur de la Salle."

La Salle's face had lost its pallor. A new look came into it.

"You asked for two ships; well, I shall give you four— one, the *Joly,* armed with thirty-six guns. You asked for a hundred men; I shall give you two hundred and fifty, and, besides, on these ships men and women of France shall go for a settlement at the mouth of the Mississippi. One of my best naval captains, Captain Beaujeu, shall go with you. I resolve that Spain be conquered, and you will bring your Indians down from Fort St. Louis and we shall break the power of Spain in Mexico. Spain would rival us, but we are supreme in Europe, and we shall be supreme over there."

While Louis spoke every pulse of La Salle had pounded life, hope and vitality back. He could scarce believe that all he asked for had been granted, and he knew not why, for yesterday Seignelay had given him no hope. How his future was spread before him! All that he had planned would come to pass. He raised his head slowly and moisture came to his eyes. He saw he was expected to reply. He controlled himself.

"Sire, I have but this to say: Louis, the great, King of France, by the grace of God, rules. The work you have set me, Sire, I will do. I will obey the spirit of France in all things. I have lived for my native land; I have loved her, and to my last moment I am the faithful son and friend of France. I am the King's loving, true devoted servant."

Louis stretched out a hand, and La Salle knelt and kissed the fingers which had carried on the work of Richelieu and Mazarin and Colbert.

As La Salle stood again, King Louis said to all: "I would I had a hundred such as he. The name of France would be secure."

As La Salle drew slowly back and mingled with the excited, admiring crowd on the way to exit, Seignelay came to him. There was a look in Seignelay's eyes which said: "Well done, La Salle. The way is now clear!"

He whispered, however, "I knew yesterday what the King would do, for he heard our talk, Sieur de la Salle."

La Salle's eyes were startled. "Name of God!" he said, and that was all.

Chapter XXXIX: GOD KNOWS

ALL Versailles and Paris rang with the triumph of La Salle. Outwardly he was not changed. His motions were as deliberate as usual. His walk was firm and quiet, but in his voice and eyes was the spirit of conquest. He had seen the Abbé Potin as he left Versailles, and in the priest's face was the hatred of one beaten in the struggle for the favor of the King.

Few knew of the branding of Barbe Ranard, but every official of the Church understood why she had been punished. Weeks passed. She saw the Abbé Potin but once since her branding, for a few moments. She was on her way to the Invalides when she met him in the street, and stopped him. Looking at her haggard face and piteous, beautiful eyes, he said, sadly: "You have failed. Henceforth you work no more in the service of our Order."

Bitterness and revolt were in her heart, but she answered, quietly: "So, only success matters! If that were true, Abbé Potin, what of the priests who have given all after torture." She bowed her head. "For me—for me—all is done forever!" and she buried her face in her hands.

When she looked up again the Abbé was gone, and she would never see his face as a friend again. His lips she had kissed, upon his breast her face had lain, but it was all over, and forever, and she shrank into her dark and everlasting torture.

As she returned slowly to her apartments, her feet heavy as the gargoyles on Notre Dame, her eyes with all brightness gone, her soul in dark turmoil, for her husband had been dismissed from his post in Canada and he had deserted her before her branding; she shuddered. Every face that looked at her had in her thought stark reproof. The world turned its shoulders on her, and she knew that she was alone in the universe. Even Duchesneau never came now. He had broken with her, the discredited official whom Louis might send to the Bastille! He, even he to whom she had been so much, turned his back on her too. Her shoulder was unhealed still, and it gave her pain as she walked. Voices rang out in the street around her, songs were sung in cafés, and one came to her ears:

> "I have to take a long journey,
> I don't know who will go with me:
> I have to take a long journey,
> I don't know who will go with me:
> It will be Rossignolette
> Who will go with me,
> La violette double, double,
> La violette doubleron,
> La violette, double, double,
> La violette, doubleron."

Again she shuddered, and her face became tortured. She was no longer beautiful.

"Yes, I must take a long journey," she said in an agonized voice, "and there is no Rossignolette. I am alone. Oh, God in Heaven!"

La Salle's four ships, the *Joly*, which had thirty-six guns; the *Aimable*, with six guns; the *Belle*, the direct gift of Louis; and a ketch, *St. François*, loaded with stores and ammunition, tools and implements and things needed at the mouth of the Mississippi—all these were at Rochelle. Here began La Salle's dealings with Captain Beaujeu, whom he distrusted because Beaujeu's wife was a friend of the Jesuits, and he could trust no one under their influence. Difficulties started at once between him and Beaujeu, who wrote protesting letters to Seignelay.

He said in one letter:

I find it very hard to submit to the orders of the Sieur de la Salle, whom I believe to be a man of merit, but who has no experience of war except with savages, and who has no rank, while I have been captain of a ship for thirteen years and have served thirty by sea and land. Besides, he has told me that in case of his death you have directed that the Sieur de Tonty shall succeed him. . . . I beg, Monseigneur, that I may at least share the command with them. . . .

Seignelay rebuffed him, told him to have no further anxiety about the command, for it was settled.

This irritated Beaujeu, who wrote again:

Monseigneur, I represented to you the hardship of compelling me to obey Monsieur de la Salle, who has no rank and never commanded anybody but schoolboys. . . . He pretends that I am only to command the sailors and have no authority over the volunteer officers and the hundred soldiers who are to take passage in the *Joly*, and that they are not to recognize or obey me in any way during the voyage. . . . He is a man who wants smoke. I will give him his fill of it, perhaps more than he likes.

To his friend, Cabart de Villermont, one of his friends in Paris with whom La Salle was also on friendly terms, he wrote:

I do not like his suspiciousness. I think him a good honest Norman, but Normans are out of fashion. It is one thing to-day and another to-morrow. . . . Pray do not show my letters for fear of committing me with him, but he is too suspicious already, and never was a Norman so Norman as he, which is a great hindrance to business. I am myself *un bon gros Normand*, but I have traveled far, have seen much, and am broad in mind. I shall go straight forward without regarding a thousand whims and bagatelles. His continual suspicion would drive anybody mad except a Norman like me; but I shall humor him as I have always done, even to sailing my ship on dry land, if he likes. . . . I could not help telling him that I saw he was brought up in the provinces. . . . Let Abbé Renaudot glorify Monsieur de la Salle as much as he likes, and make him a Cortez, a Pizarro, or an Almagro. That is nothing to me, but do not let him speak of me as an obstacle in his hero's way. Let him understand that I know how to execute the orders of the court as well as he.

It will thus be seen that Beaujeu was a man of irritable nature, generous impulses, and distinct capacity. He was round, plump, and vigorous, with blazing eyes, grayish hair, and a pugnacious nose, but he was a man through and through, and La Salle could have trusted him more than he did at the start; but he had been beset by too much exterior friendliness to accept any man at his own valuation, and Beaujeu did not lack in self-importance.

Nika, the Indian servant, with whom La Salle had more in common than with Beaujeu, one day said to him: "Great chief, that captain he not so bad. Him honest fool. His ways, not yours—no, but Nika could march with him, yes."

He looked at Nika with understanding eyes, and far beyond Nika into the past out on the great Lakes of the far continent and into the future with its hoped-for success, and he smiled and nodded, but made no reply in words.

Time went on, difficulties arose not only with Beaujeu, but with the officials who superintended the loading of the ships and provided the stores—things done at the expense of the King. La Salle could not object, but when Louis complained of delay, La Salle said to Seignelay by letter:

I am eager to start, but delay comes from official tardiness. They do not expedite purchase of stores or loading of the ships. They recruit the soldiers slowly, and not always from the best class, and I do not wish to take offscourings of the prisons of France. Be sure, monsieur, that I mean well by my native land and by the great monarch who has commissioned me.

Then came a sharp command from King Louis that new officials be appointed, and they were chosen by Seignelay himself. Then the work moved on. King Louis became aware that even yet the foes of La Salle were working.

To Rochelle came Joutel, the son of a gardener, who had once been in the employ of La Salle's uncle and was a native of Rouen, had been sixteen years in the army and was to become the honest historian of the expedition. Father Le Clerc and the Abbé Cavelier also wrote, but the Abbé was at no time an honest chronicler of his brother's deeds and doings. The Abbé Cavelier had arrived in France and come to Rochelle with Moranget, nephew of La Salle, and another nephew, Cavelier, a schoolboy, to join the expedition. La Salle's faith in his brother was small, but this was no time for personal distrust, and he accepted the Abbé and also his two nephews.

La Salle said: "You have seen me in dark days with death and disaster round me. Now you see me with my face in the rising sun, and my life stirring with new purpose. All goes well with me."

The Abbé's reply was significant. He was fundamentally unsound and the good streaks in him were the feeblest muscles of his whole constitution. He should never have been a priest. He was La Salle's antithesis, a man with meager face, long nose, acquisitive hands, and attenuated soul. Yet La Salle loved his captious brother as he loved his devoted mother, to whom he wrote a letter just before he sailed. These were among his words to her:

We are setting sail with four vessels and nearly four hundred men on board. We all have good hope of a happy success. I passionately wish, and so do we all, that the success of this voyage may contribute to your repose and comfort. . . . Madame, my most honored mother, from your most humble and obedient servant and son, de la Salle.

My brother, my nephews, and all the others greet you, and take their leave of you.

The ships were loaded and they were ready to start, but they awaited a favorable wind. Louis had at once sent La Forest to Fort Frontenac, commanding him to take control there, and Tonty to continue in control at Fort St. Louis on the Illinois. He wrote as well to La Barre, the Governor, a scathing letter which warned him that he had lied about La Salle. He concluded with these words: "I am satisfied that Fort Frontenac was not abandoned, as you wrote to me that it had been."

He wrote also to the Intendant of Canada, Meulles, that La Forest was to suffer no impediment and that La Barre was to surrender to him without reserve all that belonged to La Salle.

A letter had also come from Frontenac, full of delight that La Salle had triumphantly overcome difficulties, that Barbe Ranard had been punished, that La Forest had been returned to Canada, and that the girl, Lya, had been a pivot on which La Salle's success had swung.

My wife sends you her good wishes and hopes, and for myself I give you, as I always have, my entire faith and deep affection. As for myself, I shall go to Canada again. Please God, I shall leave my bones in that great land which in centuries to come shall be the memorial of endurance, power, and glorious endeavor and achievement. My hand is on your shoulder, dear La Salle. I bid you Godspeed.

On the four ships a goodly sprinkling of gentlemen and women of the middle and lower class made up the members of the new colony who were to settle at the mouth of the Mississippi. Among these were the Marquis de la Sablonnière, a noble whose only fortune was his sword; the Sieur le Gros; Sieur de Merle; Bartholemy, a young Parisian; Barbier and Talon, Canadians; Liotot, a surgeon, the brothers Duhaut, Paget, a Huguenot; Heins, a Wurtemberger, an ex-buccaneer, known as "English Jem"; Friar Zenobe Membré and others; Recollet Friars and the priests Esmanville and Desloges; Minet, the engineer; and so many others.

The day before La Salle sailed, there came to Rochelle with Madame Louvigny Lya Darois, and he did not know. She did not seek La Salle, or try to speak with him. She only wished to see him start upon his long journey, though she did not know it was to be his last. They must not meet and greet and say farewell.

Standing with Madame Louvigny, she saw him pass to his ship with firm, quiet tread, Saget, his servant, and Nika, his Shawanoe hunter, behind him. The look in his face was that of one who was entering on his greatest achievement. She knew, as Frontenac had said, her interview with King Louis had been one of the swivels on which had swung La Salle's fortunes, and she was glad. In her heart was that which deepens faith and hope in all mankind. She watched the evening mists fall upon this little fleet, and she did not know what its fate would be, but in her heart was an unexplainable sadness, with sure sense of victory.

She saw night descend and she returned to her apartments with Madame Louvigny, but next morning at daybreak in a favoring wind she was out upon the dock with numbers of folk who had come to see the ships depart. She saw Captain Beaujeu, the Abbé Cavelier, and the priests Zenobe Membré, Douay, and Le Clerc. She saw the soldiers and the settlers, the women and girls who were bidding farewell to friends on shore and were kissing their hands and waving handkerchiefs in good-bye. She saw La Salle's face in the distance, the upright resolution of his figure, the look of command on him, and she said aloud:

"Great man, great patriot, farewell!"

La Salle did not hear this, but he looked at the four ships and the people on them, and he too felt a strange sadness and an enormous exhilaration as he gazed into the far distance to the sky-line beyond which were the Mississippi and Mexico.

The wind caught the sails, they filled, and with the rising sun upon the canvas they moved upon the infinite sea. Lya did not go until the ships were almost lost to view beyond the horizon's line.

"God knows—God knows!" she said.

Chapter XL: "ALL SHALL BE WELL"

IN two months after leaving France the four vessels reached the island of St. Domingo. Here came the first misfortune of the expedition, owing to the mistake of Beaujeu, who ran past the Port de Paix and cast anchor at Petit Goave on the other side of the island. La Salle was indignant, because he wished to meet the Marquis de Saint-Laurent, Lieutenant-General of the island, at Port de Paix, Bégon, the Intendant, and De Cussy, Governor of La Tortue, who had orders to supply him with provisions.

La Salle and others of the expedition were ill and the *Joly* had more than fifty sick men on board. The *Joly* was alone, the other vessels having sailed slowly. A "Te Deum" for safe arrival had scarcely been sung, when two of the delayed vessels came, bringing news that the ketch, *St. François*, had been taken by Spanish buccaneers. She had carried provisions, tools, and other needs of the colony, and the loss was irreparable. Not La Salle alone, but the Lieutenant-General spoke scathingly to Beaujeu, who was answerable for the loss of the ketch and all that it involved. In vain Beaujeu protested; they turned and left him, bitter and difficult. Meanwhile, La Salle's illness increased and he was taken to the house of a goldsmith in the town, where he lay near to death. The men of the ships roamed on shore and plunged into excess of debauchery, contracting dire diseases. Joutel in his journal said, "The air of this place is bad and so are the fruits, and there are plenty of women worse than either."

In his bed, La Salle could hear the songs of the evil streets, and he knew the men were on the broad path to perdition. To his troubled brain the songs and noise were horrible and disgraceful. They shouted outside the home where he lay so ill. One of the chansons struck him like a blow in the face, it was so vile:

> "To the Saint Jean I was welcome,
>   I was welcome for six francs all round.
> La vesi, la veson,
>   La veson don don,
> Dancing la vesi,
>   Mi!
> Jumping la veson,
>   Mon!"

This would be followed by shrieks of laughter, and salacious mutterings, and ugly little simperings and ejaculations, and the shame of it all lowered his vitality. He was helpless, he could do naught, and again the tide seemed against him. Even the Intendant and Governor did not visit him. They were little better than their people, and were aware of the strife between La Salle and Beaujeu, and had no faith in the expedition.

There was a mirror opposite La Salle's bed; it was evening, the blinds were up, and all was dark in his room. His servant, Saget, had left him, as he thought, asleep, and had not pulled down the blinds. La Salle could see the soldiers in the street—his own soldiers, sailors, and colonists—and the negro women and girls, some of them half dressed, some of them drunk, and all of them *exalté* in a crude, primitive way. There was an attempt at a procession in which black and white were one, and Frenchmen were masked like Indians. It was a melancholy sight for La Salle to see men of his ships with their arms around black women. He had seen posts in the far West when Indian girls were brought in numbers, but the licentiousness of the barbaric West was not like the shameless abandon of this civilized island under the French flag.

The men seemed lost in the ribaldry of it all, and among them was the Marquis de la Sablonnière, and Duhaut and Hiens and Teissier, the pilot, and many others, and La Salle's pulses of indignation beat faster. To think that a marquis of France should be in such a crowd! Thank God, none of the women and girls of the ships were present, for the priests had seen to that, but they had no control over the men, now that La Salle, the leader, was ill and Beaujeu was not in command. They had no regard for their leader when they were in this salacious circle and they were nearly all drunk.

More than once La Salle in his black misery tried to rise from his bed to command them to begone. He heard one shrill voice singing:

> "My father married me,
>   On one of the harvest days, laridon,
>   He gave me a man who wouldn't listen to reason,
>   So, laridon, don dame, I love you!
>   Laridon, don, don!"

This was sung by a pretty drunken girl of not more than sixteen years of age, only partially dressed, with lovely neck and shapely legs, and she now threw herself in the arms of the Marquis de la Sablonnière, whose name was already at a discount in the expedition. La Salle saw them hurrying up the street, but among the revelers came Barbier, a young Frenchman born in Quebec, and he stormed with good round oaths. He asked them if they wished to make their leader, La Salle, worse that they rioted so near his sick-room. Had they no feeling, no decency? Were they abandoned beasts?

It was now that the Abbé Cavelier and Friar Membré

came and with sharp commands drove the crowd away and threatened them with punishment by the Intendant.

"He is not on this island now—ha! ha! ha! ha!" they shouted as they ran away, the women and girls gathering their gay clothes about them.

"And he not say no!" said a native girl, sticking her tongue out as she tossed a skirt at the priests, showing her bare limbs. She was very young and very bad.

The priests entered La Salle's room and found him excited and almost delirious. "I will stay no longer here. It is infamous," he said.

"My brother," said the Abbé, "we take you away from this shamelessness to the home of a Capuchin friar."

At this moment Saget and Nika entered and they helped La Salle to dress. Then he was led shaking from the house, and presently the Capuchin friar met them in the street, a little godly man of gentle heart and cheerful eyes.

"In my home you shall have peace, Sieur de la Salle," he said, and La Salle liked the man and took his arm, and the peace promised was his in the friar's home.

The expedition was now without a recognized head, and Beaujeu, in a letter to Seignelay, told him that La Salle was dangerously ill; that great numbers were sick; that the Abbé Cavelier had asked him to take charge, but he had refused; that the Spaniards are well armed with six vessels, but that he is not afraid, and if Sieur de la Salle died he should go a different course, for he did not approve of his plans.

La Salle could not resume the voyage until near the end of November, and the stay in the island had been bad for all the men in the ship. The island had bad government and the place was a hotbed of vice and evil living. Even the clergy had limited influence over the soldiers, sailors and colonists. Most had become demoralized already. La Salle, as he grew better, hoped that the life at sea would greatly help. He stiffened his courage.

He was ever on ill terms with Aigron, the captain of the *Aimable,* whom he had reason to distrust, for Aigron was an agent of La Salle's foes, who had placed him on the ship in spite of King Louis' caution. Fearing some mishap might befall the *Aimable,* La Salle embarked on her himself with his brother, Membré, Douay, and the trustiest of his followers. On the *Aimable* they coasted the shores of Cuba. La Salle meanwhile, haggard from his recent illness, was buried in meditation, because of the apparent enmity of Beaujeu and the loss of the *St. François.* Weeks passed. The spirits of nearly all grew again discontented, for there were three ships, and La Salle could only be on one where he had influence and he kept his fellow-passengers fairly contented in spite of Aigron.

At length a sailor at the masthead of the *Aimable* saw land, and on New-Year's Day they anchored three leagues from the shore. Then came a thick fog, and when it cleared the *Joly* was not to be seen, but La Salle, in the *Aimable,* with the *Belle* explored the coast. He was not aware that they had already passed the mouth of the Mississippi. At length they came upon a wide opening between two points of land, and the adjacent sea was discolored with mud. It was no doubt the entrance to Galveston Bay. La Salle lay there five or six days, waiting for Beaujeu. Then thinking that Beaujeu must have passed the *Aimable,* he resolved to follow. They coasted the shores of Texas. Indians swam out and were taken on board, but their language was not understood, and as he approached the land he saw vast plains and a dim expanse of forest and prairie and buffalo and deer. At length he landed between Matagorda Island and Corpus Christi Bay. Into the lagoons where he was he thought the Mississippi must empty itself. At last the *Joly* drew near and all were encouraged again.

La Salle and Beaujeu met upon the deck of the *Joly*. Beaujeu was irritated; the coast was dangerous, the weather bad, and supplies scanty.

La Salle said to him: "I fear we have missed the principal mouth of the river. I ask you to sail back in search of it."

Beaujeu replied that La Salle was to blame for their separation, but he would sail back if the ship was given provisions.

La Salle said, "I will give rations for fifteen days, no longer."

Beaujeu replied: "Fifteen days' rations are not enough. I decline."

La Salle retorted, bitterly: "Very well. I will land soldiers and they shall find the chief mouth of the Mississippi."

Minet, the engineer, standing by, said he doubted that the Mississippi discharged into the lagoon at all. La Salle, in his confusion and uncertainty, resented this, and Minet shrugged his shoulders and turned away, saying, afterwards, "He treated me as if I were the meanest of mankind."

La Salle persisted, and sent Joutel and Moranget with soldiers to explore the coast.

Joutel in his diary said: "The difficulty was that few of our men were fit for anything except eating. Our company was like Noah's Ark, which contained animals of all sorts."

At last they set themselves to build a raft on a good shore into which a great stream flowed, but before it was finished they saw the ships which had followed them along the coast. La Salle now landed, announcing that here was the western mouth of the Mississippi. He decided to bring the *Aimable* and the *Belle* to safe harborage.

The *Aimable* was ordered to enter, and she weighed anchor, La Salle watching her from the shore.

Suddenly there came word to La Salle that the Marquis de Sablonnière with several men had been set upon by Indians and carried off. The moment was critical; the men must be recovered. He led his followers in haste towards the camp. There behind him was the *Aimable* nearing the shoals. They reached the Indian huts. As they entered the camp there was a report of cannon on the seashore. La Salle knew the shot was a signal for disaster, and, looking back, he saw the *Aimable* furling her sails, and knew she had struck a reef. With his followers he entered the chief's lodge, where the men were naked and the women nearly so, and an ugly crew swarmed round them. They were given buffalo meat and dried porpoise meat and pipes to smoke, but La Salle hastily closed the interview, with difficulty recovering the kidnapped men, and returning to the beach. On his way he saw the *Aimable* on the reef. She contained nearly all the colony's provisions—sixty barrels of wine, cannon, grenade, vast amounts of iron and lead, tools, a forge, a mill, cordage, boxes of arms, nearly all the medicines, and most of the baggage of the soldiers and colonists. Aigron had disobeyed orders, and, though little else was saved, his own personal property was landed safely!

La Salle had always doubted Aigron, and now he recalled the face of the Abbé Potin when he left the palace of Versailles after being commissioned by the King. He was convinced that the delays at Rochelle and the sinking of the *Aimable* were due to his enemies, who still defeated him in these smaller but terrible ways. The loss of the *St. François* had been bad, the loss of the *Aimable* was infinitely worse. He was convinced that the power which had indirectly tried to kill him had destroyed the *Griffon*, ruined Fort Frontenac, and strove so persistently against him,

[287]

was that which now broke before his eyes another of his tools to achievement. When Joutel said the boat which hung at the stern of the *Aimable* had been staved in, he was the more convinced.

Beaujeu sent a boat from the *Joly* and La Salle urged his men to hasten the saving of the cargo. Gunpowder and flour were landed. Indians came, greedy for plunder, but all night long sentinels guarded the miserable bivouac among the casks and boxes yielded up by the sea, and La Salle, encompassed by treachery, darkness, and the storm, straightened his shoulders, set his teeth, and fought on. It was useless to put Aigron under arrest. That would be done in France, and in time it was so done.

On the morning after the wreck of the *Aimable*, La Salle, who believed profoundly in the fidelity of Joutel, said to him: "These are dark days, but I have had darker and may have darker still. That is the fate of all explorers, of whom I am——"

He paused. He had meant to say, "not the most important," but his inveterate honesty prevented; he felt beneath all the far-reaching effects of this expedition, no matter what its present fate. His native land would see that its purpose was fullfilled. His eyes lighted. He drew his shoulders up and added to his words, "Of whom I am the most opposed, but the more persistent, Joutel."

Joutel's reply was: "Many have been against you, Sieur, but you conquer. You have conquered even Captain Beaujeu. He was against you at first; he did not believe in you. He thought you distrusted him. Now he knows what you are, and his energy and capacity are for you."

La Salle smiled. "We Normans do not long misunderstand each other. We have a faith of our own, and it makes us greater patriots. This Captain Aigron"—La Salle's brow darkened—"is a servant of my foes, and through them again I have been struck. We are not at the chief mouth of the Mississippi, I know now, but in the *Belle* we shall find it, and there build a fort and start again upon the long path of France's glory."

Joutel nodded, and after a moment said: "There is great sickness now, due to brackish water and bad food, and many of our people have died. The sailors eat wild fruits to excess. Men have died from diseases caught at St. Domingo. Fifty of our company are already gone. Besides, we are unsafe here with the Indians near and the Spaniards possible. We are defenseless in some sense."

La Salle replied: "I understand. We must make a rampart to protect the camp." Here, among bales, boxes, casks, and pens for fowls and swine, were gathered the sorrowful men and women who came to hold for France a region larger than half of Europe, and they built a fort under the eye and with the help of La Salle.

Slowly but surely the settlement grew. There were quarters for the women and the men, and a small chapel was built, and at length a sort of village became evident and Indians came and traded, and gardens were planted, and men hunted and women and girls sewed and gave a sense of settled life to the transitory place. It was all lonely, but not secluded. Vast plains stretched behind them, a wide and beautiful sky was above them, and they were free from all danger of cold and only the bad water was their foe in the daily life. Wells were sunk, but still the water was brackish, and there was food in plenty from the prairie, and oysters from the beds near by, and, had it not been for discordant elements, all would have seemed in some degree promising.

Never did priests behave better than on this expedition. Not one of them but would have cut off his hand rather than have gone back to France with Beaujeu. They went among the people guiding, encouraging, hopeful, sustaining.

They had the social gifts of women, the piety of saints, the adaptability which was so needed in the pioneer life. They had the primitive sense. Some of them came of high lineage in France, they were ever faithful and useful, advising well, attending the sick, administering to the dying, and burying the dead. Their cassocks might be worn and frayed, but their vestments of the Mass were ever clean and rich and beautiful, and attendance at Mass was a comfort to those whose clothes were becoming worn and grimy, and not easily renewed, for much cloth had been lost in the *St. François* and the *Aimable*.

It was hard to imagine that this expedition would prove in the end a failure.

"Shall we lose faith in our great star, La Salle?" said the wife of a dissident mason. "But no, he may not always succeed, but he triumphs as he has always done. I am for standing steady—yes."

"*Zut!* the man is a wonder for sure," said a builder from Rochelle, "I take my compass from his pocket."

"I drink to him," said a laborer who had a bottle of wine for his dinner. "This is good enough for me. We have enough to eat, and if the water ain't good, then drink wine, say I. *Parbleu*, drink wine, say I."

Father Le Clerc, in passing, said, "The wine of life for you, my friend, and don't forget that, either."

The laborer made the sign of the cross. "That's my answer, *pardieu!*"

On the whole the settlement was very busy, for La Salle realized that only by work could discontent be diminished, and Joutel, his faithful friend, fought his fight with understanding heart.

One of the wives of the settlers came to Joutel. "You think we shall come through this all right, M. Joutel? Are we at the mouth of the Mississippi? Is it now—that?"

"Do you think the Sieur de la Salle would rest until the expedition was a success? But no, madame, we are on the way to happiness. Be sure of that."

The woman smiled. "You are like the priests, M. Joutel; you make us believe the best."

"If I am like a priest that is good for me. If they believe, trust them, and all will come right."

"Come right—yes, *comme ci, comme ça,*" she replied.

A girl went by singing:

> "We were ten girls in a meadow
> All ten waiting to marry,
> There was Diane, there was Chine,
> There was Claudine, et Martine,
> Ah, ah, Cath'rinette et Cathrina—
> Finally they sent us away,
> All were sent away,
> Drove away, Diane,
> Drove away Chine—ah!"

The woman laughed. "There is spirit for ye!"

Joutel exclaimed: *"Comme ci, comme ça,"* and he laughed.

As time passed disaffection grew. There were, from the first, discordant elements. These became vocal. Such men at Liotot, the surgeon, the brothers Duhaut, Hiens, Teissier, the pilot, young Barthelemy, and one or two others sought to increase the disaffection. They moved about sowing discord, unmindful of the fact that without La Salle the project must wholly fail. They were never successful among the few women, with whom La Salle was popular, and the priests, aware of the conspiracy, did their best to stem it, though they did not speak of it to La Salle. They were loyal from first to last, and admired and loved him. They succeeded in preventing the worst.

Said Friar Membré, head of the priests on the expedition, to Father Esmonville, "We must cheer the settlers, or all will be hopeless."

Esmonville replied, "We are in the hands of God—it shall be well with us."

His cassock was torn and mended; he was lean and ill fed, for the water was poor and many were ill because of it, but he held himself, as did all his colleagues, with heroic dignity. His sunburnt face showed little, but it had a look of patient hope.

"Naught can come of naught," said Duhaut, passing them with a sarcastic smile.

"We do not know the word," said Friar Membré.

It became known that the Indians had set fire to the prairie, meaning them ill, but La Salle caused the grass to be cut about the camp, especially near where the powder was. Then the Indians stole and carried things away.

La Salle sent his nephew, Moranget, and others to reclaim them, which they did, and they seized canoes and made slow progress back. They were attacked by Indians at night and two men were killed, and Moranget was wounded by an arrow through the arm.

When they returned, La Salle sternly reproved Moranget and placed him in the hands of Liotot, the surgeon. Liotot detested Moranget, as he saw how selfish and mean he was and how little likely to help La Salle. Liotot had invested money in the expedition and was eager for its success.

At last Beaujeu, who in the *Joly* was slowly coming to understand La Salle and did all possible to help him, prepared to return to France. His ship was in danger on this exposed coast and he was anxious to find shelter. Two days before the wreck of the *Aimable* he had said to La Salle: "I wish you to have more confidence in me. I will always make the first advances and I will follow your counsel whenever I can do so without risking my ship. If you wish,

I will go to Martinique for provisions and reinforcements. There is nothing I am not ready to do. You have only to speak."

La Salle replied with emotion: "I am proud of your confidence. I ask you to send ashore a quantity of iron stowed in the *Joly* for the use of the colony."

Beaujeu shook his head sorrowfully: "It is almost impossible save in harbor, for it is on my ballast and under my spare anchors and all my stowage. It will take days to get it here where the sea runs like mountains when the slightest wind blows."

To this La Salle replied: "I am near the place I sought; my expedition will succeed if I can have the iron stowed on board the *Joly*."

Beaujeu shook his head in negation and his round face seemed troubled, but after some further talk, a glass of wine and a biscuit, while the *Joly* scorched in the sun, and seagulls fluttered and sailors quarreled, La Salle returned to shore.

Beaujeu looked after him with admiration and said to himself: "We Normans must stand together. The man is wholly to be trusted. He is a great patriot and gives all for the love of our native land."

Suddenly he sent for his lieutenant, Aire. "I shall get out the iron for La Salle. See that it is done."

Aire's face clouded and he said, "In this uncertain sea?"

Beaujeu hardened. "Carry out my commands. There is naught to fear."

Beaujeu now wrote to La Salle:

I have ordered your iron to be got out in spite of my officers, who tell me I endanger my ship. I will bring provisions from Martinique. My work is over, the settlers are landed, and your responsible work begins. With all my heart I wish you well, my good Norman comrade.

When La Salle received this letter he said to Joutel: "You are right. Now our way seems clearer, and Beaujeu will carry the good news that my work is well begun."

Joutel raised an arm in salutation. "Good master, all comes your way in time."

At last La Salle bade good-by to Beaujeu on the shore. With great respect Beaujeu had come to say farewell, and in the wretched camp, with its poor ramparts and surrounded by oyster beds and broad flats of mud, the farewell took place with all the colonists present. Some had lost heart and nine embarked for home with Beaujeu. Among these was Minet, the engineer.

This bright day, the sun shining, the mists clearing, the waters of the great Gulf rippling in the light (for there was no roughness), faced by the departure of the *Joly,* La Salle smiled upon his followers, then swept the land in a vast semicircle with an outstretched arm:

"This land, Captain Beaujeu, will bring honor and great prosperity. Spain shall be conquered in Mexico, and France shall be triumphant there and here. Take with you the message of our hope and love. To Monseigneur Seignelay please say all shall end well here."

In Beaujeu's eyes was not the light of confidence, save in La Salle himself. "I shall take to France, Sieur, my faith in you and in your vast energy and patriotism and administration. Hardships lie before you, but prosperity shall come. It is a great land and I shall speak of it well and warmly."

They were dressed in the best they had, La Salle in his laced scarlet coat, Beaujeu in the uniform of the navy, which had distinction and handsomeness, and behind Beaujeu were his officers in showy uniforms. Behind La Salle were his chief men, all dressed in their best—laces and ribbons and swords, and all the women and girls in their

gayest clothing in the bright sun. It was outwardly promising.

When Beaujeu entered his small boat he was acclaimed,
and there were tears and waving handkerchiefs of the
women, but in the eyes of some behind La Salle were anxiety
and the glimmer of tragedy. They watched the *Joly* disappear, and as they turned to the camp again one of the
chief men was bitten by a snake in the ankle, and though
Joutel killed the snake, a sudden depression went through
the crowd. They were superstitious and this was like a
warning.

La Salle turned again to where he could see the tips of
the sails of the *Joly*. He laid a hand upon his sword. "All
shall be well," he said.

A pretty young girl heard him and she shook her head
and said to Barbier, "Shall all be well, m'sieu'?"

Barbier, a good colonist, looked at her forlornly, but made
no reply at first. The girl's name was Babette Laroque.
She came from La Salle's old home, Rouen, and she was of
the lower middle-class, with an intelligent mind, and in her
was the rare spirit of adventure and travel which few women
have. She had come because she had a brother of whom
she was fond and they were orphans, and when he said he
would go with the expedition, she willed to go with him;
and she was heart free when she started, but was not heart
free now.

From the first she had liked Barbier, who was a man of
men and as loyal to the expedition as though it was his own,
and an intense admirer of La Salle, in whom he ever
believed.

At last, as he walked with Babette and they turned and
watched the *Joly* grow smaller as she sailed, he said: "If
La Salle says it shall be well, then we must believe, but to

be *well* has many meanings. He has the big view— his *well* may not be ours."

She raised her head swiftly and she said, "Well, and well, and well—haven't we the big view, too?"

He turned and looked into her deep-blue eyes. "You give me hope, Babette." This was the first time he had called her by her Christian name.

Chapter XLI: TWO WOMEN

"SO, Captain Beaujeu, you come from the mouth of the Mississippi, where you left the Sieur de la Salle?"

"Monseigneur," replied Beaujeu to Seignelay, "I am not sure I left Sieur de la Salle at the mouth of the Mississippi—no."

Seignelay lifted his eyebrows and said, sternly, "If not the mouth of the Mississippi, then where?"

Beaujeu, though frightened by the sarcastic voice of the Minister, tried to fortify himself. "I am a Norman, monseigneur, and——"

Seignelay interrupted: "That touches not the point. You are a Frenchman. Where did you leave La Salle?"

Beaujeu wilted before the hard voice and said: "I know not, but it was not the mouth of the Mississippi discovered by the Sieur de la Salle, and not only I, but Monsieur Minet, the engineer——"

Seignelay interrupted: "Oh, Minet the engineer! Then by the Heaven above, in the confinement to which I shall assign him Monsieur Minet shall have time to think why he deserted La Salle. Go on, if you please."

Beaujeu was now thoroughly upset, but he controlled himself and said: "Monseigneur, the Sieur had never seen the Mississippi from the sea. I am sure we passed it and came to the mouth of a river further west, which also has lagoons and mud flats. I do not think Sieur de la Salle himself believes he has found the Mississippi mouth."

Something like satire filled the quiet but severe face of

[297]

the Minister. "So much for that, then. Why did you leave the Sieur de la Salle?"

"Because the *St. François,* the ketch, had been wrecked at Saint Domingo and it contained tools and ammunitions, and the *Aimable* was wrecked and it contained provisions and other things needful for the colony, so it was that I left——"

Seignelay intervened again: "The ketch, *St. François,* was wrecked and the *Aimable* was wrecked. Where is Aigron, captain of the *Aimable?* France would lay hands upon him."

Beaujeu told him Aigron's address in Paris.

In Seignelay's mind was the belief that the *Aimable* had been purposely wrecked and that behind the false captain was what prevented the quick loading of the ships at Rochelle, the power of the Jesuits. His lips compressed, his eyes grew cold with indignation.

"Well then, what more?"

"The Sieur de la Salle needed iron and provisions, and so I made for Cuba to get him both; but head winds were against me. My crew were discontented, and so I did not touch at Cuba but came direct to France."

Beaujeu almost sank through the floor before the anger in the eyes of the Minister.

Seignelay looked at him for a moment without speaking, and then these harsh words came: "Captain Beaujeu, as master of your ship why should discontent stop you from doing your duty? Does, then, a captain of the navy of France kneel before the will of his crew?" Seignelay got to his feet. "By God! I would rather see the ship sunk, and you with it, than that you should come to France with this dastardly tale."

When he had finished, Beaujeu's face was haggard. "Monseigneur, I did my duty after the light given me. On my word of honor, at last I acted to the Sieur de la Salle as I would to my own brother. His greatness conquered me and I came to respect and love him. He was worth all of us put together—an explorer without parallel, a patriot without measurement. I take back every word I ever said against the Sieur de la Salle. At last I gave him all I had, the best that was in me. The man conquered me." There were tears in his eyes, his head drooped.

Seignelay looked for a moment, then placed a hand upon his shoulder. "Captain Beaujeu, that redeems you in my eyes. What you have said I believe, but you must not repeat elsewhere your uncertainty as to the mouth of the Mississippi. It should not reach the ears of the King, who sent this expedition at his own expense. Captain Beaujeu, the Bastille was for you, but your words assure me you are an honest man and a faithful servant of the King—according to your lights—not the lights of Heaven! You have an obtuse but an honest mind. Now get you gone, Captain Beaujeu."

With tears streaming down his cheeks, Captain Beaujeu said: "Monseigneur, with all my soul I thank you. God preserve the Sieur de la Salle."

With these words he left the room and Seignelay watched him go with unhappy premonition of La Salle's defeat. He sat slowly down and thought. The *St. François* had been lost, the *Aimable* had been lost, and there was some black conspiracy behind it all. Minet and Captain Aigron! He took a pen, wrote an order, blotted the ink, and rang a bell. His secretary answered.

"This is for the arrest of Minet, the engineer who went with the Sieur de la Salle, and Captain Aigron. Have them brought to my office."

The secretary bowed and retired, and Seignelay made his way to King Louis.

He told King Louis of the loss of the *St. François* and of the *Aimable,* at which King Louis' eyes and face grew stern and hard, and of the return of Captain Beaujeu and Minet, the engineer. He did not tell Beaujeu's suspicions about the mouth of the Mississippi, but he spoke well of Beaujeu and harshly of Minet and Aigron, who had deserted La Salle and returned to France.

After a moment's silence King Louis said: "Captain Beaujeu did his duty, I suppose. But why did these men desert their master, La Salle?"

"Sire, I ordered the arrest of Minet and Aigron, believing it Your Majesty's will. I took the responsibility."

After a moment Louis said, "You believe that La Salle will succeed, then?"

There was an instant's pause, and then Seignelay said: "He has never yet failed, Sire, but has done honor to you who are his country. All will come right to the Sieur de la Salle—all in time. In him I have unchangeable faith and hope."

King Louis' face lighted. "This I like to hear. That vast new empire must conquer Spain in Mexico. That was why I sent La Salle. Settlement there, and the conquest of Spain. Now, Seignelay, what are your latest news from Quebec?"

"The very worst, Sire. The Iroquois are more than troublesome and De la Barre has failed."

"I gave La Barre warning, and now he shall retire—the useless one! In his place I will send Denonville, a better man. He may succeed."

"Sire, do you not think that Count Frontenac should return?"

Louis smiled now. "If Denonville does not succeed I can turn to Frontenac and say: 'Go back to the land where you ruled so well—yes, in spite of all—conquer the vile Iroquois, and lay the stable base for the future of my Canada.'" He added: "Frontenac is poor. I will send him three thousand livres. So he will know I have forgiven him and he will have patience."

Seignelay bowed his head. France was greater than she had been in all her history, and it was due to this sage being who, like all great men, made mistakes, but did his own thinking, played his own great part, and loved France more than aught else in all the world.

Rojet Ranard had been recalled from Quebec, and at first lived with his beautiful, dejected, humiliated wife in complete seclusion in Paris. Then he left her forever, as Duchesneau had done, and she lived alone. No old friends visited her, for the shame of her punishment had gone abroad.

On the day that Lya Darois, with Madame Louvigny, returned to Canada, she and the girl met. It was in the street where La Salle had lived—La Truanderie—for Lya had come to see where he had defeated the garrotters at the door of his apartments. She looked at it as though while life remained the picture of it would stay in her mind.

Barbe Ranard had not passed through this street since her own tragedy, but as a murderer comes again to the scene of his crime, so she had been drawn against her will to the spot where the great explorer had defeated her murderers. She went with bowed head, and was astounded to meet Lya coming from the door where La Salle had been the cause of her banishment from all civilized life. For a moment they looked at each other and then Barbe Ranard said, bitterly, "So, mademoiselle, you come to see where Sieur de la Salle made my tragedy."

"No, madame. I came to see the home where lived in anxiety one of the noblest men God ever gave the world. I had no thought of the crime committed here."

The honesty of her eyes and the sweet beauty of her face conquered this lost woman, as La Salle had conquered her at her branding. For a moment she looked at Lya without speaking. Then she turned gravely away, weeping, and walked swiftly to her own home. Lya watched her go with pity in her heart, for the woman had paid her price.

That night when the clocks struck twelve Barbe Ranard in her lonely room walked up and down in misery. As in her terrible shame she walked, now a little bent to one side as though her seared shoulder still hurt her, and her lips moaning and her body trembling, she raged in impotency. She had had place and even power; she had none now. Pictures of Versailles, of Quebec, of Paris in days past came to her mind's eye, and they tortured her as no martyr had ever been tortured by natives in the frozen wastes of Canada. Now there came to her sounds of singing from the street:

> "Pass, pass, Tribonet,
> Through the door of Saint-Jacquet,
> Pass, pass, Tribonot,
> Through the door of Saint-Jacquot."

As she listened she shook her head and said: " 'Pass, pass, Tribonot!' Yes, that is it—to Saint Jacquot! There is naught left for me. Even Duchesneau deserted me, and he is in confinement. All my friends are gone forever. O God, I am alone—all alone! No one cares now." She suddenly stood still and tore open her gown, exposing her bare breasts. "They are beautiful still," she said, "but none shall ever kiss them now. Behind them is the mark of the red-hot iron!" She gave a frenzied laugh. Again she walked, swaying from side to side. The clock of a church now began to strike, and the words of a chanson came to her:

"Orleans, Boisgency,
  Notre Dame of Clery,
Vendome, Vendome,
  What sorrow, what a bore,
To count all the night,
  The hours, the hours!"

That was it—"to count all the night, the hours, the hours!" No, she could not do it—no! It was too black, too awful. "What sorrow, what a bore!" She ran to a cupboard and took out a bottle of poison. Pouring out some, she added a little wine and, looking round the room, so loathsome to her eyes, with a sudden cry she closed her eyes, raised the glass, and drank her own eternal silence.

Then she knelt upon the floor blindly, her brilliant eyes opened, glazing with torture. For a moment or two she swayed, her fingers closing and unclosing, at last raised in agonized prayer, and then she fell. There in the ghostly silence she lay still, the light burning until morning. And the life in the streets went on.

Lya landed in Quebec with Madame Louvigny and was met with honor, for news had come of her reception by King Louis, of how she had helped in the success of La Salle, and of the favor shown by distinguished folk in France; though certain members of the Sainte Famille were still secretly bitter against her.

As she and Madame Louvigny came to the cathedral to Mass, little groups of people gathered to see them pass. Never before had Mass seemed so comforting to Lya. She had in her pocket a letter from Henri de Tonty.

Denonville, the new Governor, had come from France, and Tonty had received a letter from him. This was Tonty's letter to her; it was in her pocket as she attended Mass:

DEAR MADEMOISELLE: I regret I have bitter news. I was displaced by La Barre, the Governor, from command of Fort St. Louis on the Illinois, but I was reinstated by the King, and, having had word from Denonville, the new Governor, of the loss of the *Aimable*, the return of Beaujeu, the arrest of Aigron, the captain of the *Aimable*, and Minet, I determined to go to La Salle. So I gathered twenty-five Frenchmen and eleven Indians. Leaving here, I swiftly descended the Mississippi, where I had been with La Salle, and reached its mouth in Holy Week. I came upon loneliness and desolation. There were no white men on river, marsh, or sea. I sent canoes to search the coast for many leagues, but found no trace of La Salle, so I wrote him a letter, leaving it in charge of an Indian chief, hoping he would receive it at some time. I cannot tell you with what sorrow I ascended the Mississippi, some of my men remaining at the villages of Arkansas, Couture, Delaunay, and four others.

One thing, alas, seems clear, that La Salle missed the mouth of the Mississippi, and is no doubt in territory farther west which from the sea resembles the Mississippi mouth. He must be in a sad way, for he lacks tools and food and stores, but in the past he has overcome all obstacles, no matter how tremendous. I doubt not the end will be all we can desire, but it may not be soon. I must consolidate the work he so splendidly began here. The Iroquois are troublesome, but I have other tribes whom La Salle conquered by his indomitable soul, and here, at Fort Frontenac, at Michillimackinac, and elsewhere they will be kept ready to resist attack; but no permanent good will come to this vast region, unless Frontenac returns. Everything depends on that. The great *coureur de bois*, Du Lhut, a cousin of Louvigny, will take this letter to you. He is a man of worth and enormous skill in trade and with the Indians, and a gentleman in all. He takes this to you with the loving respect and timeless admiration of

HENRI DE TONTY.

Lya had not yet seen Du Lhut, but the letter from Tonty had been left with Monsieur Louvigny, and she read it with mournful heart, for she realized that all was not well with La Salle.

In vain Madame Louvigny sought to cheer her; an unexplainable pathos was in her eyes and around her lips. She read again with how proud and, strangely enough, how happy a heart, the words, "With the loving respect and timeless admiration of Henri de Tonty." It sent her to sleep that night depressed and yet elated, sorrowful in anticipation of bad news, but hopeful.

Next night at dinner she met the big and adventurous Du Lhut, but he knew no more than Tonty had told him and he had learned in Quebec, but he was high in praise of La Salle and in admiration of Tonty. "He has a metal hand," he said, "but his heart is of true metal also. The hand can kill, but the heart can save. He is a man of a million!"

There was in Du Lhut the wide spirit of a man without jealousy, without smallness, without malice; trusted, beloved, criminal if you will, but a great man after his kind. There was no Governor but spoke well of him. It was only the Intendants who persecuted him, and they, like Duchesneau, were rivals in trade, or, like Ranard, were corrupt officials.

"Will you tell me, monsieur," said Lya, her eyes intent on his, "whether the Iroquois are likely to conquer?"

All three watched closely the face of Du Lhut. It grew somber, but behind the somberness there was the light of hope.

"They are powerful, the Iroquois. The Indians of the West cannot stand against them, for they are not combined as the Six Nations are. I do not say they will take Quebec, because it is not the destiny of this vast estate to be under the rule of the heathen. The lives of Jesuit priests and Recollets—how many—are proof that the white man has come to stay!"

He suddenly got to his feet and both hands went up. "By the souls of all the saints it shall not be. Frontenac must return. With him, all shall be safe."

He walked the room for a moment, excited, dominant,

then sat down again with a little laugh. "We primitive people are easily roused but not easily conquered . . . and a little more of that excellent ragoût, my cousin!"

Lya watched him, and her figure trembled with happy agitation. For long they talked, though Lya little. She watched and listened, and when Du Lhut kissed her hand in good-bye she suddenly said: "May I kiss you, monsieur? May I kiss you?"

She put her hands on his shoulder and kissed each cheek. With his arms he drew her close: "God be good to you, my dear," he said. The Louvignys smiled. They loved the girl.

Outside in the hallway, where he would not let them come —for he hated this sort of formality; to his mind it was en-feebling—Du Lhut was faced by Luce Hontard who happened to pass to the staircase. He stopped her and he learned by shrewd questioning of this noble soul, fat, faithful and silent, that Lya had enough to live on humbly but comfortably all her days.

Du Lhut laughed. "She kissed me, Luce Hontard, just now. May I kiss you, good woman?"

"Oh, m'sieu', m'sieu'! Oh, la! la!" she said, and he kissed her on both cheeks and on the lips.

"Now Time be good to us all," he said, and a moment later he was in the street with a new pulse of adventure and hope in his veins.

Chapter XLII: IN THE HOUR OF TRIAL

ON the last day of October La Salle started with fifty men to find the mouth of the Mississippi, and they were saluted by cannons and were cheered as they started. Some wore corselets made of staves to ward off arrows, and they descended the La Vache, where La Salle had built a temporary post. It was two leagues above the mouth of the river and Joutel was in command. Lodgings were built for the women and girls, separate lodgings for the men, a small chapel was added, and the whole was palisaded. At the four corners of the house were mounted pieces of cannon and all the surrounding prairie swarmed with game—buffalo, deer, turkeys, ducks—there were plenty of turtles in the river and the bay was full of oysters.

Yet death, meanwhile, made withering havoc among La Salle's followers. Many of the soldiers were useless, nearly all fell ill, and the graveyard received more than thirty tenants that summer. The new post was given the name of Fort St. Louis. Under the eye of La Salle the men had worked hard. The carpenters brought from Rochelle proved worthless and La Salle himself had made the plans of the work and directed the whole.

After La Salle's going Joutel kept all at work, for busy folk had not time for disillusion. Plenty of buffalo were killed. A scaffold was built near the fort and all were set to work to smoke buffalo meat against the day of scarcity.

Autumn passed and January came, but without snow or

bitter weather, for it was far south. One day from the opposite side of the river came a shout of, "Dominic!" One man was in a canoe, and as it came near Joutel recognized the elder Duhaut, the rascal who had gone with La Salle. Duhaut, well born, had deserted La Salle, but to Joutel he falsely said he had stopped to mend his moccasins and, trying to overtake the party, had lost his way. He had fired his gun to no answering shot, and under great hardship he returned to Fort St. Louis. Dominic was his younger brother.

Time dragged on and at last Joutel saw seven or eight men approaching. La Salle headed them. They were greeted with joy by all, but La Salle, seeing Duhaut, asked why this deserter had been received. Then the wily and clever Duhaut explained, and La Salle's anger at length grew less.

La Salle had come upon a large river which he at first mistook for the Mississippi, and, building a palisaded fort, he left there several of his men whose fate was now unknown to him. He found he was mistaken about the river. After long search he had at length returned slowly to Fort St. Louis.

Presently La Salle was taken ill. His strength had been overcome, but not his courage or fortitude. In the fort he could command the care of all whom his brother, the Abbé, and Joutel, would let come to him. Liotot, the surgeon, looked after him, not loving him, but doing his duty. He had money in the expedition, and in France had not been a bad man, but here in the wilds a crude strain in him showed, and he was now disappointed and surly. Yet their only safety lay in keeping La Salle alive now, and Liotot admitted to himself that no man ever in this hemisphere had proved so great as La Salle.

As he lay sick, and at times delirious, due to over anxiety and a sense of bitter mistake, he had visions. As a rule La Salle preferred to be waited on by men—by Saget and Nika, who loved the ground he trod—but Liotot urged that one of the women of the expedition should come to his room. She was a woman of about forty-five, a mother, and of the lower middle class, and she was swift and gentle in her ways.

La Salle was but dimly aware of her presence, and why she was there he did not know. One night she came out of the dark with a lantern and La Salle in semi-delirium said:

> "The poor woman,
> She is the wife of a carter,
> She goes all about the country,
> From tavern to tavern,
> Searching for her husband,
>   Tirelli,
> With a lantern."

The woman was the widow of a man who had died on the expedition and for an instant her eyes gazed wildly at La Salle. She saw, however, that he was delirious and her distress abated. She put out the lantern, went to his bed, lifted up his head, and gave him a cup of soup to drink. He nodded at her kindly and she said:

"God save you to us, exalted man!" Then she made the sign of the cross, and presently sat down and watched him, with Nika standing near.

La Salle had visions again, but now with eyes closed. He dreamed he was in vast fields of settlement at the mouth of the Mississippi, and he saw oxen in the fields, and at the threshings, and all was prosperity. He remembered the splendid work done by the farmers of France, and with quivering voice said:

"Thresh out for yourselves,
  Thresh out for yourselves,
        Oxen.
Thresh out for yourselves,
  Thresh out for yourselves,
Many bushels for your masters!"

His was a strange elation in the leader of an expedition which had not in some ways justified itself in its time, but was for all time. Death and disaster had followed it, yet here was its sick leader exultant in his dream. He saw in prophetic vision the fulfillment of his hopes, and these lines are written not so far from the spot where he had his vision and the oxen threshed out prosperity to their masters.

One by one members of the expedition came to inquire, for he was its life and soul. Others might despair, but never he. Gentlemen in faded uniforms came, peasants, woodmen, mechanics, some of the offscourings of the streets of Rochelle and elsewhere, and even young girls were permitted to inquire. To these Saget and Nika were kind, for they were chaste and they were giving all for no present return, and these servants of La Salle knew it—for these girls there was no future; they could not marry among the men of the expedition, for the best were dead.

The Abbé Cavelier came much to his brother's bedside, and Friar Membré, the head of the priests, knelt and prayed for the recovery of this stricken hero, and at Mass in the small chapel he was remembered. At last their prayers were heard, and La Salle came out again into the open world on the arm of Liotot, and greeted kindly those who were to do him ill Duhaut, Hiens, Teissier, and the rest.

He determined to make his way by the Mississippi and Illinois to Canada to bring succor to his colonists. The Abbé, his brother, Moranget, his nephew, the Friar Anastase Douay, and twenty altogether were chosen to go with

[310]

him. The whole colony was ransacked for outfit. Men labored to patch their fading garments or take their place with buffalo or deer skins.

In April, loaded with weapons, kettles, axes, and gifts for Indians, they issued from the gate, and bravely set forth once more. They disappeared into the misty waste, the sun behind them and all the country glowing with the verdure of spring. Again La Salle cheered his followers.

Left with a gradually dwindling colony, Joutel kept the people occupied building, hunting, and planting vegetables. Meanwhile Duhaut the elder, a vain man, had fomented discontent among the colonists, telling them that La Salle would never return, and he tried to make himself their leader. The priests did their best to counteract these disgraceful acts, watched Liotot and Duhaut continually and reasoned with the settlers, trying to stem the conspiracy, and at last they spoke to Joutel.

Joutel sternly rebuked the offenders and did his best to encourage the dejected settlers. To Duhaut he said: "You are no explorer, you have few qualities of worth. You have no gift for leadership at all. You are as a pinhead beside the Sieur de la Salle. Have done!"

The strange thing was that, like Father Anastase Douay, Friar Membré was injured by a furious buffalo bull, and Father Maxime LeClerc by a boar. Thus the three priests had come to grief in the wild life, and Friar Membré was three months before he recovered. Women and girls went out with the hunters to aid in cutting up the meat. The young Canadian, Barbier, became enamored of one of the girls, and he came to Joutel:

"Monsieur, Babette Laroque is beautiful and young and sweet, and I would marry her."

Joutel replied, "I must consult the clergy."

This was done, and consent was given, and in these

strange surroundings came the happy sacrament of matrimony with what gayety and cheerful rites as were possible. There were few ribbons, but a feast of wild·meat and fancy pudding and pies and cakes were prepared, but all the wine was gone. There was but one bottle of brandy for all, and each had a sip. In these somber surroundings—somber not where nature was concerned, because it was bright and buoyant—the awful isolation preyed upon the minds of all 'and they were lost in melancholy.

One day the Marquis de la Sablonnière begged leave to marry another of the girls:

"Monsieur Joutel, I would give myself the honor to marry Manette Ridot. I am lonely, and she is beautiful and would be a good wife to me."

Joutel, the gardener's son, gazed at him with stern re·serve. Two things weighed with him. The Marquis de la Sablonnière was of the aristocracy; this girl was of the peasant class! His mind revolted from it. Besides, the Marquis was suffering from disease got at St. Domingo and it would be shameless and criminal to marry Manette.

He said, sternly, "Monsieur le Marquis, if she married you she would have a quicker dispatch from this world than by the bite of a venomous snake."

The Marquis was furious. He dropped a hand upon his sword, but Joutel said, sternly: "Stop that! You know what you are. Keep what you are to yourself. In a few months you will not be able to join any expedition, Monsieur le Marquis."

De la Sablonnière was of the outcasts of high society. He was young, corrupt, kindly, hopeless. He had no real courage. This gardener's son was far beneath him socially, but as high above him morally as the sky is from the earth. He plucked at his small moustache, but his weak eyes could not face the resolute Joutel. He turned on his heel and walked away.

This was not the kind of man to build up a new colony, but three-fourths of the people who came were right, and one-fourth were worthless. The women and girls were of the better peasant and lower middle class. They were decent, wholesome, and upright. There was no immorality in the camp. They lived in hope of a ship coming from France to rescue them, and in dread of Spanish ships landing troops to destroy them, for Spaniards had been here, as they all knew from the Indians who came and went.

At last one evening they heard shouts from beyond the river, and Joutel recognized La Salle's voice. Twenty men had gone with La Salle and eight returned with him. Four had deserted, one had been lost, one had been killed by an alligator, and the rest had perished in regaining the fort. The joy of the settlers was great because La Salle had that which gave them confidence and faith. His failures did not put the colony against him—only the few!

These were Joutel's words to La Salle when asked about the *Belle:*

"Alas! On May day I heard a voice crying out, '*Qui vive!*' I answered, '*Versailles!*' which was the password given to Barbier should he come back in the night, but I heard other voices than his. Among the rest was Sieur Chefdeville, who told me that the *Belle* was wrecked on the other side of the bay, and that all were drowned save the six in the canoe—himself, Teissier the pilot, a soldier, and three others."

"This is indeed disaster," said La Salle in a troubled voice. "She contained my papers, our baggage, and what was needed to take us from this spot."

"But they brought back your papers and some baggage," replied Joutel.

La Salle and his followers had journeyed towards the northeast over green plains and through prairie covered with buffalo. They reached the bank of a river, where Hiens was mired and nearly suffocated in a mud-hole and was saved by La Salle. They came upon Indian towns, and the Cenis Indians, then powerful but now extinct, overwhelmed them with kindness. The lodges of the Cenis were forty or fifty feet high, covered with meadow grass, looking like huge beehives. The spoil of the Spaniards was seen on every side. These Cenis spoke with contempt of the Spaniards. They moved on, but after two months they found the stock of ammunition nearly spent and their condition was such that they could do naught but return to Fort St. Louis.

The excitement of La Salle's return soon gave place to deep dejection. They watched with anxious eyes for an approaching sail, but none came. Less than forty-five remained out of near two hundred colonists. La Salle, by his composure, his hardihood, his adamantine temper, his audacity of hope, his words of encouragement and cheer, was the breath of life of this unhappy company.

He prepared once more to go to Canada and to take Joutel with him, intending to send Joutel to France with his brother to ask succor for the colony. They were in sad straits for clothing, but the sails of the *Belle* were cut up to make coats for the adventurers, and the colony was racked to find odd bits of clothing for the neat but ragged members of the expedition.

Here in his little colony, reduced now, La Salle looked back at all he had tried to do. His heart was strong within him. He and his friends might pass, but what he had done would stay.

Looking back, La Salle saw Fort Frontenac enlarged, Fort Louis on the Illinois the center of great development, Fort Louis on the Mississippi the beginning of greatest development; all under the will of God. He had become responsible for those thousands of leagues of luxurious land: his hand, his brain, his soul had made all possible. On Christmas day there was to be Mass in the crude, unhandsome chapel, and he and his colony would be there in the best clothes they had—and they were meager and patched and worn, except for his own wonderful scarlet tunic, which he had scarcely worn. The festivities of the day had, of course, been limited. There was no wine or brandy left, but there was good coffee and bread, and fresh meat from the prairies, and at dinner, soup, entrée and roast and vegetables, and pudding made of flour and rice and raisins. All were in cheerfulness, because, somehow, the spirit of La Salle, which again was self-possessed and resolute, affected all. It was folly to say he had only influence with Indians. It was his nearness to the elemental soul that gave him power over the Indians, but he had also power to influence great minds in Europe, to get money when he was bankrupt, to found faith when he stood almost alone in the entire sphere of French influence. Wherein he lacked was the capacity of Tonty—to give himself freely in the casual ways of life; his spiritual concentration made him a lonely, isolated figure, and yet he was the heart and soul of this martyr expedition. How few of all who had come from France would ever see it again—how few! Yet these men and women would live on.

At the Christmas dinner La Salle made a brief speech. On his left was his brother, on his right was Friar Membré, and at the same table were the other priests of the expedition and its few dissident and some faithful members.

La Salle rose. His soul was in his dark eyes. Somehow, all applauded, for he seemed lifted up. They were all lost, even the worst of them, in his atmosphere for the moment.

"Fellow-countrymen," he said, "this is the day of Christ,

and in the chapel we shall celebrate Mass in honor of the blessedness of life. We have had trials and misfortunes. The *Joly* has returned to France, the *Aimable* was wrecked, the *St. François*, the *Belle*, were lost, but behind these misfortunes is the everlasting truth: that we, a few faithful souls, have started for France a work which will live long. Many of our fellow-settlers are gone, but we live on. I go with a small company to Canada and rescue shall come for those who stay behind. We cannot all go. The women may not, they could not endure the journey. We must not yield this settlement; it shall stay." He raised his hand. "Please God, prosperity will come to those left behind; to the vast populations of Frenchmen who will live in these wide spaces. Two years have passed since we landed. They have been filled with toil and faith and loss and love. I have gone on explorations three times; I now go the fourth time, and this will be the last, for I shall come to a happy destiny for us all. Now may the love of God sustain us!"

He made the sign of the cross and everyone present did the same, and all stood up and with smiles and tears cheered.

In the crude, unhandsome chapel, in primeval surroundings, the priests officiated, and when Friar Membré raised the consecrated wafer, and the lamps shone dimly through the mists of incense, the kneeling group knew well that the beautiful vestments of the priests, compared with their own humble clothing, was the difference between the permanent success of this expedition and its momentary relapse. Some spirit of divinity seemed to fill the space. It was like a strange dream through which shone the glorious splendor of France and of the Church. The humblest intelligence present was under a hypnotic spiritual influence. Even Liotot, Duhaut, and Hiens were impressed.

Through the mists came the ringing of the bell twice—

first for the elevation of the Host, and then for the chalice, and as Friar Membré raised the sacred vessel there came the words from all the congregation:

"Savior of the world, save us, for by Thy Cross and by Thy Blood Thou hast redeemed us. Help us, we beseech Thee, O our God. Amen."

After the "Agnus Dei," these words pierced the tender mists:

"In saying to thine apostles, 'My peace I leave with you, my peace I give unto you,' Thou hast promised, O Lord, to all Thy Church that peace which the world cannot give—peace with Thee and peace with ourselves."

TWELFTH Night came, and on the morrow La Salle and his little expedition would start for Canada. They met in the hall where they dined on Christmas Eve, and held the Twelfth Night revels. Twelfth Night cake made of good flour and raisins and some dried orange peel and other pleasant ingredients was brought in with burning candles, and it was cut by La Salle. All had their share, and it was small, and when they had eaten it La Salle stood up. He raised a glass high. In it showed no wine or brandy. There was none left:

"The King drinks!" he said, and everyone present raised a tin cup holding a little cold water.

"The King drinks!" said every voice, and as they drank hearts grew suddenly hopeful, then presently sad.

The King was drinking at Versailles, with all the wealth and splendor of modern France round him, and not in spaces like these. King Louis and his courtiers, with wine in plenty, drank to the happiness and peace of all the French Empire. He and they were in luxury and plenty. La Salle and his people were in misery and lonely fear, but as La Salle lowered his cup he looked round and said:

"We go a long travel, a hard path. We shall have much to endure. Will the friar bless us?"

With bowed heads before him, Friar Membré lifted up his arm and solemnly said:

"The peace of God which passeth all understanding be with you and remain with you forever. Amen."

The next morning at daylight La Salle's company, with five horses bought from the Indians, stood in the yard of the fort, ready for the march. Barbier was to remain behind in control, with Sablonnière, the Friar Membré and the Sieur Chefdeville, with a surgeon, soldiers, laborers, women and girls and several children, who faced the dark uncertainty of the future. With the sun shining bright, and equipped and weaponed for their journey, the little band turned and looked upon those who they were leaving behind. They were laden with meager baggage and presents for Indians.

With La Salle were his brother, the Abbé, his two nephews, Moranget and the boy Cavelier, Joutel, and Friar Anastase Douay. Besides these were Duhaut, and Liotot, both now evil-hearted men who were ready to do dark things, though in France they had held good positions. Hardship and misfortune had poisoned them. There were also the German Hiens, the Sieur de Marle, Teissier, a pilot, Barthelemy and Talon, L'Archeveque, a servant of Duhaut, and Nika and Saget, La Salle's servant and guide. In all were seventeen.

La Salle shook hands warmly with all who were to stay, and he stooped and kissed a little girl, his eyes amiable, yet mystical. Then standing at salute, he raised a hand to his cap, as though to say farewell and God be with you, but he did not speak. In his face was the pathos of his one awful mistake, hidden from them, and the resolution of his grave, enduring character. Slowly he and his friends filed silently from the gate, crossed the river, and marched slowly through the staring sun and over the limitless prairies where wild life teemed, till Fort St. Louis was hidden from their sight.

When they were far out La Salle, at the head of his company, turned to Joutel and said, "This journey solves my fate."

"And the fate of us all, Sieur de la Salle," was Joutel's reply.

La Salle nodded. "Yes, the fate of all."

Joutel was young and full of vigor, not a gentleman, but with the spirit of the best that belongs to France—a man, an ardent follower of La Salle, the reliable friend. Of him La Salle had never had the shadow of a doubt. He had not the same thought concerning others, and yet he felt himself on the highway to better days.

As they trudged on, Duhaut and Liotot, who walked together, talked in low words, glaring darkly at La Salle. The priests walked together, and the Abbé Cavelier, lean, ascetic, wiry, and physically strong, conversed in a low voice with Father Douay, and in his keen furtive eyes was the look of the pioneer. It had got there at last. He had never talked much to his brother, and he talked less as time went on. His coming at all had been one of the mysteries of his nature and life. He had never been a traveling missionary like Père Marquette and many others. The soul of the life was not in him. But he adored success, and by instinct he was a courtier and a miser, and riches were his ever-present thought. If La Salle had not succeeded at Versailles he would have abandoned him; because he had succeeded he would be his critical follower; but since the expedition had started he had shown a fluttering interest and at last something of the pioneer spirit had entered him. He had little heart. Friar Membré was nearer to La Salle than his own brother—his was an unwholesome nature.

Father Douay said to him: "I feel, somehow, we are on the way to better days. But we shall have hard going—eh?"

The Abbé shook his head somberly. "I know not, but I

hope." Then he shook his head again. "I like not that Duhaut and Liotot. They will give trouble. We are not united—no."

Moranget, his nephew, was in talk with Duhaut and Liotot now, and he said, "I'll eat my pantaloons if we don't come out of this all right." He laughed vapidly, for he was of thin intellect and had a quarrelsome and violent temper.

Both these men hated him, for he had more than ever shown stupid braggadocio, and they looked furtively at him. "Well, you'll have a filthy meal," said Duhaut.

Moranget with an oath flung away from him.

Nika and Saget walked together. They did not speak at all, but in Nika's eyes were forebodings of tragedy and he could not have told why, but they were present. Faithful and devoted to La Salle, he had been with him many years. How often had he provided food for them all when they were near starvation!

Hiens, behind them, alone, as though to himself said, "It's a long way to the Mississippi, that's so!" He laughed satirically.

Nika heard, but his eyes only glowed the deeper.

Prairie and forest, wood and river, rain and shine, buffalo and wild game in plenty, and so they trudged on day after day. They were sadly in want of shoes, so they made coverings of buffalo hide, which they must keep always wet, because when dry it hardened about the foot like iron, and they bought deer skins from the friendly Indians to make good moccasins. Herds of buffalo, whose tread through the forest made good paths for the weary travelers, passed them. When bad weather came they built huts of bark and meadow grass; they set a rude stockade about their camp. They met Indians constantly, visited them in their camps, sat within their lodges on buffalo robes, and watched them killing herds of buffalo with lances of sharpened bone.

Keeping a northernly course, they reached the waters of the Trinity and they endured unfavorable weather for days at a time. It was not a happy company. La Salle, who could not pretend, became cold and reserved to those in whom he had no faith, like Liotot and Duhaut. They had money in the enterprise, and were bitter. Liotot was at heart a foe of La Salle. He charged him with the death of a relative who, on a previous journey, had failed in strength and was ordered by La Salle to return to the fort, and was killed by Indians on the way. Besides, young Moranget, with foolishly impulsive temper, was hated by Liotot, who had treated him for a wound by an Indian arrow and nursed him with care and had been rewarded with abuse.

They came at last in the middle of March to a spot not far from where La Salle had, on a preceding journey, left a quantity of Indian corn and beans in *cache*. He sent Liotot and Duhaut and l'Archeveque and Nika to bring in the corn. When the *cache* was opened the contents were spoiled, but as they were returning Nika shot two buffalo, and a servant was sent to inform La Salle that he might send horses to bring in the meat.

La Salle directed Moranget and De Marle to go with his servant, Saget, to the hunter's camp. There Moranget found that Duhaut and the others, having cut up the meat, had reserved for themselves the marrow bones, to which by custom they had right, but Moranget violently scolded them, and ended by seizing the whole of the meat. Thereupon Liotot, Duhaut, and Hiens resolved to kill Moranget that night. Also, Nika and Saget must die with him, for they were faithful to La Salle.

It was a night ill suited to crime, with the young moon, bright stars, the fresh smell of the green wood and the verdure round. They ate their evening meal and pipes were smoked, apparently at peace, but there was no peace. Rancor, hatred, dark purpose were in the minds of those who arranged that the first three guards of the night should be Moranget, Saget, and Nika.

Each in his turn stood watching, and saw the moon slowly rise, and the stars glimmer in the far blue sky; then at last each rolled in his blanket and was soon deep in slumber. The night was beautiful and clear. The moon shone.

Slowly Liotot with an ax stole towards the three sleepers and struck a rapid blow at each. Duhaut and Hiens stood with guns cocked, but there was no need to fire. All three were killed instantly, and the murderers looked scornfully at these men, of whom Nika was an infinite loss to this little company—faithful, skillful, wise in his primitive way, and he had been with La Salle so many years and was trusted and resourceful.

Liotot turned to Duhaut. "Now for the dastardly La Salle!"

Duhaut grimly inclined his head, but Hiens hesitated, for La Salle had saved his life and there was in him some touch of definite loyalty. They did not bury the men. They left them in their blankets with stark eyes staring at their eternal night.

Only six miles away, with all the details of a camp about him, with idle Indians lounging or strolling, with men sleeping or smoking, with black kettles hung from tripods over the fires, and the horses grazing near by, La Salle sat silent, but disturbed. His nephew, Moranget, and Saget and De Marle had been expected the night before, but they had not come. La Salle resolved to go and find them. To Joutel he said, "Have you heard of any evil purposes against Moranget and the others?"

"Nothing. They have complained and blasphemed, that

is all. They would not tell me of evil purpose; they know me loyal."

La Salle shook his head and a grim look came to his eyes and mouth. He smoked hard, he thought much, but he was silent. The next morning he started with an Indian guide. He now directed Joutel to remain in charge of the camp and to keep faithful watch. He summoned Friar Douay to go with him and they borrowed Joutel's gun and pistol.

During the six miles walk La Salle spoke of naught at first but religion, of grace and predestination, acknowledging the debt he owed to God in all his twenty years of exploration. Then suddenly he became overwhelmed with profound sadness, for which he did not seek to account. He sat down on the bough of a fallen tree and buried his face in his hands. At last he rose, grown serene and calm, and there came from his lips the sixteenth-century prayer. He lifted his face to the quiet sky and said:

O Lord support us all the day long of this troublous life until the shades lengthen and the evening comes and the busy world is hushed and the fever of life is over and our work done. Then in Thy mercy grant us safe lodging and holy rest and peace at the last.

When he had finished, the Friar made the sign of the cross and his lips murmured the benediction. After a moment they moved on.

They came near to the camp of Duhaut on the farther side of the small river. La Salle fired his gun as a summons to any of his followers. Guessing he had fired the shots, Duhaut and his evil friends crossed the river, though trees hid them from sight. Liotot and Duhaut crouched like Indians in the long dry grass, while l'Archeveque stood in sight near the bank.

La Salle advancing, saw l'Archeveque, and asked where was Moranget.

The servant did not lift his hat, but replied in a tone of studied insolence that Moranget was no doubt strolling somewhere.

La Salle rebuked him. l'Archêveque's insolence increased, drawing back as he spoke, towards the ambuscade, while La Salle advanced upon him. The day was beautiful, the trees whispered in a slight breeze, birds sang, and the sun was like a soft cauldron of light. It was not a scene for trouble, but for peace. Yet a copperhead snake crossed the path, the deadly venom of the wilds. In the air some distant spirit sang—a low, clear, loving sound. All seemed well, and yet the devil's son, l'Archêveque, backed towards the trees.

Then suddenly there came from the grass a shot, followed by another, and, stricken through the brain, the intrepid La Salle dropped to the ground dead.

Thus, at the age of forty-three, one of the greatest men of all the ages, Réné Robert Cavelier de la Salle, whose name abides forever, disappeared from the scene of his work, but enshrined himself in the immortality which comes to such as he.

The Friar was terror-stricken, but Duhaut called out that he had naught to fear. They came forward and with wild looks gazed at La Salle.

"There thou liest, great Bashaw! There thou liest!" exclaimed Liotot, in gross exultation over the quiet body.

With mockery and insult they stripped it and dragged it into the bushes.

Friar Anastase Douay returned to La Salle's camp in horror, and rushed into the hut of the Abbé Cavelier. At the sight of him the priest, reading the catastrophe in his face, cried out, "My poor brother is dead!"

Then entered on them Liotot, Duhaut, and the rest.

The Abbé, his young nephew, and Douay fell on their

knees, expecting instant death, the Abbé begging piteously for half an hour to prepare. But Duhaut shook his head. "No more blood shall be shed. We have done our duty. The tyrant is gone forever."

The party was now reduced to Joutel, Douay, Cavelier, Teissier, De Marle, and Hiens, and his young nephew, two other boys, the orphan Talon, and a lad called Barthelemy, and Liotot, Duhaut, and l'Archeveque.

Joutel was absent, and l'Archeveque, who liked him, went to find him. When Joutel saw him coming he was astounded and anxious. L'Archevéque seemed all confusion.

"You have bad news. What is it?" Joutel's voice was broken.

L'Archevéque, faltering, answered that La Salle was dead, also that Moranget, Nika, and Saget had been killed.

Joutel was overcome. "Good God! Do they mean to kill me, too!"

"They said no more blood was to be shed."

Joutel did not know what to do. He had no gun, only one pistol, no balls or powder.

L'Archevéque read the look in his face: "Do not fear, m'sieu' Joutel; they will not kill you—no. I beg you return to camp."

After a moment's study Joutel raised his head and returned to camp. In the tent he saw the Abbé Cavelier and Father Douay praying in a corner, but he did not go towards them until he knew the will of the assassins.

They were in terrible excitement and uneasy and embarrassed.

Duhaut at length said: "No more killing! Each will take command in turn, and all shall be well now."

At dinner that night, when the murderers shared out the meat without regard to proportion, as had been the past custom, the Abbé, Father Douay, Joutel, and others were told to mount guard as usual; that what was done came through despair, and they meant no more harm to anybody.

To this the Abbé Cavelier said that when they slew the Monsieur de la Salle they had slain themselves, for there was no one else who could get them out of this country. To this Duhaut and Liotot made angry replies, Liotot saying: "He was not the only bushman or voyageur. We too have traveled, and we will find our way."

Then they quieted, and arms were handed to their former comrades. The Abbé Cavelier, Joutel, and the others spent a sleepless night, but they pledged themselves to stand together to the last and to escape as soon as possible.

Joutel said they should kill the murderers in their sleep, but the Abbé Cavelier said vengeance should be left to God, and that he himself had more to revenge than the others, having lost his brother and his nephew. So Duhaut and Liotot were for the moment safe. In the morning Duhaut and Liotot determined to go to the Cenis village and to take Joutel with them. At the Cenis Indian villages they were received with honor and sumptuously fed with sagamite, corn cake, beans, bread made of the meal of parched corn, and other bread made of the kernels of nuts and the seeds of sunflowers. Then the pipe of peace was lighted and all smoked together. The Frenchmen proposed traffic in provisions, and they exchanged knives, beads, and other trinkets for corn and beans.

In Indian villages they were well received, and some of these dwellings were of great size. The travelers were lodged in one of the largest. One night as Joutel lay between sleeping and waking on buffalo robes that covered his bed of canes, and all round the lodge the inmates were buried in sleep, with the fire still burning, the sound of a footstep wakened him. He saw at his side the figure of an Indian armed with bows and arrows.

Joutel said, "Who are you?" in a hoarse whisper, reaching for his pistol.

As, not answering, the intruder turned and sat by the fire, Joutel followed and saw that the face and body, though tattooed, were not that of an Indian. Indeed, the figure presently rose and threw his arms around Joutel's neck, saying he was a Breton sailor named Ruter; that he and his sailor friend, Grollet, had feared to come to the village lest they should meet La Salle, whom they had once deserted.

Joutel said: "Have no fear, the Sieur de la Salle has gone to Heaven. He was sent there by Duhaut, Liotot and Hiens, having also killed Moranget, La Salle's nephew, and Nika and Saget, his servant and his guide.

Joutel bowed his head in sorrow, but Ruter replied: "I deserted from the Sieur de la Salle, but he was great. What devils they were to kill that man!"

He moved his body backwards and forwards in agitation. He left in the morning, carrying with him a present of beads for his wives, of whom he had several, and in a few days he returned, bringing Grollet with him, each wearing a bunch of turkey feathers dangling from his head and wrapped in native blankets.

Duhaut and Liotot had separate camps, and Douay and the two Caveliers had been treated with harshness and disdain and were obliged to eat their meals apart. The assassins quarreled among themselves, and Hiens, fierce against Duhaut and Liotot, who had seized all the plunder, went about morosely.

Joutel and his comrades talked of naught but how to make their way to Canada; and so they devised a simple plan of escape.

The Abbé Cavelier was to be too tired for the journey and wished to stay among the Cenis Indians. To this the old priest consented, for truth was not an indispensable thing to him, and they gained the assent of Liotot and Du-haut, but Ruter, the French savage, told Duhaut of Joutel's plan and Duhaut said that he and his men would also go to Canada.

"We have had enough of lies and tricks," he said, fiercely, "and we will go to Quebec city, where we shall be well received."

He said this with a disdainful smile, for he knew that many merchants would welcome the disappearance of the Sieur de la Salle. Hiens and the others, hearing of Duhaut's plan of going to Canada, said they would not consent.

One morning Hiens appeared at the camp of Duhaut and Liotot with Ruter and Grollet and about twenty Indians. Duhaut and Liotot were practicing with bows and arrows in front of their hut. They were excitedly rivaling each other.

"Good morning," said Liotot to Hiens, but Hiens said, sullenly, "Good night!"

Hiens then said to Duhaut, "I want my share of the goods."

Duhaut's reply was: "The goods are ours. La Salle owed them for what we invested and lost."

He looked at Hiens fiercely.

Hiens then said: "So you will not give them to me—no? You are a wretch; you killed my master," and, flashing a pistol from his belt, he fired at Duhaut, who staggered and fell dead.

At the same instant Ruter fired at Liotot, shot three balls into his body, and mortally wounded him.

Joutel, Douay, and the two Caveliers stood in terror, thinking that their turn would come next, and they held their guns ready to defend themselves, but Hiens said:

"Have no fear. I killed them to avenge the death of La Salle."

Liotot, still alive, tried to raise himself and said to Hiens: "I killed La Salle; this man has killed me. I pay my price. God forgive me for my sin. O God forgive—forgive!" He sank slowly back, and was killed by Ruter exploding a pistol with a blank charge of powder against his head.

While this was done the Indians looked on amazed, for here were Frenchmen killing one another in a most atrocious way. Joutel anxiously said to them: "These men murdered our great leader, La Salle, and he has been avenged; that is all. They earned death, and it is theirs."

Hiens and others of the French promised to join the Cenis against a neighboring tribe, and six Frenchmen went with Hiens and the rest, including Joutel, Douay, and the Caveliers. They remained a week or more among the Cenis, but at length came news of a great victory, and with the return of the Indians it was said that the French guns had won the battle, and several days were spent in ceremonies and feasts of triumph.

Joutel and his comrades explained to Hiens their plan to reach home by way of the Mississippi, but he angrily said he would not run the risk of losing his life; but after argument he agreed to their going, but the Abbé Cavelier must give him a certificate of innocence of the murder of La Salle, and this the priest did.

"Good," said Hiens as he read the certificate. "You are free to go!"

He supplied them with hatchets, knives, beads, and other articles of trade, and several horses, showing that, with all his evil, there was some good in him, yet he walked about the camp in a scarlet coat laced with gold, which had belonged to La Salle!

Joutel's party consisted of the Caveliers, Father Douay,

De Marle, Teissier, and the young Parisian named Barthelemy. Teissier had received from Cavelier a form of pardon in the crime against Moranget and La Salle.

Hiens embraced them at parting and said, "Go in peace, and may the end be good!"

So they left the Cenis villages and Hiens, on the morning when the sun was bright and all the trees and all the grass was green. After a safe journey of about two months, in which De Marle was drowned while bathing, they approached the river Arkansas, not far from its junction with the Mississippi. Beneath the forests of the farther shore they saw the lodges of a large Indian town and their weary bodies and sad hearts became elated. They saw a tall wooden cross, and near it a small house evidently built by Christian hands. Falling on their knees, they raised their arms to Heaven in thanksgiving.

Two men in European dress fired welcoming guns for the excited travelers. Canoes came and they were ferried to the town, where they were welcomed by Couture and De Launay, two assistants of Henri de Tonty!

The Indian town was moved to tears by the stories of their disasters. La Salle's death was carefully hidden from the Indians, who had held him in respect. They feasted and danced before Joutel, Cavelier, and the others, from sunset until dawn.

With guides they continued their journey in a canoe on the 1st of August, went down the Arkansas, and reached the bleak, powerful Mississippi in its shady provinces of loneliness and shadow. They passed the mouth of the Ohio, saw Marquette's picture rock and the line of craggy heights called on old French maps "The Ruined Castles." In September they saw the cliff of Fort St. Louis, and as they came near, a troop of friendly Indians, headed by a Frenchman, fired guns. They replied, and Boisrondet,

Tonty's comrade in the Iroquois war, greeted them and asked where was La Salle.

The Abbé Cavelier, with a glance of understanding at Joutel, concealed his brother's death, and replied that La Salle had been with them as far as the Cenis villages and that they had left him in good health.

They waited at the fort for Tonty, who was absent, fighting the Iroquois, but his garrison of bushrangers greeted them with salutes of musketry and the whoops of Indians. In the spacious chapel the "Te Deum" was sung, and thanks were given to God who had preserved and guided them. At length October arrived, and meanwhile Tonty returned from the Iroquois war, where he had fought Senecas with Du Lhut.

Tonty listened with profound interest to the mournful story of his guests. The Abbé Cavelier knew his generous character and his faithful service to La Salle.

Tonty said to him: "I had every faith in him, and I have still. Nothing overcomes him, nothing can. Life, wealth, is naught to him save for his native land."

In Tonty's eyes, always generous, was a glimmer of tears; in the face of La Salle's brother was deception. Four thousand livres in furs, besides other goods and a canoe, were delivered to him by the unsuspecting Tonty. At the doors of the settlement they bade good-by to the man who had cared for them for months and whom the Abbé Cavelier had so brutally misled.

Tonty watched them go, with a sudden inexplainable sense of mistrust. He did not suspect the real truth, for he believed in Joutel, but the face of the Abbé Cavelier had always been to him a symbol of deceit.

"NO, La Salle is dead," said Louvigny.

Lya's face turned almost white and her lips trembled.

"But the Abbé Cavelier, who passed through Quebec, said he left him in good health among Cenis Indians."

Louvigny shook his head. "Yes, I know. He had got money and skins from Monsieur Tonty. He sold the skins at a profit before he came to Quebec, then he went to France. There for long he hid the death of La Salle because he hoped that Seignelay would pay what his brother owed him. At last he told the truth and petitioned the King for all La Salle's property in Canada. This I came to know to-day. I have a letter from the Abbé Renadout."

Louvigny paused. The face of the girl was shocked and bitter. "The Abbé has a heart of stone," she said, "and from first to last he has been false to his great brother. A liar and a thief!" she added.

"Some good was in him or he would not have gone with La Salle. He loaned his brother money. If he could love anyone, he loved La Salle."

"God save the world from love like that," was the response. "He went because La Salle owed him money. He was only the friend of success."

At that moment a servant entered. "Monsieur Tonty has come," he said.

Lya's hand went swiftly to her breast. It seemed all was coming at once. Her eyes dimmed, she trembled.

Louvigny smiled, because he and his wife had long known the deep friendly spirit Lya had for Henri de Tonty.

"I will see monsieur first," he said, "then send him in to you."

It was the time of year when all the trees were taking on the colors of the rainbow, when a wild blaze of tender color lay upon all the land in the bright sun. Flights of gulls were overhead, droves of pigeons sailed by, wild geese and turkeys honked past, and all over was the splendor of autumn, the sweetest season in this new land. She saw the *habitants* coming to market with vegetables, jars of maple syrup and slabs of maple sugar, and all kinds of cordials. How good, how bad it was, for behind it all was the threat of the Iroquois, who, reduced in numbers, were daily becoming more menacing. Peace was here, but not a permanent peace, for weakness was in high places.

She saw the Château St. Louis, high above the waters, the Bishop's palace, the seminary, the hospital, the Basilica and the residence of the Intendant where had been her unhappy interview with Duchesneau. All was not well in Quebec, for Denonville, the Governor, had completely failed to destroy the Iroquois.

She raised her eyes. White clouds were moving fast, but in the air of this new land was the thrill of life, of hope, of faith, of noble destiny. La Salle was gone forever. She recalled his leaving Rochelle with the four ships and her words as she saw them pass.

"God knows, God knows!" she had said.

She had only met Tonty once, yet there had grown up between them a sense of deep comradeship and what was far deeper still. It was the soul of this land.

Now Henri de Tonty was here. She turned from the window, the door opened, and Tonty made a swift, sad gesture and with glowing eyes came forward. She gave him her hand; he kissed it, then, after a few moments of broken words, he said: "I have come from where La Salle was murdered."

"And gained his immortality," she said, nodding. "I have just learned that the Abbé had hidden his brother's death to get goods and money from you."

Tonty waved a hand, then said, satirically: "The Abbé Cavelier will die rich, but none will mourn his going."

"Will you not sit down?" Lya said.

They seated themselves in the big comfortable room where the rugs were the skins of wild animals and on the walls were trophies of the chase, and ever the bright happy sun shone through the window.

Tonty spoke again: "Over a year ago I learned from Couture and De Launay, whom I had left at Fort Illinois, that La Salle had been slain. With five Frenchmen and a Shawanoe Indian I set out for the abandoned colony. After hard trials we reached the Red River, where the Caddoes Indians were, and learned that Hiens was about eighty leagues distant. Here the men would go no farther, and I could not force them. The Shawanoe and one Frenchman stayed with me. When I came to the village where Hiens had remained, I did not find him. I charged the Indians with killing him, and when the women raised their voices in wailing, I knew that what I said was true. And one of the squaws, an old woman, came in the night and told me all.

"So we retraced our steps to the Red River and found the whole country flooded. It rained night and day. We fought through canebrakes with hatchets, and sometimes were to the neck in water. We had no meat; we were forced to eat our dogs. Never have I suffered so much, and never with greater grief. I was detained in the Arkansas villages by fever, but at last I reached my fort on the Illinois!"

Tears were in the girl's eyes. She rose to her feet.

"You have the soul of a martyr—yes that!"

"I am naught, but La Salle!"

"La Salle will live forever," she said.

Their eyes met and all each felt rose and conquered them. Tonty reached out an arm with love and passion in his handsome eyes. She understood. With a little cry she put her hands on his shoulders and he drew her close.

An instant after, with tears in her eyes, she reached down and raised his metal hand and kissed it.

"Oh, hard hand! Oh, tender heart!" she said.

EPILOGUE

NEVER had the city of Quebec been in such gorgeous spirit, never so gay with flags and bunting or brighter with sun or more vital with crisp, inspiring air. From every public building flags flew and every house had a touch of color on the Heights and in Lower Town.

A ship had just anchored in the harbor and eager crowds could see three boats row towards the shore. When the first boat touched land all shouted with joy, and the aged ecclesiastic, Laval, greatly changed, noble, serenely glad, with the Lieutenant-General De Lothbinière and many others, proudly hailed it. They had come to welcome again to New France Louis, Count Frontenac. The greeting was like the laugh of a man saved from drowning. Presently, the excited crowd behind him, Laval made a short, sincere, congratulatory speech, to which Frontenac, much moved, replied.

Cannon roared from the cliffs, people shouted from the shore. The green meadows, the cloudless blue sky, declared eloquently that once again New France looked up with a sense of security. Even in the fields the cattle seemed to stand at gaze, birds fluttered overhead.

All day it was so, and at night were full illuminations, making the ancient place a scene of gayety, and a few Iroquois looked on with indignant gaze—they knew their master was come again. All night the splendid carnival went on, and Quebec flamed forth in certain hope.

Not far behind the main body of sightseers were Luc Maste, Jules Ladaux, and Luce Hontard.

Luc Maste said to Luce Hontard: *"Tonnerre!*—Canada shall now be safe. The Iroquois shall be beaten—yes."

Fat, silent, beautiful in her simplicity, Luce Hontard said, "So—so—so!" and a smile showed at her slow lips.

Then Jules Ladaux said, *"Bidemme,* but it is good!"

Suddenly Luc Maste's face darkened. "Nearly all Sieur de la Salle's colony have gone to Heaven. How know I? A French prisoner led Spaniards to the fort where all had been and none were left, but near were skeletons, and fragments of a dress showed one was a woman. So—so! In the fort itself were rags of the life—kettles, well-bound books in the mud. Near by stood Indians in buffalo robes to the chin, speechless. Indians had come to trade at the settlers' camp. They would not let them into the fort, but trade began outside. Then up from ambuscade sprang hosts of Indians and killed them all, priests and people, and so the end."

Luce Hontard's brow knitted. "Who brought this news to Canada—eh?"

"Ah, that is it, name of God! The Frenchman escaped from the Spaniards and came here. From him—the truth!"

Luce Hontard's eyes were dim; yet she was happy.

Behind the three, a voice said: *"Sacré bleu,* that Frontenac he too old—yes, much too old!"

The fingers of Luc Maste dropped to the sword at his hip. His face went black. He turned savagely and said: *"Tiens,* not too old to save clean and sweet New France and your dirty skin, pig!"

With fright in his face the little riverman turned and ran.

Slowly up the steep hill towards the Château St. Louis, Count Frontenac, erect, powerful, the exile returned in triumph, with Laval beside him, made his way to the ringing of bells and wild shouts of welcome.

Luce Hontard gazed with shining eyes. "Ah, God is good—but yes!" she said.

La Salle lives on.

THE END

CONTENTS

v

vii

BIOGRAPHY

E.P.

Born, Hailey, Idaho, 30 Oct. 1885.
Educ. U. of Penn. and Hamilton. PhB. '05. M.A. '06.

Published. 1908. Venice; A Lume Spento.

1909, Mathews, London. Personae, Exultations.
Thereafter some 40 volumes, in London till 1920.
N. York 1920–'30.
1930 onwards, with Faber, London, and in U.S.

1918 began investigation of causes of war, to oppose same.
Lectured in the Università Bocconi, Milan, 1931, on Jefferson
and Van Buren.

From 1932 continual polemic in two languages, moving from
Social Credit to Gesellism.

Obtaining imprint in Italy of Social Credit and Gesellite
doctrines, comparing them with Catholic canonist theory
and local practice.

1939 first visit to U.S. since 1910 in endeavour to stave off
war. D.Litt, honorary, from Hamilton.

1940 after continued opposition obtained permission to use
Rome radio for personal propaganda in support of U.S.
Constitution, continuing after America's official entry into
the war only on condition that he should never be asked to
say anything contrary to his conscience or contrary to his
duties as an American Citizen. Which promise was faithfully
observed by the Italian Government.

CINO

Italian Campagna 1309, *the open road*

Bah! I have sung women in three cities,
But it is all the same;
And I will sing of the sun.

Lips, words, and you snare them,
Dreams, words, and they are as jewels,
Strange spells of old deity,
Ravens, nights, allurement:
And they are not;
Having become the souls of song.

Eyes, dreams, lips, and the night goes.
Being upon the road once more,
They are not.
Forgetful in their towers of our tuneing
Once for wind-runeing
They dream us-toward and
Sighing, say, "Would Cino,
Passionate Cino, of the wrinkling eyes,
Gay Cino, of quick laughter,
Cino, of the dare, the jibe.
Frail Cino, strongest of his tribe
That tramp old ways beneath the sun-light,
Would Cino of the Luth were here!"

Once, twice, a year—
Vaguely thus word they:

 "Cino?" "Oh, eh, Cino Polnesi
 The singer is't you mean?"

"Ah yes, passed once our way,
A saucy fellow, but . . .
(Oh they are all one these vagabonds),
Peste! 'tis his own songs?
Or some other's that he sings?
But *you*, My Lord, how with your city?"

But you "My Lord," God's pity!
And all I knew were out, My Lord, you
Were Lack-land Cino, e'en as I am,
O Sinistro.

I have sung women in three cities.
But it is all one.
I will sing of the sun.
. . . eh? . . . they mostly had grey eyes,
But it is all one, I will sing of the sun.

" 'Pollo Phoibee, old tin pan, you
Glory to Zeus' aegis-day,
Shield o' steel-blue, th' heaven o'er us
Hath for boss thy lustre gay!

'Pollo Phoibee, to our way-fare
Make thy laugh our wander-lied;
Bid thy 'fulgence bear away care.
Cloud and rain-tears pass they fleet!

Seeking e'er the new-laid rast-way
To the gardens of the sun . . .

.   .   .   .   .

I have sung women in three cities
But it is all one.

I will sing of the white birds
In the blue waters of heaven,
The clouds that are spray to its sea."

NA AUDIART

Que be-m vols mal

NOTE: Anyone who has read anything of the troubadours knows
well the tale of Bertran of Born and My Lady Maent of Mon-
tagnac, and knows also the song he made when she would none
of him, the song wherein he, seeking to find or make her equal,
begs of each preëminent lady of Langue d'Oc some trait or some
fair semblance: thus of Cembelins her "esgart amoros" to wit,
her love-lit glance, of Aelis her speech free-running, of the Vicom-
tess of Chalais her throat and her two hands, at Roacoart of Anhes
her hair golden as Iseult's; and even in this fashion of Lady Audiart
"although she would that ill come unto him" he sought and praised
the lineaments of the torse. And all this to make "Una dompna
soiseubuda" a borrowed lady or as the Italians translated it "Una
donna ideale."

Though thou well dost wish me ill
                    Audiart, Audiart,
Where thy bodice laces start
As ivy fingers clutching through
Its crevices,
                    Audiart, Audiart,
Stately, tall and lovely tender
Who shall render
                    Audiart, Audiart,
Praises meet unto thy fashion?
Here a word kiss!
                    Pass I on
Unto Lady "Miels-de-Ben,"

3

Having praised thy girdle's scope
How the stays ply back from it;
I breathe no hope
That thou shouldst . . .
                    Nay no whit
Bespeak thyself for anything.
Just a word in thy praise, girl,
Just for the swirl
Thy satins make upon the stair,
'Cause never a flaw was there
Where thy torse and limbs are met
Though thou hate me, read it set
In rose and gold.[1]
Or when the minstrel, tale half told,
Shall burst to lilting at the praise
                    "Audiart, Audiart" . . .
Bertrans, master of his lays,
Bertrans of Aultaforte thy praise
Sets forth, and though thou hate me well,
Yea though thou wish me ill,
                    Audiart, Audiart.
Thy loveliness is here writ till,
                    Audiart,
Oh, till thou come again.[2]
And being bent and wrinkled, in a form
That hath no perfect limning, when the warm
Youth dew is cold
Upon thy hands, and thy old soul
Scorning a new, wry'd casement,
Churlish at seemed misplacement,

[1] *I.e.*, in illumed manuscript.
[2] Reincarnate.

4

Finds the earth as bitter
As now seems it sweet,
Being so young and fair
As then only in dreams,
Being then young and wry'd,
Broken of ancient pride,
Thou shalt then soften,
Knowing, I know not how,
Thou wert once she
                    Audiart, Audiart
For whose fairness one forgave
                    Audiart,
Audiart
        Que be-m vols mal.

VILLONAUD FOR THIS YULE

Towards the Noel that morte saison
(*Christ make the shepherds' homage dear!*)
Then when the grey wolves everychone
Drink of the winds their chill small-beer
And lap o' the snows food's gueredon
Then makyth my heart his yule-tide cheer
(Skoal! with the dregs if the clear be gone!)
Wining the ghosts of yester-year.

Ask ye what ghosts I dream upon?
(*What of the magians' scented gear?*)
The ghosts of dead loves everyone
That make the stark winds reek with fear

5

Lest love return with the foison sun
And slay the memories that me cheer
(Such as I drink to mine fashion)
Wining the ghosts of yester-year.

Where are the joys my heart had won?
(*Saturn and Mars to Zeus drawn near!*) [1]
Where are the lips mine lay upon,
Aye! where are the glances feat and clear
That bade my heart his valour don?
I skoal to the eyes as grey-blown mere
(Who knows whose was that paragon?)
Wining the ghosts of yester-year.

Prince: ask me not what I have done
Nor what God hath that can me cheer
But ye ask first where the winds be gone
Wining the ghosts of yester-year.

THE TREE

I stood still and was a tree amid the wood,
Knowing the truth of things unseen before;
Of Daphne and the laurel bough
And that god-feasting couple old
That grew elm-oak amid the wold.
'Twas not until the gods had been
Kindly entreated, and been brought within
Unto the hearth of their heart's home

[1] *Signum Nativitatis.*

6

That they might do this wonder thing;
Nathless I have been a tree amid the wood
And many a new thing understood
That was rank folly to my head before.

THE WHITE STAG

I ha' seen them 'mid the clouds on the heather.
Lo! they pause not for love nor for sorrow,
Yet their eyes are as the eyes of a maid to her lover,
When the white hart breaks his cover
And the white wind breaks the morn.
  " 'Tis the white stag, Fame, we're a-hunting,
  Bid the world's hounds come to horn!"

SESTINA: ALTAFORTE

Loquitur: *En* Bertrans de Born. Dante Alighieri put this man in hell
for that he was a stirrer up of strife. Eccovi! Judge ye! Have I dug
him up again? The scene is at his castle, Altaforte. "Papiols" is his
jongleur. "The Leopard," the *device* of Richard Cœur de Lion.

I

Damn it all! all this our South stinks peace.
You whoreson dog, Papiols, come! Let's to music!
I have no life save when the swords clash.
But ah! when I see the standards gold, vair, purple, opposing
And the broad fields beneath them turn crimson,
Then howl I my heart nigh mad with rejoicing.

7

II

In hot summer have I great rejoicing
When the tempests kill the earth's foul peace,
And the lightnings from black heav'n flash crimson,
And the fierce thunders roar me their music
And the winds shriek through the clouds mad, opposing,
And through all the riven skies God's swords clash.

III

Hell grant soon we hear again the swords clash!
And the shrill neighs of destriers in battle rejoicing,
Spiked breast to spiked breast opposing!
Better one hour's stour than a year's peace
With fat boards, bawds, wine and frail music!
Bah! there's no wine like the blood's crimson!

IV

And I love to see the sun rise blood-crimson.
And I watch his spears through the dark clash
And it fills all my heart with rejoicing
And pries wide my mouth with fast music
When I see him so scorn and defy peace,
His lone might 'gainst all darkness opposing.

V

The man who fears war and squats opposing
My words for stour, hath no blood of crimson

But is fit only to rot in womanish peace
Far from where worth's won and the swords clash
For the death of such sluts I go rejoicing;
Yea, I fill all the air with my music.

VI

Papiols, Papiols, to the music!
There's no sound like to swords swords opposing,
No cry like the battle's rejoicing
When our elbows and swords drip the crimson
And our charges 'gainst "The Leopard's" rush clash.
May God damn for ever all who cry "Peace!"

VII

And let the music of the swords make them crimson!
Hell grant soon we hear again the swords clash!
Hell blot black for alway the thought "Peace!"

BALLAD OF THE GOODLY FERE

Simon Zelotes speaking after the Crucifixion. Fere = Mate, Companion.

Ha' we lost the goodliest fere o' all
For the priests and the gallows tree?
Aye lover he was of brawny men,
O' ships and the open sea.

When they came wi' a host to take Our Man
His smile was good to see,
"First let these go!" quo' our Goodly Fere,
"Or I'll see ye damned," says he.

Aye he sent us out through the crossed high spears
And the scorn of his laugh rang free,
"Why took ye not me when I walked about
Alone in the town?" says he.

Oh we drank his "Hale" in the good red wine
When we last made company,
No capon priest was the Goodly Fere
But a man o' men was he.

I ha' seen him drive a hundred men
Wi' a bundle o' cords swung free,
That they took the high and holy house
For their pawn and treasury.

They'll no' get him a' in a book I think
Though they write it cunningly;
No mouse of the scrolls was the Goodly Fere
But aye loved the open sea.

If they think they ha' snared our Goodly Fere
They are fools to the last degree.
"I'll go to the feast," quo' our Goodly Fere,
"Though I go to the gallows tree."

"Ye ha' seen me heal the lame and blind,
And wake the dead," says he,

"Ye shall see one thing to master all:
'Tis how a brave man dies on the tree."

A son of God was the Goodly Fere
That bade us his brothers be.
I ha' seen him cow a thousand men.
I have seen him upon the tree.

He cried no cry when they drave the nails
And the blood gushed hot and free,
The hounds of the crimson sky gave tongue
But never a cry cried he.

I ha' seen him cow a thousand men
On the hills o' Galilee,
They whined as he walked out calm between,
Wi' his eyes like the grey o' the sea,

Like the sea that brooks no voyaging
With the winds unleashed and free,
Like the sea that he cowed at Genseret
Wi' twey words spoke' suddently.

A master of men was the Goodly Fere,
A mate of the wind and sea,
If they think they ha' slain our Goodly Fere
They are fools eternally.

I ha' seen him eat o' the honey-comb
Sin' they nailed him to the tree.

PLANH FOR THE YOUNG ENGLISH KING

That is, Prince Henry Plantagenet, elder brother to Richard Cœur de Lion.

If all the grief and woe and bitterness,
All dolour, ill and every evil chance
That ever came upon this grieving world
Were set together they would seem but light
Against the death of the young English King.
Worth lieth riven and Youth dolorous,
The world o'ershadowed, soiled and overcast,
Void of all joy and full of ire and sadness.

Grieving and sad and full of bitterness
Are left in teen the liegemen courteous,
The joglars supple and the troubadours.
O'er much hath ta'en Sir Death that deadly warrior
In taking from them the young English King,
Who made the freest hand seem covetous.
'Las! Never was nor will be in this world
The balance for this loss in ire and sadness!

O skillful Death and full of bitterness,
Well mayst thou boast that thou the best chevalier
That any folk e'er had, hast from us taken;
Sith nothing is that unto worth pertaineth
But had its life in the young English King
And better were it, should God grant his pleasure,
That he should live than many a living dastard
That doth but wound the good to ire and sadness.

From this faint world, how full of bitterness
Love takes his way and holds his joy deceitful,